A First Course in

Atmospheric Radiation

Second Edition

Grant W. Petty
ATMOSPHERIC AND OCEANIC SCIENCES
UNIVERSITY OF WISCONSIN-MADISON
MADISON, WISCONSIN

Sundog Publishing
Madison, Wisconsin

Library of Congress Control Number: 2006900201

Petty, Grant, W., 1958–

    A first course in atmospheric radiation.

    Sundog Publishing
    Includes index.
    1. Atmosphere—Radiative transfer. I. Title.

ISBN-13: 978-0-9729033-1-8

ISBN-10: 0-9729033-1-3

Printed in the United States of America

10 9 8 7 6 5 4 3

Preface to the Second Edition

Considering that the first edition of this book was rushed into print so as to be available in time for the Spring 2004 semester, it is not surprising that a number of errors and typesetting problems survived the proofreading process. In the spirit of modern software development — and isn't a book just software distributed on the oldest of storage media? — we may now look back on the first edition as the Beta Release.

This Second Edition offers the first opportunity not only to correct errors but also to add a few other embellishments that had to be skipped the first time around. Examples include a table of symbols, a discussion of the Poynting vector and its relationship to flux, and several additional exercises. Since the first edition is already sold out as of this writing, other planned revisions and enhancements will unfortunately have to wait for yet a third edition.

I am indebted to the following individuals for having taken the time and effort to send me written comments and corrections based on their experience with the first edition: Jack Barrett, Dan Bednar, Ralf Bennartz, Wann-Jin Chen, Christine Chiu, Kenneth Davis, Caryn Erlick, Howard Evans, Brian Fiedler, Piotr Flatau, Neil Fox, Tim J. Garrett, Jason Harder, Harshvardhan, Eric M. Hudish, Katja Hungershöfer, Brian W. Kabat, Lazaros Oreopoulos, Keith P. Shine, Junshik Um, Mark Weitz, and Ping Yang.

I would like to especially thank Prof. David E. Stooksbury and Dr. Robert Pincus for their insightful and fair book reviews which appeared in the *Bulletin of the American Meteorological Society* and *EOS*, respectively. Dr. Pincus not only pointed out the need for a broader selection of exercises, but he also helped partly correct this deficiency by generously contributing ideas for several of the new exercises that appear in this edition.

Above all, I thank my wife Antje and daughters Sonia and Annika for patiently accepting the sometimes onerous demands this book has made on both my time and their living space over the past four years.

GRANT W. PETTY

Preface to the First Edition

Most meteorology and climatology students require a basic grounding in the principles and practical consequences of atmospheric radiation but do not necessarily intend to specialize in radiation or remote sensing. I have written this textbook with those students in mind. My goal is to cultivate a firm (if basic) grasp of "how radiation works," without overwhelming the student with a mass of technical details. Although it is impossible to avoid a substantial reliance on mathematics in a book on this subject, I have tried to emphasize physical insight rather than blind reliance on equations. My measure of this textbook's success will be not how much students *could have learned* had they been sufficiently diligent in picking their way through a vast thicket of facts and equations, but rather how much they *still remember*, and can correctly explain to others, a year or more after the course has ended.

Consequently, a great deal of material that is found in other widely used textbooks on atmospheric radiation has been deliberately omitted. My decisions concerning what to include were guided by the following two questions: "What does the *non-specialist* really need to know about atmospheric radiation in order to appreciate its essential (and pervasive) role in modern meteorology and climatology? Which topics are better left to advanced courses designed for future remote sensing or radiation specialists?" Wherever I give a cursory (and often over-simplified) overview of a complex topic, I try to also cite the relevant sections of other textbooks offering a more complete and nuanced treatment.

Whenever possible, key concepts are illustrated by reference to observable phenomena encountered both in everyday life and in "real world" meteorology, climatology, and remote sensing. Homework problems are interspersed throughout each chapter rather than being grouped at the end in the traditional manner. These are designed not to stump the student but rather to facilitate his/her internalization of the immediately preceding material. Boxed equations highlight key results or relationships that deserve special attention. The appearance of a dagger (†) after a chapter or section heading warns of more advanced material that may be skipped in an undergraduate-level course.

A word on notation and terminology: There is no standard system of symbols, terms, and units for radiative transfer quantities; each radiation subcommunity has its own distinctive and mutually incompatible traditions. In the end, I settled on a set of symbols that seemed reasonably compatible with the recent literature in mainstream atmospheric science while minimizing ambiguity.

Both in my own education in atmospheric radiation and in the preparation of this book I have referred to lecture notes and other unpublished materials by S.A. Ackerman, Harshvardhan, Conway B. Leovy, Gary E. Thomas, and Stephen G. Warren, as well as the published textbooks cited at the end. I am grateful to Ryan Aschbrenner, Jason Brunner, Monica Harkey, and David Santek for their invaluable assistance with proofreading. Any errors of fact or interpretation are of course my own responsibility. Last but not least, I owe much to Prof. Ronald Rinehart, whose willingness to share his experience with self-publishing *Radar for Meteorologists* gave me the confidence to follow his example.

Despite having now been committed to print for the sake of this year's generation of students, this first edition remains very much a work in progress. I intend to undertake revisions and corrections with each new print run, following a model that more nearly resembles that of regular software updates rather than traditional textbook publishing. Comments, corrections and suggestions for future revisions are therefore encouraged and may be sent to the author c/o Sundog Publishing (see contact information on copyright page). Errata, as well as supplemental resources, will be posted on the publisher website at `www.sundogpublishing.com`.

GRANT W. PETTY

One should write not to be understood, but rather so as to make it impossible to be misunderstood. - Marcus Fabius Quintilianus

Contents

Preface to the Second Edition   iii

Preface to the First Edition   v

1   Introduction   1
   1.1   Relevance for Climate and Weather   1
       1.1.1   Solar Radiation   2
       1.1.2   Thermal Infrared Radiation   3
       1.1.3   The Global Heat Engine   4
       1.1.4   Components of the Earth's Energy Budget   . .   6
   1.2   Relevance for Remote Sensing   7

2   Properties of Radiation   11
   2.1   The Nature of Electromagnetic Radiation   11
   2.2   Frequency   16
       2.2.1   Frequency Decomposition   18
       2.2.2   Broadband vs Monochromatic Radiation   . . .   19
   2.3   Polarization   20
   2.4   Energy   22
   2.5   A Mathematical Description of EM Waves[†]   24
   2.6   Quantum Properties of Radiation   31
   2.7   Flux and Intensity   33
       2.7.1   Flux   33

2.7.2 Intensity 35

2.7.3 Relationship between Flux and Intensity . . . 46

2.8 Applications 49

2.8.1 Global Insolation 49

2.8.2 Regional and Seasonal Distribution of Insolation 50

3 The Electromagnetic Spectrum   **55**

3.1 Frequency, Wavelength and Wavenumber 56

3.2 Major Spectral Bands 57

3.2.1 Gamma Rays and X-Rays 61

3.2.2 Ultraviolet Band 61

3.2.3 Visible Band 63

3.2.4 Infrared Band 64

3.2.5 Microwave and Radio Bands 66

3.3 Solar and Terrestrial Radiation 68

3.4 Applications 69

3.4.1 UV Radiation and Ozone 69

4 Reflection and Refraction   **74**

4.1 A Closer Look at N 76

4.1.1 The Real Part 76

4.1.2 The Imaginary Part 76

4.1.3 The Dielectric Constant[†] 79

4.1.4 Optical Properties of Heterogeneous Mixtures[†] 80

4.2 Refraction and Reflection 82

4.2.1 Angle of Reflection 82

4.2.2 Angle of Refraction 84

4.2.3 Reflectivity 86

4.3 Applications 90

4.3.1 Rainbows and Halos 90

5 Radiative Properties of Natural Surfaces   **96**

5.1 Natural Surfaces Idealized as Planar Boundaries . . . 97

5.2 Absorptivity and Reflectivity 98

5.2.1 Examples of Reflectivity Spectra 99

5.2.2 The Graybody Approximation 100

5.3 Angular Distribution of Reflected Radiation 102

5.3.1 Specular and Lambertian Reflection 102

5.3.2 Reflection in the General Case[†] 105

5.4 Applications 107
    5.4.1 Solar Heating of Surfaces 107
    5.4.2 Satellite Imaging at Visible and Near-IR
        Wavelengths 109

6 Thermal Emission   **113**
6.1 Blackbody Radiation 115
    6.1.1 Planck's Function 117
    6.1.2 Wien's Displacement Law 120
    6.1.3 Stefan-Boltzmann Law 122
    6.1.4 Rayleigh-Jeans Approximation 123
6.2 Emissivity 123
    6.2.1 Monochromatic Emissivity 124
    6.2.2 Graybody Emissivity 124
    6.2.3 Kirchhoff's Law 125
    6.2.4 Brightness Temperature 127
6.3 When Does Thermal Emission Matter? 130
6.4 Applications 132
    6.4.1 Radiative Equilibrium in a Vacuum 133
    6.4.2 Top-of-the-Atmosphere Global Radiation Bal-
        ance 136
    6.4.3 Simple Radiative Models of the Atmosphere . 139
    6.4.4 Nighttime Radiative Cooling 144
    6.4.5 Radiative Cooling at Cloud Top 146
    6.4.6 IR Imaging from Space 148
    6.4.7 Microwave Imaging from Space 151

7 Atmospheric Transmission   **155**
7.1 Extinction, Scattering and Absorption Coefficients . . 159
7.2 Extinction Over a Finite Path 160
    7.2.1 Fundamental Relationships 160
    7.2.2 Mass Extinction Coefficient 163
    7.2.3 Extinction Cross-Section 166
    7.2.4 Generalization to Scattering and Absorption . 167
    7.2.5 Generalization to Arbitrary Mixtures of Com-
        ponents 168
7.3 Plane Parallel Approximation 169
    7.3.1 Definition 171
    7.3.2 Optical Depth as Vertical Coordinate 173

7.4   Applications 174
    7.4.1   The Transmission Spectrum of the Atmosphere 174
    7.4.2   Measuring Solar Intensity from the Ground . . 185
    7.4.3   Transmittance in an Exponential Atmosphere 187
    7.4.4   Optical Thickness and Transmittance of a
            Cloud Layer 194

8   Atmospheric Emission   **204**
8.1   Schwarzschild's Equation 205
8.2   Radiative Transfer in a Plane Parallel Atmosphere . . 210
    8.2.1   The Emissivity of the Atmosphere 211
    8.2.2   Monochromatic Flux [†] 212
    8.2.3   Surface Contributions to Upward Intensity . . 215
8.3   Applications 217
    8.3.1   The Spectrum of Atmospheric Emission 219
    8.3.2   Satellite Retrieval of Temperature Profiles . . . 228
    8.3.3   Water Vapor Imagery 233

9   Absorption by Atmospheric Gases[†]   **236**
9.1   Basis for Molecular Absorption/Emission 238
9.2   Absorption/Emission Lines 240
    9.2.1   Rotational Transitions 243
    9.2.2   Vibrational Transitions 251
    9.2.3   Electronic Transitions 256
    9.2.4   Combined Energy Transitions and Associated
            Spectra 258
9.3   Line Shapes 258
    9.3.1   Generic Description of Lines 260
    9.3.2   Doppler Broadening 261
    9.3.3   Pressure Broadening 263
    9.3.4   Comparing Doppler and Pressure Broadening 266
9.4   Continuum Absorption 267
    9.4.1   Photoionization 268
    9.4.2   Photodissociation 268
    9.4.3   Continuum Absorption by Water Vapor 269
9.5   Applications 270
    9.5.1   Atmospheric Absorbers in the IR Band 270

10 Broadband Fluxes and Heating Rates[†]   **280**
  10.1 Line-by-line Calculations 281
  10.2 Band Transmission Models 286
        10.2.1 Absorption by an Isolated Line 288
        10.2.2 Defining a Band Model 293
        10.2.3 The Elsasser Band Model 294
        10.2.4 The Random/Malkmus Band Model 297
        10.2.5 The HCG Approximation 298
  10.3 The k-Distribution Method 299
        10.3.1 Homogeneous Path 300
        10.3.2 Inhomogeneous Path: Correlated-k 303
  10.4 Applications 306
        10.4.1 Fluxes and Radiative Heating/Cooling 306

11 RTE With Scattering   **320**
  11.1 When Does Scattering Matter? 321
  11.2 Radiative Transfer Equation with Scattering 322
        11.2.1 Differential Form 322
        11.2.2 Polarized Scattering[†] 324
        11.2.3 Plane Parallel Atmosphere 324
  11.3 The Scattering Phase Function 326
        11.3.1 Isotropic Scattering 327
        11.3.2 The Asymmetry Parameter 329
        11.3.3 The Henyey-Greenstein Phase Function 330
  11.4 Single vs. Multiple Scattering 332
  11.5 Applications 336
        11.5.1 Intensity of Skylight 336
        11.5.2 Horizontal Visibility 338

12 Scattering and Absorption By Particles   **343**
  12.1 Atmospheric Particles 344
        12.1.1 Overview 344
        12.1.2 Relevant Properties 345
  12.2 Scattering by Small Particles 347
        12.2.1 Dipole Radiation 347
        12.2.2 The Rayleigh Phase Function 351
        12.2.3 Polarization 353
        12.2.4 Scattering and Absorption Efficiencies 354
  12.3 Scattering by Spheres — Mie Theory 358

    12.3.1 Extinction Efficiency for Nonabsorbing Sphere 359
    12.3.2 Extinction and Scattering by Absorbing Spheres 363
    12.3.3 Scattering Phase Function 365
  12.4 Distributions of Particles 372
  12.5 Applications 373
    12.5.1 The Scattering Properties of Clouds 373
    12.5.2 Radar Observations of Precipitation 376
    12.5.3 Microwave Remote Sensing and Clouds 382

13 Radiative Transfer with Multiple Scattering   **387**
  13.1 Visualizing Multiple Scattering 389
  13.2 The Two-Stream Method 392
    13.2.1 Azimuthally Averaged RTE 392
    13.2.2 The Two-Stream Approximation 393
    13.2.3 Solution 398
  13.3 Semi-Infinite Cloud 400
    13.3.1 Albedo 401
    13.3.2 Flux and Heating Rate Profile 404
  13.4 Nonabsorbing Cloud 406
  13.5 General Case 408
    13.5.1 Albedo, Transmittance, and Absorptance . . . 409
    13.5.2 Direct and Diffuse Transmittance 412
    13.5.3 Semi-Infinite Cloud as Approximation 414
  13.6 Similarity Transformations[†] 416
  13.7 Clouds Over Non-Black Surfaces 418
  13.8 Multiple Cloud Layers 423
  13.9 Accurate solution methods[†] 424

A Representing the Phase Function   **427**
  A.1 Legendre Polynomial Expansion 427
  A.2 δ-Scaling of the Phase Function 430

B Symbols Used   **438**

C Further Reading   **445**

D Useful Physical and Astronomical Constants   **447**

Ordering Information   **448**

CHAPTER 1

Introduction

Electromagnetic radiation is an omnipresent part of our lives. Take a look around you. The fact that you can see, and interpret in astonishing detail, both your immediate and distant surroundings is made possible by radiation arriving at your eyes from every possible direction. Because the properties of this radiation, including both intensity (brightness) and spectral characteristics (color), are strongly influenced by its interactions with matter, you are able to instantly distinguish objects, faces, textures, material compositions, and many other details, some as small (in relative terms) as the period at the end of this sentence or the shape of a bird perched on a distant telephone wire.

1.1 Relevance for Climate and Weather

By now, if you are a student of atmospheric science, you are probably already aware of the distinction between adiabatic and diabatic processes in the atmosphere. It is common — because it is so convenient — to idealize many dynamic and thermodynamic processes as adiabatic. That is to say, it is often assumed that there is no significant energy exchange between the air parcel under consideration and its surrounding environment. In fact, this is not a bad assumption for processes taking place in the free atmosphere on time scales of a day or less. Over longer time periods, and even over short time periods (hours or less) in close proximity to the earth's surface, diabatic processes cannot be ignored. One such process is thermal conduction, which is quite slow in air *except* in the presence of very large temperature gradients — i.e., a degree per centimeter or more. Another diabatic process is latent heating and cooling in connection with the phase changes of water – melting, freezing, evaporation, condensation, etc. Although latent heating is a very important factor in cloud and precipitation formation, it operates only intermittently and, conveniently, it can almost always be understood and computed entirely in terms of *local* thermodynamic and microphysical processes.

Atmospheric radiation, the subject of this book, is the sole energy exchange process that operates both *continuously* throughout the atmosphere and *over long distances*. The fact that net heating or cooling due to radiation depends strongly on *nonlocal* processes greatly complicates the problem of computing this diabatic heating term in weather prediction and climate models. It is also one of several reasons why an entire textbook can be devoted to the subject and still only scratch the surface in terms of both the implications and applications (e.g., satellite remote sensing) of atmospheric radiative transfer processes.

1.1.1   Solar Radiation

When you go outside and look up at the sky, you are directly observing one form of atmospheric radiation. In fact, all of the natural light you can see during the day — and a great deal that you can't — originates from the sun, and we refer to this as solar radiation. It is of course the absorption of solar radiation by the atmosphere and the earth's surface that is ultimately responsible for maintaining the atmosphere's overall temperature structure, including the horizontal gradients that drive atmospheric circulations. If the sun were switched off, the world would quickly chill to the point where it would sustain neither life nor even wind and weather.

Not all of the radiation arriving from the sun is visible to the eye. For example, a significant fraction of solar radiation arrives in the form of *infrared* (IR) radiation. Although the cloud-free atmosphere is rather transparent to visible radiation, it is somewhat less so to solar IR radiation. Furthermore, clouds and snow cover, both of which are highly reflective to visible radiation and therefore appear bright white to the eye, would appear rather dark to an eye capable of perceiving only IR radiation.

Ultraviolet (UV) radiation, another invisible component of solar radiation, is responsible for the burn you get when you spend too much time exposed to the sun. It also plays a key role in the formation of smog in industrialized regions of the world. In its harsher forms, UV radiation can injure or kill living organisms. Fortunately, oxygen and ozone in the upper levels of the atmosphere attenuate the worst components of solar UV radiation, protecting life at the surface from its most damaging effects. Ironically, ozone itself is a product of the interaction of UV radiation with ordinary oxygen. Indeed solar UV radiation plays a decisive role in almost all aspects of the chemistry of the atmosphere.

1.1.2 Thermal Infrared Radiation

There are other forms of invisible EM radiation that continuously flood your surroundings, both day and night, but do not originate directly from the sun. The most important of these is also classified as infrared, but is often called *thermal* IR radiation to distinguish it from the solar variety. You personally experience the effects of long-wave IR radiation whenever you feel warmth radiating on your face from a hot oven across the kitchen even though the temperature of the intervening room air is moderate. Even when we are not directly conscious of it in this way, every object and surface in our surroundings, including the air itself, is constantly exchanging energy in the form of thermal IR over both short and long distances.

Thermal IR plays a major role in the redistribution of heat energy within the atmosphere and between the surface and the atmosphere. It is also *the* mechanism by which the earth-atmosphere system invisibly sheds excess heat back to space. Without this mechanism, the earth and atmosphere would continue to heat up indefinitely as they absorbed more and more solar radiation from the sun. It is also the downward emission of thermal IR by clouds and water

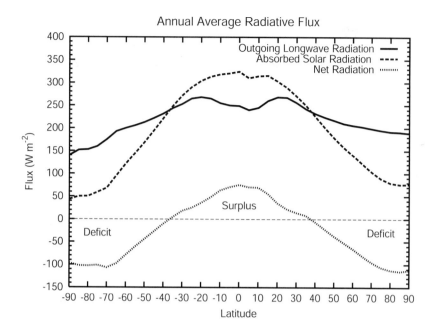

Fig. 1.1: Annual average radiation budget as a function of latitude.

vapor in the lower atmosphere that explains why nighttime temperatures do not fall nearly as sharply on humid or overcast nights than they do on clear, dry nights.

1.1.3   The Global Heat Engine

In broadest terms, the importance of radiation for weather and climate can perhaps best be appreciated by examining Fig. 1.1. The top two curves represent the long-term zonally averaged distribution of absorbed solar radiation and outgoing longwave radiation, as seen at the top of the atmosphere. The bottom curve depicts the difference between the input of energy from the sun and the loss of energy to space. In the tropical belt, more energy is received from the sun than is lost to space in the form of longwave radiation. If there were no compensating processes at work, the tropical belt would continue to heat up to well above its current temperature, and the poles would plunge to even lower temperatures than exist there now. The net effect of this radiative imbalance is the creation of a meridional temperature gradient.

Horizontal temperature gradients in a fluid such as our atmosphere inevitably create pressure gradients that in turn initiate circulations. These fluid motions serve to reduce the temperature gradient by transporting heat from warm to cold regions. In fact, they intensify until the net horizontal heat transport exactly offsets (on average) the imbalance in radiative heating and cooling. *All circulations observed in the ocean and atmosphere — from ocean currents to the Hadley circulation to extratropical cyclones to hurricanes and tornadoes — can be viewed as mere cogs in a huge and complex machine serving this higher purpose.*

In fact, if you have previously taken a course in thermodynamics, you might recall that a *heat engine* is defined as a system that converts a temperature gradient into mechanical work. It does this by taking in heat energy at a high temperature and discharging the same amount of heat at a cooler temperature. If you take a second look at Fig. 1.1 you will agree that that is exactly what is occurring in the earth-atmosphere system: a net intake of heat energy in the warm tropics and a net discharge of heat from the cool polar regions.

Problem 1.1:   Referring to Fig. 1.1:

(a) Estimate the latitude L_C where the net radiation crosses over from positive to negative in the Northern Hemisphere. Through that point, use a straightedge to sketch a line that best fits the trend in net radiation toward the North Pole. Find the value Q_{np} of the net radiation where your straight line intercepts the right axis. Use the two pieces of information to find the linear equation that approximately describes the net radiation (in W m^{-2}) as a function of latitude L between 10°N and the North Pole.

(b) The latitude L_C is where the northward transport of heat by the atmosphere and ocean is at a maximum in that hemisphere. Explain why.

(c) The rate of meridional heat transport at that latitude equals the total radiation deficit integrated over the surface area of the earth from L_C to the North Pole. Compute this value using the equation you obtained in part (a), keeping in mind that a unit change in latitude is not proportional to a unit of surface area.

(d) Convert your result to a power per unit distance (east or west along the line of constant latitude at L_C), using units of kilowatts per kilometer. The mean radius of the earth $R_E = 6373$ km.

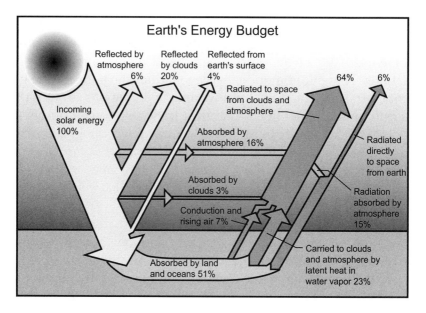

Fig. 1.2: Components of the globally averaged energy budget expressed as percentages of the incoming solar radiation. *Redrafted from an illustration by J.T. Kiehl and Kevin E. Trenberth.*

1.1.4 Components of the Earth's Energy Budget

Just as we looked at how incoming and outgoing radiation is partitioned, on average, between high and low latitudes, we can also break the energy budget down in terms of average exchanges *within* the earth-atmosphere system. Fig. 1.2 schematically depicts the fate of the solar radiation that is intercepted by the earth. Approximately 30% is immediately reflected back to space by the atmosphere, clouds, and the surface. The remaining 70% is absorbed. Almost three-quarters of that radiation is absorbed by the land and ocean surfaces; the remainder by the atmosphere (including clouds).

Of the energy absorbed by the surface, a mere tenth is emitted right back to space and lost forever. The remainder is transferred to the atmosphere, either by conduction of sensible heat, evaporation of water (which carries latent heat of vaporization), or via the emission and reabsorption of radiation.

Ultimately, the atmosphere itself is responsible for radiating about nine-tenths of the total absorbed solar energy back to space.

The loss of radiation to space is the major cooling term in the atmospheric energy budget, offsetting the direct or indirect heating from the ground and (to a lesser extent) the direct absorption of solar radiation. The magnitude and vertical distribution of this cooling at any given location and time depends on the profile of temperature, humidity and cloud cover, among other variables. When it occurs mainly at high altitudes, it helps to destabilize the atmosphere, making verical convection more likely. When it occurs near ground level, the effect is to stabilize the atmosphere and suppress convection.

By now, you should be persuaded that it is impossible to understand, let alone accurately predict, the medium- to long-term evolution of weather or climate without accounting for radiative transfer processes in the atmosphere. Even on very short time scales (hours), radiative absorption and emission at the earth's surface and at the bases and tops of cloud layers have noticeable effects on everyday weather. Key examples are the initiation of convection by solar heating, and the formation and subsequent evaporation of frost, dew, and ground fog. In general, the longer the time scale, the more decisive radiative processes become at all levels in the atmosphere.

Problem 1.2: Averaged over the globe, about 342 W m^{-2} of solar radiation is incident on the top of the earth's atmosphere. Using the information in Fig. 1.2, compute the average rate at which the atmosphere (including clouds) would be heated by *direct* absorption of solar radiation if there were no other processes at work. Hint: You will need the values of g, p_0, and c_p from the back of the book. Combine these with the rate of absorbed solar radiation to find a value that can be expressed in degrees per day.

1.2 Relevance for Remote Sensing

I have just outlined the role that atmospheric radiation plays in redistributing energy over potentially long distances, both within the atmosphere and between the earth-atmosphere system and outer space. But that is not the whole story. EM radiation carries not only energy but also a wealth of *information* about the environment within which it originated and through which it subsequently propagated. Since the early 1960s, virtually all areas of the atmospheric sciences have been revolutionized by the development and application of *remote sensing* techniques — that is, measurements of atmospheric properties and processes at a distance, using radiation sensors placed in space, on aircraft, and/or on the earth's surface.

As we shall see, the interactions of various forms of EM radiation with the environment are extremely rich and complex. Consequently, there are few important atmospheric variables that cannot be directly or indirectly estimated from the vantage point of a satellite in orbit if one is clever enough in the design of both the instrument and the analytical techniques. Today, there are large parts of the globe — especially the oceans, polar regions, and sparsely populated land areas — where meteorologists depend almost entirely on satellite observations for up-to-date information about temperature and humidity structure, wind, cloud cover, precipitation, etc.

The three images in Fig. 1.3 give just a hint of the variety of information contained in satellite observations of the atmosphere at different wavelengths. Panel (a) is a snapshot of the Eastern Pacific at a wavelength in the visible part of the spectrum. This is essentially the view of Earth you would see with the naked eye if you were on board a spacecraft, except that it's in black and white. The source of the illumination is of course the sun, and brightest areas in the image correspond to highly reflective features, such as clouds and snow. The ocean, which is not very reflective of sunlight, appears very dark. Land areas fall in between. Images of this type are primarily useful for observing the extent and evolution of cloud features associated with storms and other atmospheric circulations. Also, by observing the cloud coverage over time, it is possible to estimate what fraction of the sun's energy, on average, is absorbed by the earth and atmosphere.

Panel (b) shows the same scene but the image was taken at an infrared wavelength for which the cloud-free atmosphere is very transparent. The shades of gray in this image give an indication of the *temperatures* of the various surface and cloud features visible from space. Light shades correspond here to cold temperatures, and dark shades correspond to warm temperatures. Note that many of

a) Visible, 0.65 μm   b) IR window, 10.7 μm

c) IR water vapor band, 6.7 μm

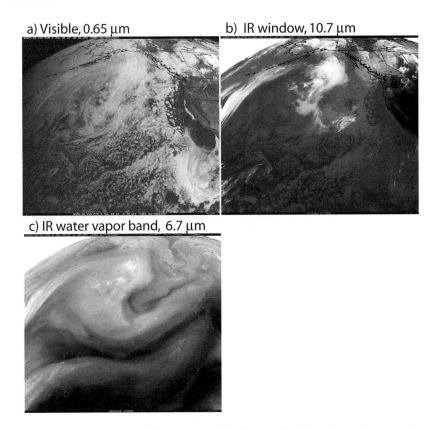

Fig. 1.3: Geostationary satellite images of the Eastern Pacific taken at the same time but at three different wavelengths.

the bright clouds seen in panel (a) appear dark in panel (b), indicating that their tops occur at a low, warm altitude. Other clouds, such as those in the upper center of the image, appear bright, indicating that they have high, cold tops. Rain clouds are usually deep and therefore have cold tops, so infrared images can often help distinguish deep precipitating clouds from shallow nonprecipitating clouds. The California lowlands appear as the darkest shade, so we can conclude that they have the warmest temperatures in this image. The Sierra Nevada mountain range, however, is visible as a light streak parallel to the coast, because the surface temperatures at high elevations are much cooler than those in the lowlands.

Panel (c) is very similar to panel (b) except that it was taken at an infrared wavelength for which water vapor is nearly opaque. The temperature patterns we see in this case correspond to the temperature of the atmosphere at some level above the majority of the atmospheric water vapor. Where the image shade is bright, the temperature is cold, and we can infer that the atmosphere is humid over a fairly deep layer; where it is dark, the atmosphere must be quite dry, because we are observing radiation emitted from the lower, warmer levels of the atmosphere.

This book will not delve too deeply into the details of atmospheric radiation as it relates specifically to remote sensing techniques and applications — for that, I recommend the book by G. Stephens (hereafter S94[1]). However, once you have mastered the basic radiative transfer facts and principles covered in the following chapters, you will be well prepared for further study in this area.

---

[1]Abbreviations like S94 will be used as a shorthand for the textbooks recommended for further reading. See Appendix C for the full bibliographic information.

CHAPTER 2

Properties of Radiation

The first order of business in a book about atmospheric radiation is to clarify what radiation *is*, how it behaves at the most fundamental physical level, what conventions are used to classify it according to wavelength and other properties, and how we define the characteristics (e.g. intensity) that appear in quantitative descriptions of radiation and its interactions with the atmosphere. We will start from absolute basics, which requires us to at least touch on some topics in classical physics. Our forays into such matters will be as brief and descriptive as the subsequent material allows, in keeping with the title of this book. Here, and throughout the book, students interested in a more comprehensive treatment should consult the more specialized textbooks and other sources cited at the end of this book.

2.1 The Nature of Electromagnetic Radiation

Electric and Magnetic fields

Everyone has experienced the effects of electric and magnetic fields. A nylon shirt pulled from a dryer may be found to have several socks clinging firmly to it. A magnet may be used to affix a note or photograph to a refrigerator door. In the first case, an electric field induced by excess charge on one item of clothing exerts an attractive force on the excess opposite charge found on the others. In the second, a magnetic field exerts an attractive force on the iron atoms in the door.

Both magnetic and electric fields are detectable at some distance from their source. A plastic balloon that was rubbed on a sweater may attract your hair from a foot or so away. A refrigerator magnet may deflect the needle of a compass from a meter or more away. Taking the magnet away, the needle returns to a position aligned with the magnetic field of the earth's iron core, thousands of kilometers beneath your feet.

The basic laws governing *static* electric and magnetic fields are well known and probably already at least somewhat familiar to you from an earlier physics course. According to Coulomb's Law, the electric field at any point is determined entirely by the distribution of electric charge in the space surrounding that point. According to Faraday's Law, magnetic fields are determined by the distribution of electric *current* (moving electric charge) in the neighborhood.

The latter law is what makes electromagnets possible, without which electric motors and most audio speakers would not exist in their current form. A related law tells us that a changing magnetic field induces an electric field that can drive a current. Thus, an electric motor that is caused to rotate by an external torque (e.g., a steam-driven turbine) can reverse roles and become a generator instead.

Thus, although static magnetic and static electric fields — as illustrated by the examples given at the beginning — may appear to have little or nothing to do with each other, they are in fact intimately connected: a *changing* electric field induces a magnetic field, and a *changing* magnetic field induces an electric field. Quantitatively, this interplay of electric and magnetic fields is embodied both completely and remarkably succinctly in Maxwell's Equations (see Section 2.5). However, one does not need to look at equations themselves to appreciate a few of the implications of this interplay.

Electromagnetic Waves

Imagine a refrigerator magnet resting on the kitchen table. It creates a magnetic field that extends essentially indefinitely (though with ever-weaker strength at increasing distances from the source) in all directions. Pick up the magnet and stick it back on the refrigerator door. Because the magnet has moved (and probably changed its orientation as well), its induced magnetic field has also changed. But a changing magnetic field creates an electric field, which persists as long as the magnetic field continues to change. Once the magnet is stationary again, the magnetic field stops changing and the electric field must disappear. But wait: this means the electric field is undergoing a change, which leads to the reappearance of a magnetic field!

You can see where this is leading. A change in either an electric or magnetic field, however brief, leads to a disturbance that is self-perpetuating. Less obvious to the casual observer is the fact that this electromagnetic disturbance propagates away from the source at a finite speed, just as ripples propagate outward from the point where a pebble strikes the surface of a pond (in the latter case, the interplay is not between magnetic and electric fields but rather between the kinetic and potential energy of the water's surface).

In the case of both electromagnetic waves and ripples on a pond, the disturbances carry energy. In the absence of viscosity, the pond ripples will transport the original energy outward, with no net loss, until they encounter something that can convert some or all of that energy to another form, such as heat or/and sound — e.g., through the breaking of the waves on the muddy bank.

Likewise, in a perfect vacuum, where there is no opportunity to convert the energy carried by electromagnetic waves into another form, such as heat, kinetic, or chemical energy (all of which can only exist in association with matter), the waves propagate indefinitely without net loss, though distributed over an ever-larger volume of space. Furthermore, it has been observed that, unlike pond ripples, electromagnetic waves always travel in a vacuum at an absolutely constant speed. This *speed of light* is approximately 3.0×10^8 m s^{-1}. By convention, it is represented by the symbol c.

The direction that an EM wave travels in a vacuum is always perpendicular to the wave crest, again just like pond ripples. And because c is a constant in a vacuum, the wave can only propagate directly away from the source. Any change of direction would imply a slowing down or speeding up of part of a wave crest at some point during its travels. This *can* happen in the presence of matter, but remember we're still talking about a vacuum here.

Sometimes it is helpful to visualize the propagation of waves in terms of *rays*. A ray is an imaginary line that always crosses wave fronts at right angles. Thus at any point on a ray, the direction of propagation of the wave is along that ray. In the case of pond ripples, all rays would be straight lines originating at the point where the pebble strikes the surface. If you like, you can think of each ray as carrying a unit of energy. Thus, the density of their intersections with a given wave front is a measure of the energy content of the wave at that location. If a given wave front propagates outward from a source without losses, the total number of rays remains constant (implying conservation of energy), but the density of intersections along the wave front decreases with distance from the source. This is consistent with the spreading of the wave's energy over a larger area and thus of its weakening as it gets further and further away.

Again, the bending of rays can only occur in the presence of local changes in wave propagation speed. This phenomenon, known as *refraction*, is the subject of Section 4.2.

Imagine throwing two pebbles into a pond at the same time. Each one produces its own set of ripples that propagate outward from the source. Sooner or later, the ripples from one pebble encounter those from the other. What happens? Do they bounce off of each other? Do they annihilate each other in a flash of heat and gamma rays? Of course not; each passes through the other as if it didn't exist. At each point on the water surface, the height perturbations associated with each set of waves simply add in a linear fashion. Where two crests intersect, the water surface is (temporarily) raised to about twice the height of either crest individually. Where a crest from one wave intersects the trough from another, the two may partially or completely cancel, leaving the water (temporarily) at its original level. This effect is called *interference* — constructive interference in the first case, destructive in the second. It must be emphasized however that nothing is created or destroyed; the ef-

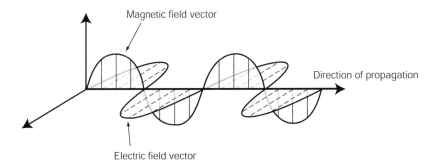

Fig. 2.1: Schematic depiction of the interplay between the electric and magnetic fields in an electromagnetic wave.

fect is purely local at the points where the waves overlap and has no influence on the subsequent propagation of the individual waves.

Exactly the same principle of linear superposition applies to EM waves. If you shine a flashlight on a wall in a dark room and then turn on the overhead light, the latter adds its illumination to that of the flashlight but otherwise has no influence on the propagation of the flashlight beam.

There is one further analogy to pond ripples that we can use to illustrate an important property of EM waves. Unlike sound waves in air, which entail oscillations of air molecules parallel to the direction of propagation, water waves arise from vertical displacements of the water surface; i.e., *perpendicular, or normal, to the direction of propagation*. Likewise, EM waves are associated with an oscillating electric field vector that is normal to the direction of propagation (Fig. 2.1). Both are therefore *transverse* waves, unlike sound waves, which are *longitudinal*.

Now we finally come to a couple of points where the analogy to pond ripples starts to break down:

- Unlike sound waves, water waves, and all other everyday kinds of waves, EM waves require no material medium in which to propagate. You can't have pond ripples without a pond; you can't have sound without air (or some other medium). But EM waves are quite at home, and indeed easiest to understand, in a perfect vacuum. It is when matter, such as the atmosphere and its various resident particles, gets into the picture that the propagation of EM waves become considerably more complex and interesting.

- Whereas pond ripples are confined to the water surface and therefore propagate in only two dimensions, EM waves propagate in three dimensional space, like sound waves (imagine if you could only hear your stereo when you put your ear on the floor!).

- Whereas the transverse oscillations of water particles in pond ripples are constrained to be vertical, there is no similar constraint on the electric field oscillations in EM waves. The orientation of the electric field vector may lie in any direction, as long as it is in the plane normal to the direction of propagation. Occasionally it is necessary to pay attention to this orientation, in which case we refer to the *polarization* of the wave as vertical, horizontal, or some other direction. A more detailed discussion of polarization will be taken up in Section 2.3

2.2   Frequency

Up until now, we have imagined an arbitrary EM disturbance and given no thought to its detailed dependence in time. In principle, we could assume any kind of EM disturbance we like — a lightning discharge, a refrigerator magnet dropping to the kitchen floor, the radiation emitted by a radio tower, or a supernova explosion in deep space. In each case, Maxwell's equations would describe the propagation of the resulting EM disturbance equally well.

Let's consider a special case, however. Imagine that we take our magnet and place it on a steadily rotating turntable. The fluctuations in the magnetic field (and in the associated electric field) are now periodic. The frequency of the fluctuations measured at a distance by a stationary detector will be the same as the frequency of rotation ν of the turntable. But recall that the periodic disturbance propagates outward not instantaneously but at the fixed speed of light c. The distance λ that the fluctuation propagates during one cycle of the turntable is called the *wavelength* and is given by

$$\lambda = \frac{c}{v} . \qquad (2.1)$$

In the above thought experiment, v is extremely low (order $1 \sec^{-1}$) and the wavelength is therefore extremely large (order 10^5 km).

In nature, electromagnetic waves can exist with an enormous range of frequencies, from a few cycles per second or even far less to more than 10^{26} cyles per second in the case of extremely energetic gamma waves produced by nuclear reactions. According to (2.1), EM wavelengths can thus range from hundreds of thousands of kilometers or more to less than the diameter of an atomic nucleus.

Because it is a common point of confusion, it bears emphasizing that the wavelength is *not* a measure of how *far* an EM wave can propagate. In a vacuum, that distance is always infinite, regardless of wavelength. In a medium such as water or air, wavelength *does* matter, but in a rather indirect and highly complex way.

Problem 2.1:
  (a) Visible light has a wavelength of approximately 0.5 μm. What is its frequency in Hz?
  (b) Weather radars typically transmit EM radiation with a frequency of approximately 3 GHz (GHz = "Gigahertz" = 10^9 Hz). What is its wavelength in centimeters?
  (c) In the U.S., standard AC electrical current has a frequency of 60 Hz. Most machinery and appliances that use this current, as well as the power lines that transport the electric power, emit radiation with this frequency. What is its wavelength in km?

Problem 2.2:
  Whenever we talk about a single frequency v characterizing an electromagnetic wave, we are tacitly assuming that the source and the detector are stationary relative to one another, in which case v is indeed the same for both. However, if the distance between the two is changing with velocity v (positive v implying increasing separation), then the frequency of radiation v_1 emitted by the source will

be different than the frequency v_2 observed by the detector. In particular, the frequency shift $\Delta v = v_1 - v_2$ is approximately proportional
to v, a phenomenon known as *Doppler shift*.

(a) Derive the precise relationship between Δv and v, by considering the time Δt elapsed between two successive wave crests reaching
the detector with speed c.

(b) For the case that $v \ll c$, show that your solution to (a) simplifies to a proportionality between Δv and v.

2.2.1   Frequency Decomposition

The above discussion of periodic waves is interesting, but what does
it have to do with real EM radiation? After all, the EM disturbance
that arises from a lightning discharge, or from dropping a magnet
on the floor, is clearly not a steadily oscillating signal but more likely
a short, chaotic pulse! What sense does it make to speak of a specific
frequency or wavelength in these cases?

The answer is that any arbitrary EM fluctuation, short or long,
can be thought of as a *composite* of a number (potentially infinite)
of different "pure" periodic fluctuations. Specifically, any continuous function of time $f(t)$ can be expressed as a sum of pure sine
functions as follows:

$$f(t) = \int_0^\infty \alpha(\omega) \sin[\omega t + \phi(\omega)] \, d\omega \qquad (2.2)$$

where $\alpha(\omega)$ is the amplitude of the sine function contribution for
each specific value of the angular frequency ω and $\phi(\omega)$ gives the
corresponding phase. If $f(t)$ itself is already a pure sine function
$\sin(\omega_0 t + \phi_0)$, then of course $\alpha = 0$ for all values of ω except ω_0.
For more general functions $f(t)$, $\alpha(\omega)$ and $\phi(\omega)$ may be quite complicated. It is beyond the scope of this book to explain *how* we find
$\alpha(\omega)$ etc. for any given $f(t)$; it is only important to recognize that it
can, in principle, always be done.[1]

---

[1]This so-called *Fourier decomposition* is extremely useful throughout the physical and engineering sciences, including other areas of atmospheric dynamics and
climatology, so if you haven't seen anything like this before, it is certainly worth
taking the time to read up on it.

Now recall what I pointed out earlier: individual EM disturbances propagate *completely independently* of one another. They may intersect, or even travel together, but the presence of one does not *influence* the other. This principle applies equally well to the pure sine wave components of a Fourier decomposition. Thus, not only can you regard any arbitrary electromagnetic disturbance as a mixture of pure sine waves of differing angular frequencies ω, but *you can then track the propagation of each frequency component completely separately from all the others.*

The implications of this observation are profound for atmospheric radiative transfer. The most basic path to understanding and/or modeling the interaction of EM radiation with clouds, water vapor, oxygen, carbon dioxide, etc., is to consider one frequency at a time and then, if required, to sum the results over all relevant frequencies. There are shortcuts that sometimes allow you to forget you are doing this, but that is nevertheless what is going on under the surface.

2.2.2 Broadband vs Monochromatic Radiation

Now is a good time to introduce a few more definitions:

- EM radiation composed entirely of a single frequency is termed *monochromatic* ("one color").

- Radiation that consists of a mixture of a wide range of frequencies is called *broadband* radiation.

As already noted, the transport of broadband radiation in the atmosphere can always be understood in terms of the transport of the individual constituent frequencies. Therefore, we will tend to focus at least initially on the monochromatic radiation.

It is quite common to have to deal with radiation that is not strictly monochromatic but is nevertheless confined to an extremely narrow range of frequencies. Such radiation is often called monochromatic, even though *quasi-monochromatic* would be a more precise term. Another way to distinguish between the two cases is via the terms *coherent* and *incoherent*:

- *Coherent* radiation is what you get from a single oscillator, like the magnet on a turntable described earlier, or from a group of oscillators that are, for whatever reason, in perfect synchronization with one another. Imagine a stadium full of people doing "the wave" at a football game, or an audience clapping in unison for an encore at the end of a rock concert. Microwave ovens, radars, lasers, and radio towers all produce coherent radiation. Note that these are all artificial sources. As an atmospheric scientist, you are most likely to encounter coherent radiation in the context of the artificial sources used in remote sensing, such as radar and lidar.

- *Incoherent* radiation is what you get from a set of independent oscillators that may have nearly the same frequency (quasi-monochromatic) but are not phase-locked to one another. Imagine a large audience applauding at the end of a speech. There is no synchronization of the claps of different individuals, even if everyone is clapping with about the same frequency. Natural radiation in the lower atmosphere is, for all practical purposes, incoherent.

2.3 Polarization

As mentioned earlier, *the orientation of the oscillating electric field vector in an EM wave can be any direction that is perpendicular to the direction of propagation.* In some radiative transfer applications (especially remote sensing) it is sometimes important to keep track of that orientation and how it evolves over the course of a complete cycle.

In coherent radiation, there is a unique, repeating pattern to the oscillating electric field vector when viewed along the direction of propagation. There are several basic possibilities for this pattern:

1. It may vibrate back and forth in a fixed plane, like a pendulum or plucked guitar string. This is called *linear polarization* [Fig. 2.2 (a)–(c)].

2. It may oscillate in spiral fashion about the direction of propagation, either clockwise or counterclockwise, for *circular polarization* [Fig. 2.2 (f)].

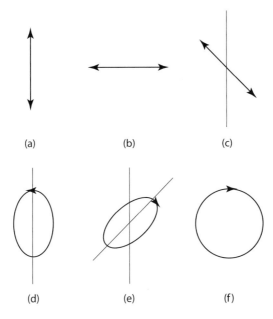

Fig. 2.2: Examples of different types of polarization, depicted in terms of the vibration of the electric field vector in a fixed plane perpendicular to the direction of propagation. (a) vertical linear, (b) horizontal linear, (c) linear at 45°, (d) elliptical counterclockwise, with vertical major axis, (e) elliptical clockwise, with the major axis oriented at a 45° angle, (f) circular, clockwise. Note that an infinity of combinations of orientation, ellipticity, and sense of rotation are also possible.

3. *Elliptical polarization* is essentially a hybrid of the first two. Note that elliptical polarization can be viewed as including both linear and circular polarization as limiting cases [Fig. 2.2 (d)–(e)].

Standard weather radar equipment typically transmits coherent radiation with linear polarization (either vertical or horizontal) and then measures the backscattered radiation with the same polarization. More sophisticated radars may transmit in one polarization but then separately measure the returned radiation in both vertical and horizontal polarizations in order to gain additional information about the targets.

In incoherent radiation, a systematic tendency toward one type of polarization may or may not be discernible. Therefore, in addition to the above *types* of polarization, one must specify the *de-*

gree of polarization. As a general rule, natural emissions of radiation in the atmosphere are completely unpolarized, but the radiation may become partially or completely polarized in the course of its interactions with particles and/or the surface. In particular, it will be shown later that a smooth surface, like calm water, preferentially reflects radiation having horizontal linear polarization. This is the phenomenon that motivated the invention of polarized sunglasses, which block the reflected horizontally polarized radiation while transmitting the rest. It is also a phenomenon of great practical importance for satellite remote sensing in the microwave band.

The purpose of this section was just to introduce you to the existence and qualitative nature of polarization. Having done that, I'll point out that polarization is often disregarded in radiative transfer calculations, especially at the level targeted by this book. Where polarization cannot be ignored, one can often gain at least qualitative insight into its role without getting too deep into the relevant mathematics. But since some of you may eventually require a more complete and quantitative understanding of polarization, I will introduce some elements of the mathematical treatment of polarization at appropriate points along the way.

2.4 Energy

Barely mentioned so far, but central to our interest in atmospheric radiation, is the fact that EM radiation transports energy. Just as gravity waves on the surface of the ocean efficiently transport energy from a North Pacific storm to the sunny beaches of California, where that energy is violently deposited onto the bodies of inattentive bathers, EM radiation transports vast quantities of energy from the thermonuclear furnace of the sun to the vinyl seat cover in your parked car.

In view of this fact, it would seem natural to characterize radiation in terms of its energy content, using the standard SI units of joules (J). But because natural radiation is not pulsed but rather continuous, it actually makes more sense to speak of the *rate* of energy transfer, or *power*, in watts (W = J/sec). Furthermore, radiation doesn't transport its energy through a single point but rather is distributed over an area. Therefore, the most convenient way to describe the transport of energy by radiation at a location is in terms of its *flux density* F (commonly, though somewhat inaccurately, shortened to just *flux* in W/m^2. Other names you may see for the exact same quantity are 1) *irradiance*, and 2) radiant *exitance*. The term "irradiance" is often preferred when referring to the flux of radiation *incident on* a plane or surface, while the term "exitance" is usually applied to the flux of radiation *emerging from* a surface.

The magnitude of the flux depends on the orientation of the reference surface. If the radiation is due to a single source, such as the sun, one might measure the flux through an imaginary surface normal to the direction of propagation. On the other hand, one is often interested in the flux density of sunlight (or other radiation) obliquely incident on a horizontal surface. We will refine these ideas later in this chapter.

Problem 2.3: The atmospheric *boundary layer* is that region near the surface that is "well-mixed" by mechanical and/or convective turbulence originating at the surface. Its thickness may range from a few meters to several kilometers. Heat added by conduction from the surface is typically distributed quickly throughout the boundary layer.

At a certain location in the tropics, the sun rises at 06 Local Solar Time (LST), is directly overhead at noon, and sets at 18 LST (=6 PM). Assume that, during the twelve hours that the sun is up, the net flux of solar energy absorbed by dry vegetation and immediately transferred to the overlying air is $F(t) = F_0 \cos[\pi(t-12)/12]$, where t is the time of day (in hours), and $F_0 = 500$ W m^{-2}.

(a) Ignoring other heating and cooling terms, compute the total solar energy (in J/m^2) added to the boundary layer over one 24-hour period.

(b) If the boundary layer depth $\Delta z = 1$ km, its average air density is $\rho_a = 1$ kg/m^3, and the heat capacity at constant pressure is $c_p = 1004$ J/(kg K), compute the temperature increase ΔT implied by your answer to (a).

(c) If, instead, the boundary layer depth started out at sunrise only 10 m deep and remained at that depth throughout the day, what would be the corresponding change of temperature? Why is it much more likely that the boundary layer would deepen quickly after sunrise?

2.5　A Mathematical Description of EM Waves[†]

Maxwell's Equations

We have been able to come quite far in describing the behavior of EM radiation without resorting to many equations. Having laid the groundwork by defining terms and building mental models of electromagnetic waves, we can now tear through a more rigorous mathematical treatment with scarcely a pause for breath.

Just as the Navier-Stokes equation, the hydrostatic approximation, and the Ideal Gas Law serve as the underpinnings for virtually all of atmospheric dynamics, the so-called Maxwell equations govern classical electrodynamics. If one assumes SI units for all variables, these equations take the following form:

$$\nabla \cdot \vec{\mathbf{D}} = \rho, \tag{2.3}$$

$$\nabla \cdot \vec{\mathbf{B}} = 0, \tag{2.4}$$

$$\nabla \times \vec{\mathbf{E}} = -\frac{\partial \vec{\mathbf{B}}}{\partial t}, \tag{2.5}$$

$$\nabla \times \vec{\mathbf{H}} = \vec{\mathbf{J}} + \frac{\partial \vec{\mathbf{D}}}{\partial t}, \tag{2.6}$$

where $\vec{\mathbf{D}}$ is the *electric displacement*, $\vec{\mathbf{E}}$ is the *electric field*, $\vec{\mathbf{B}}$ is the *magnetic induction*, $\vec{\mathbf{H}}$ is the *magnetic field*, ρ is the density of electric charge, and $\vec{\mathbf{J}}$ is the electric current vector.

If we further assume (quite reasonably, for most materials) that we are dealing with a macroscopic, homogeneous medium whose electrical and magnetic properties are (i) directionally isotropic and (ii) linear with respect to $\vec{\mathbf{E}}$ and $\vec{\mathbf{B}}$, then

$$\vec{\mathbf{D}} = \varepsilon_0(1 + \chi)\vec{\mathbf{E}}, \tag{2.7}$$

where ε_0 is the *permittivity* of free space and χ is the electric *susceptibility* of the medium, which describes the degree to which the material becomes electrically polarized under the influence of an external field. Also,

$$\vec{\mathbf{B}} = \mu\vec{\mathbf{H}}, \tag{2.8}$$

where μ is the magnetic *permeability* of the medium, and

$$\vec{\mathbf{J}} = \sigma\vec{\mathbf{E}}, \tag{2.9}$$

where σ is the *conductivity*. Finally, we can usually assume that the charge density ρ is effectively zero.

With the above assumptions, Maxwell's equations reduce to

$$\nabla \cdot \vec{\mathbf{E}} = 0, \tag{2.10}$$

$$\nabla \cdot \vec{\mathbf{H}} = 0, \tag{2.11}$$

$$\nabla \times \vec{\mathbf{E}} = -\mu \frac{\partial \vec{\mathbf{H}}}{\partial t}, \tag{2.12}$$

$$\nabla \times \vec{\mathbf{H}} = \sigma \vec{\mathbf{E}} + \varepsilon_0 (1 + \chi) \frac{\partial \vec{\mathbf{E}}}{\partial t}. \tag{2.13}$$

Note that only two field variables, $\vec{\mathbf{E}}$ and $\vec{\mathbf{H}}$, appear in the above four equations. The (complex) parameters σ, χ, and μ then determine the relationship between $\vec{\mathbf{E}}$ and $\vec{\mathbf{H}}$ in any given medium.

Time-Harmonic Solution

As discussed in Section 2.2.1, we can always decompose an arbitrary EM disturbance into its various frequency components and consider each frequency separately from the others. In keeping with this approach, we will consider a general time-harmonic electric field of the form

$$\vec{\mathbf{E}}_c(\vec{\mathbf{x}}, t) = \vec{\mathbf{C}}(\vec{\mathbf{x}}) \exp(-i\omega t) \tag{2.14}$$

where $\vec{\mathbf{C}} = \vec{\mathbf{A}} + i\vec{\mathbf{B}}$ is a complex vector field, $\vec{\mathbf{x}}$ is the position vector, and $\omega = 2\pi\nu$ is the angular frequency (radians per second). An analogous representation can be written for the complex magnetic field $\vec{\mathbf{H}}_c$.

Note that the use of complex quantities is strictly a notational convenience; in physical problems, we are almost always interested in just the real part of whatever solutions we derive; e.g.,

$$\vec{\mathbf{E}} = \mathrm{Re}\{\vec{\mathbf{E}}_c\} = \vec{\mathbf{A}} \cos \omega t + \vec{\mathbf{B}} \sin \omega t \tag{2.15}$$

Substituting (2.14) into (2.10)–(2.13), we obtain the following relationships:

$$\nabla \cdot \vec{\mathbf{E}}_c = 0, \tag{2.16}$$

$$\nabla \times \vec{\mathbf{E}}_c = i\omega\mu \vec{\mathbf{H}}_c, \tag{2.17}$$

$$\nabla \cdot \vec{H}_c = 0, \tag{2.18}$$

$$\nabla \times \vec{H}_c = -i\omega\varepsilon\vec{E}_c, \tag{2.19}$$

where the complex permittivity of the medium is defined as

$$\varepsilon = \varepsilon_0(1 + \chi) + i\frac{\sigma}{\omega}. \tag{2.20}$$

Except for ε_0, which is a fundamental, real-valued physical constant, all other parameters depend on the medium under consideration as well as on the frequency ω.

Problem 2.4: Verify that (2.16)–(2.19) follow from (2.3)–(2.9) and (2.14).

Solution for a Plane Wave

Any harmonic electromagnetic field satisfying the above equations is physically realizable. However, we will restrict our attention to solutions describing a *plane wave*. Such solutions have the form

$$\vec{E}_c = \vec{E}_0 \exp(i\vec{k} \cdot \vec{x} - i\omega t), \qquad \vec{H}_c = \vec{H}_0 \exp(i\vec{k} \cdot \vec{x} - i\omega t), \tag{2.21}$$

where $\vec{E}_0$ and $\vec{H}_0$ are constant (complex) vectors, and $\vec{k} = \vec{k}' + i\vec{k}''$ is a complex *wave vector*. Thus

$$\vec{E}_c = \vec{E}_0 \exp(-\vec{k}'' \cdot \vec{x}) \exp[i(\vec{k}' \cdot \vec{x} - \omega t)], \tag{2.22}$$

$$\vec{H}_c = \vec{H}_0 \exp(-\vec{k}'' \cdot \vec{x}) \exp[i(\vec{k}' \cdot \vec{x} - \omega t)]. \tag{2.23}$$

These relationships imply that the vector $\vec{k}'$ is normal to planes of constant phase (and thus indicates the direction of propagation of the wave crests), while $\vec{k}''$ is normal to planes of constant amplitude. The two are not necessarily parallel. When they are, or when $\vec{k}''$ is zero, the wave is called *homogeneous*.

The term $\vec{\mathbf{E}}_0 \exp(-\vec{\mathbf{k}}'' \cdot \vec{\mathbf{x}})$ gives the *amplitude* of the electric wave at location $\vec{\mathbf{x}}$. If $\vec{\mathbf{k}}''$ is zero, then the medium is nonabsorbing, because the amplitude is constant. The quantity $\phi \equiv \vec{\mathbf{k}}' \cdot \vec{\mathbf{x}} - \omega t$ gives the *phase*. The *phase speed* of the wave is given by

$$v = \frac{\omega}{|\vec{\mathbf{k}}'|} \tag{2.24}$$

Substituting (2.21) into (2.16)–(2.19) yields

$$\vec{\mathbf{k}} \cdot \vec{\mathbf{E}}_0 = 0, \tag{2.25}$$

$$\vec{\mathbf{k}} \cdot \vec{\mathbf{H}}_0 = 0, \tag{2.26}$$

$$\vec{\mathbf{k}} \times \vec{\mathbf{E}}_0 = \omega\mu\vec{\mathbf{H}}_0, \tag{2.27}$$

$$\vec{\mathbf{k}} \times \vec{\mathbf{H}}_0 = -\omega\varepsilon\vec{\mathbf{E}}_0. \tag{2.28}$$

The last two equations reveal that, in a plane wave, the oscillating electric and magnetic field vectors are normal both to each other and to the direction of propagation of the wave. This property is depicted schematically in Fig. 2.1 for a horizontally polarized wave.

Problem 2.5: Verify that (2.25) follows from (2.21) and (2.16) by (a) expanding (2.21) in terms of the individual components of the vectors $\vec{\mathbf{E}}_0, \vec{\mathbf{k}}, \vec{\mathbf{x}}$ and (b) substituting this expression into (2.16) and applying the divergence operator ($\nabla\cdot$). The remaining equations (2.26)–(2.28) are derived in an analogous way.

If we now take the vector product of $\vec{\mathbf{k}}$ with both sides of (2.27),

$$\vec{\mathbf{k}} \times (\vec{\mathbf{k}} \times \vec{\mathbf{E}}_0) = \omega\mu\vec{\mathbf{k}} \times \vec{\mathbf{H}}_0 = -\varepsilon\mu\omega^2\vec{\mathbf{E}}_0, \tag{2.29}$$

and use the vector identity

$$\vec{\mathbf{a}} \times (\vec{\mathbf{b}} \times \vec{\mathbf{c}}) = \vec{\mathbf{b}}(\vec{\mathbf{a}} \cdot \vec{\mathbf{c}}) - \vec{\mathbf{c}}(\vec{\mathbf{a}} \cdot \vec{\mathbf{b}}), \tag{2.30}$$

we see from (2.25) that the first term on the right is zero, thus

$$\vec{\mathbf{k}} \cdot \vec{\mathbf{k}} = \varepsilon\mu\omega^2. \tag{2.31}$$

In the case of a homogeneous wave, the above simplifies to

$$(|\vec{\mathbf{k}}'| + i|\vec{\mathbf{k}}''|)^2 = \varepsilon\mu\omega^2 \tag{2.32}$$

or

$$|\vec{\mathbf{k}}'| + i|\vec{\mathbf{k}}''| = \omega\sqrt{\varepsilon\mu}. \tag{2.33}$$

Phase Speed

In a vacuum, $\vec{\mathbf{k}}'' = 0$, the permittivity of free space $\varepsilon \equiv \varepsilon_0 = 8.854 \times 10^{-12}$ F m^{-1}, and the magnetic permeability $\mu \equiv \mu_0 = 1.257 \times 10^{-6}$ N A^{-2}. From (2.24), we have the following phase speed in a vacuum:

$$c \equiv 1/\sqrt{\varepsilon_0\mu_0}. \tag{2.34}$$

If we substitute the above numerical values of ε_0 and μ_0 into this expression, we obtain the speed of light in a vacuum $c = 2.998 \times 10^8$ m s^{-1}.

In a nonvacuum, we can write

$$|\vec{\mathbf{k}}'| + i|\vec{\mathbf{k}}''| = \omega\sqrt{\frac{\varepsilon\mu}{\varepsilon_0\mu_0}}\sqrt{\varepsilon_0\mu_0} = \frac{\omega N}{c}, \tag{2.35}$$

where the complex *index of refraction* N is given by

$$N \equiv \sqrt{\frac{\varepsilon\mu}{\varepsilon_0\mu_0}} = \frac{c}{c'}, \tag{2.36}$$

with $c' \equiv 1/\sqrt{\varepsilon\mu}$. If N happens to be pure real (i.e., if $\vec{\mathbf{k}}'' = 0$ and the medium is therefore nonabsorbing), then c' may be interpreted as the phase speed of the wave within the medium. Even in absorbing media, this is still a reasonable, though approximate, way to view c'.

For most physical media, $N > 1$, which implies a reduced speed of light relative to that in a vacuum. It is important to keep in mind that N is not only a property of a particular medium but also generally a strong function of frequency.

The Poynting Vector

Any electromagnetic wave (harmonic or not) transports energy through space at the speed of light. The instantaneous direction and magnitude of the transported energy is given by the *Poynting*[2] *vector*, which is defined (for SI units) as

$$\vec{S} = \vec{E} \times \vec{H} \quad . \tag{2.37}$$

The above is an instantaneous value and gives the power per unit area transported by the disturbance. In the case of a time-harmonic wave, we are interested in the average over one complete cycle:

$$F = \langle \vec{S} \rangle = \langle \vec{E} \times \vec{H} \rangle \quad , \tag{2.38}$$

which is just the flux density of the wave as measure through a surface normal to the direction of propagation. For a harmonic wave, the above reduces to

$$F = \frac{1}{2} c \varepsilon_0 E^2 \quad , \tag{2.39}$$

where E is the scalar amplitude of the oscillating electric field at that location. The key point to note here is that the flux density is proportional to the *square* of the amplitude of the electromagnetic wave.

Absorption

The scalar amplitude of our harmonic plane wave at location $\vec{x}$ is

$$E = |\vec{E}_0 \exp(-\vec{k}'' \cdot \vec{x})| \quad . \tag{2.40}$$

From (2.39), it follows that, for a plane wave with initial flux density F_0 at $\vec{x} = 0$,

$$F = F_0 [\exp(-\vec{k}'' \cdot \vec{x})]^2 = F_0 \exp(-2\vec{k}'' \cdot \vec{x}). \tag{2.41}$$

---

[2]The name is easy to remember, because the Poynting vector *points* in the direction of the energy transport by the wave. However the name is simply an odd coincidence, as it was named after the English physicist John Henry Poynting (1852–1914).

If we now consider a plane wave propagating in the x direction, and note from (2.35) that

$$|\vec{k}''| = \frac{\omega}{c}\text{Im}\{N\} = \frac{\omega n_i}{c} = \frac{2\pi\nu n_i}{c} \qquad (2.42)$$

where ν is the frequency in Hz, we have

$$F = F_0 e^{-\beta_a x}, \qquad (2.43)$$

where the *absorption coefficient* β_a is defined as

$$\beta_a = \frac{4\pi\nu n_i}{c} = \frac{4\pi n_i}{\lambda}, \qquad (2.44)$$

with λ the wavelength of the radiation in a vacuum. In summary, the quantity $1/\beta_a$ gives the distance required for the wave's energy to be attenuated to $e^{-1} \approx 37\%$ of its original value.

Problem 2.6:   Within a certain material, an EM wave with $\lambda = 1\,\mu m$ is attenuated to 10% of its original intensity after propagating 10 cm. Determine the imaginary part of the index of refraction n_i.

Problem 2.7:   For red light ($\lambda = 0.64\,\mu m$), n_i in pure water is approximately 1.3×10^{-8}; for blue light ($\lambda = 0.48\,\mu m$), $n_i \approx 1.0 \times 10^{-9}$. The deep end of a typical home swimming pool is approximately 2.5 m deep. Compute the fraction of each wavelength that survives the two-way trip to the bottom of the pool and back, when illuminated (and viewed) from directly above. In light of your findings (and in view of the appearance of most swimming pools as seen from the air), comment on the common assumption that water is "colorless."

2.6 Quantum Properties of Radiation

Now that I have succeeded in indoctrinating you with the wave-based mental model of EM radiation, including even a neat mathematical expression for a plane wave, I will demolish your newly won confidence by asserting that you should view EM radiation not as waves but as particles! At least some of the time.

It may surprise you to learn that Albert Einstein won his Nobel Prize not for his famous theory of relativity but rather for his explanation in 1905 of the *photoelectric effect*. This effect refers to the phenomenon by which electrons are jarred loose from a material surface exposed to light in a vacuum. A previously mysterious aspect of the photoelectric effect had been the observation that incident light with wavelengths longer than a certain threshold, no matter how intense, would not generate free electrons, whereas light with shorter wavelengths readily dislodges the electrons and continues to do so, sporadically at least, no matter how weak the illumination.

The essence of Einstein's explanation was that light falls on a surface not as a smoothly continuous flux of wave energy, but rather as a staccato hail of little discrete packets of energy, called *photons*. The energy content E of each individual photon, and therefore that photon's ability to knock electrons loose from the surface, is determined solely by the frequency or wavelength of the radiation via the relationship

$$E = h\nu,\qquad(2.45)$$

where ν is the frequency and $h = 6.626 \times 10^{-34}$ J s is Planck's constant.

Moreover, you can't have just part of a photon; therefore very low intensity light deposits discrete packets of energy on a surface in a manner analogous to the occasional random splashes of fat raindrops on your windshield at the early onset of a rain shower. Thus, if monochromatic radiation of wavelength λ deposits F watts per unit area on a surface, then this corresponds to

$$\mathcal{N} = \frac{F}{h\nu} = \frac{F\lambda}{hc}\qquad(2.46)$$

photons per unit area per unit time. For fluxes of the magnitude typically encountered in the atmosphere, $\mathcal{N}$ is rather large, and it is therefore hard to distinguish the effects of discrete particles, just as it is hard to distinguish the contributions of each individual raindrop to your growing wetness when you get caught out in a heavy downpour.

Problem 2.8:   Only radiation with wavelengths smaller than 0.2424 μm is capable of dissociating molecular oxygen into atomic oxygen, according to the reaction

$$O_2 + photon \rightarrow O + O$$

Based on this information, how much energy is apparently required to break the molecular bond of a single molecule of O_2?

Problem 2.9:   A small light source emits 1 W of radiation uniformly in all directions. The wavelength of the light is 0.5 μm.

    (a) How many photons per second are emitted by the light source?

    (b) If the light source were on the moon and were viewed by a telescope on Earth having a 20 cm diameter circular aperture, how many photons per second would the telescope collect? Ignore atmospheric attenuation. Assume a distance $D_m = 3.84 \times 10^5$ km between the moon and the earth.

The above *quantum* description of EM radiation is completely at odds with the previous *wave* description. They cannot both be true. And yet they are! Do not trouble yourself by trying to mentally reconcile the two models — countless smart people have tried throughout the twentieth century, and all have failed to explain this paradox in terms most people can visualize.

The important things for you to know are: 1) when radiation must be viewed as waves, 2) when it must be viewed as a shower of particles, and 3) when it doesn't matter.

As a general rule of thumb, the wave nature of radiation matters when computing the *scattering and reflection* properties of atmospheric particles (air molecules, aerosols, cloud droplets, raindrops) and surfaces. By contrast, the quantized nature of radiation, and thus (2.45), comes to the forefront when considering *absorption and emission* of radiation by individual atoms and molecules, including photochemical reactions. Finally, for calculations of large-scale transport of radiation in the atmosphere, the effects of both types of interactions will have already been deeply buried in some generic extinction and scattering coefficients and can be conveniently put out of your mind altogether.

2.7 Flux and Intensity

I have already briefly introduced the concept of *flux density* (or *flux* for short[3]) as a measure of the total energy per unit time (or power) per unit area transported by EM radiation through a plane (or deposited on a surface). It is now time to extend our understanding of this property and to introduce a closely related quantity, called the *radiant intensity* , or just *intensity* for short. In some books, the term *radiance* is substituted for intensity.

Flux and intensity are the two measures of the strength of an EM radiation field that are central to most problems in atmospheric science. The two are intimately related, as we shall see shortly.

2.7.1 Flux

Recall first of all that the flux F refers to the rate at which radiation is incident on, or passes through, a flat surface. Without further qualification, flux is expressed in units of watts per square meter. The surface may be real (e.g., the ground, or the top of a cloud layer) or it may be imaginary (e.g., an arbitrary level in the atmosphere). Often, but not always, it is taken to be horizontal. Other times it may be assumed to be perpendicular to a single source of radiation, such as the sun.

Note that a flux of natural (incoherent) radiation expressed sim-

---

[3]Strictly speaking, an energy *flux* has units of W, whereas the *flux density* is the flux *per unit area* and therefore has units of W m^{-2}. Meteorologists are almost invariably concerned with quantities that are expressed per unit area, volume, mass, etc. Therefore, when a meteorologist says "flux," it is generally understood that she *means* "flux per unit area" or flux density.

ply in W/m^2 *must* be a broadband quantity.[4] That is, it includes energy contributions from all wavelengths between some specified (or implied) limits λ_1 and λ_2. Those limits might encompass all possible wavelengths (i.e., $\lambda_1 = 0$, $\lambda_2 = \infty$), or they might define a somewhat narrower range. However, the range cannot be zero ($\lambda_1 = \lambda_2$), because the power contained in that range would then also be zero!

It is, however, possible to define a *monochromatic flux* (also known as *spectral* flux) F_λ as follows:

$$F_\lambda = \lim_{\Delta\lambda \to 0} \frac{F(\lambda, \lambda + \Delta\lambda)}{\Delta\lambda}, \tag{2.47}$$

where $F(\lambda, \lambda + \Delta\lambda)$ is the flux in W/m^2 contributed by radiation with wavelengths between λ and $\lambda + \Delta\lambda$. The dimensions of the monochromatic flux are not just power per unit area but rather *power per unit area per unit wavelength*. Typical units would thus be W m^{-2} μm^{-1}.

Having defined the monochromatic (or spectral) flux as above, you get the broadband flux over some extended range of wavelength $[\lambda_1, \lambda_2]$ by integrating over the appropriate range of wavelength:

$$F(\lambda_1, \lambda_2) = \int_{\lambda_1}^{\lambda_2} F_\lambda \, d\lambda . \tag{2.48}$$

Problem 2.10: The total radiation flux incident on a surface due to wavelengths between 0.3 μm and 1.0 μm is 200 W m^{-2}. (a) What is the average *spectral* flux within this interval? Give your answer in units of W m^{-2} μm^{-1}. (b) If the spectral flux is constant with wavelength, then what is the total flux contributed by wavelengths just between 0.4 μm and 0.5 μm? (c) What is the total flux (in W m^{-2}) contributed by radiation of exactly 0.5 μm wavelength?

Let's illustrate the concept of flux with a concrete example. If you mark out an area on flat ground out in the open, the amount

---

[4]This is not necessarily true for artificial coherent radiation, for which finite power may be associated with exactly one wavelength, rather than being distributed over a range of wavelengths.

of daylight falling on it can be measured in watts per square meter. This is the *incident flux* of solar radiation, and it determines how much total radiation from the sun is available to be absorbed. If a cloud passes in front of the sun, the incident flux temporarily decreases because the transmission of radiation from the sun to the surface is partially blocked. As the afternoon wears on, the incident flux steadily decreases, this time because the light from the sun strikes the surface at an increasingly oblique angle, spreading the same energy over a larger and larger area.

An important point to remember is that the flux makes no distinction concerning where the radiation is coming *from*. 100 W m^{-2} incident on our front lawn is 100 W m^{-2}, regardless of whether it is coming from all directions more or less equally on an overcast day or primarily one particular direction (that of the sun) on a crystal-clear afternoon. *In order to completely characterize the radiation field at a given location, we must know not only the flux but also the direction(s) from which the radiation is coming and thus also in which direction(s) it is going.* This directional information is embodied in the radiant *intensity*.

2.7.2 Intensity

The radiant *intensity* I tells you in detail both the strength and direction of various sources contributing to the incident flux on a surface. For visible radiation, intensity corresponds roughly to the "brightness" your eyes see looking backward along a ray of incoming radiation. Thus, if you lie flat on your back and look up at the sky, you can visually map out which regions of the sky are associated with high radiant intensity and therefore contribute most strongly to the total incident solar flux at your location. The sun itself, if not blocked by a cloud, is seen as a very localized high intensity source, whereas the clear sky is a relatively uniform source of rather low intensity radiation. Isolated clouds, as seen from your vantage point, may be either brighter or darker than the clear sky, depending on how thick they are and from what angle they are viewed, relative to the sun.

Consider again what happens if a small cumulus cloud passes between you and the sun, casting you and your marked out area of ground into shadow. You can now look directly toward the sun without hurting your eyes. From this you can conclude that the intensity of radiation from that direction has been greatly reduced. But the contributions from the rest of the sky are unaffected. The total incident shortwave *flux* is therefore reduced but not eliminated. Although you are now in the shadow of the cloud, it is by no means pitch dark.

Clearly, there is a very close relationship between flux and intensity. In words, the flux incident on a surface is obtained by integrating the contributions of intensity from all possible directions visible from that surface. It is time to delve into the mathematics of this relationship. We will begin by setting up the necessary machinery.

Spherical Polar Coordinates

In any discussion of radiation, direction plays an all-important role. We therefore need to adopt a convention for describing directions. There is no single "right" choice, but one that is very convenient in atmospheric radiation is based on spherical polar coordinates. Fig. 2.3 depicts the geometry.

In this system, the *zenith* angle θ measures the angle from some reference direction, usually the local vertical. Thus, directly overhead usually corresponds to $\theta = 0$. In this case, the horizon corresponds to $\theta = \pi/2$ radians, or 90°. $\pi/2 < \theta < \pi$ corresponds to directions below the horizon, with $\theta = \pi$ being straight down ("nadir").

The *azimuthal* angle ϕ measures the angle counterclockwise from a reference point on the horizon, so that $0 < \phi < 2\pi$. It is not usually terribly important which point of the compass is used as the reference in any given application, and it is often chosen to be whatever is most natural for the problem at hand, such as the direction of the sun.

Any possible direction above or below the horizon may thus be described via the two angles θ and ϕ. Sometimes directions may be expressed abstractly in terms of a unit vector $\hat{\Omega}$, in which case no particular coordinate system is implied. Thus the same direction $\hat{\Omega}$ could be represented by $[\sqrt{2}/2, 0, \sqrt{2}/2]$ in (x, y, z)-coordinates, by $[\pi/4, 0]$ in (θ, ϕ)-coordinates when $\theta = 0$ defines the vertical

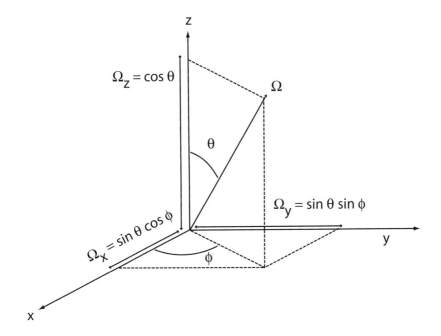

Fig. 2.3: The relationship between Cartesian and spherical coordinates.

direction, or even by $[0,0]$ if $\theta = 0$ should for some reason be chosen to coincide with the direction of the sun at a time when the latter is $45°$ above the horizon.

Solid Angle

Another essential concept is that of *solid angle*. Surprisingly many new students of atmospheric radiation find this concept confusing, presumably because they haven't had occasion to consciously use it before, unlike the angles we have been measuring with protractors since third grade. But it's really very simple: *solid angle is to "regular" angle as area is to length.* You can think of solid angle as something you might measure in "square radians" or "square degrees", except the actual unit used is called the *steradian*. We will give a precise definition of this unit later.

In absolute terms, the sun has a certain diameter in kilometers and a certain cross-sectional area in km². But absolute dimensions are often of secondary importance in radiative transfer, compared with *angular* dimensions, which describe how big an object or source of radiation *looks* from a particular vantage point. Thus, what matters for solar radiation reaching the earth is that the sun's disk has a particular angular diameter in units of degrees or radians, and it also subtends (or presents) a certain solid angle in units of steradians. Solid angle is thus a measure of how much of your visual field of view is occupied by an object. For example, the sun subtends a much larger solid angle as viewed from the planet Mercury than it does from Earth. Also, from our perspective here on Earth, the full moon subtends nearly the same solid angle as the Sun, even though the latter body is much larger in absolute terms. A half moon, of course, subtends half the solid angle of the full moon.

Definition of Steradian

Now that you understand what solid angle *is*, you can appreciate a simple definition of the unit *steradian* (abbreviation sr). Imagine you are at the center of a sphere of unit radius — it doesn't matter whether the unit is a kilometer, a mile, a furlong or what have you. The total surface area of the sphere is 4π square units. *Likewise, the combined solid angle represented by every direction you can possibly look is 4π steradians.* The surface area of just one half of the sphere is 2π units squared. *Likewise, the entire sky above the horizon* (or "celestial dome") *subtends a solid angle of 2π steradians, as does (separately) the lower hemisphere of your field of vision, representing everything below the horizon.*

Conceptually, you can determine the solid angle subtended by any object by tracing its outline on your unit sphere and then measuring the actual surface area of the tracing. (Note the analogy to radians as a measure of arc length on the unit circle.) This is generally not a practical approach, however, so we instead invoke our polar coordinate system so as to be able to define an infinitesimal increment of solid angle as follows:

$$d\omega = \sin\theta \, d\theta \, d\phi \, . \tag{2.49}$$

This relationship is depicted schematically in Fig. 2.4.

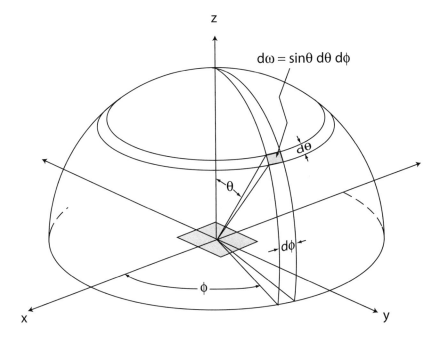

Fig. 2.4: The relationship between solid angle and polar coordinates.

In other words, if you paint an infinitesimal rectangle on the surface of your unit sphere, and it has angular dimensions $d\theta$ (zenith angle) and $d\phi$ (azimuth angle) and is positioned at θ, then the above expression gives you the increment of solid angle subtended. Why does $\sin\theta$ appear in there? Simple: for the same reason that a $1°$ latitude by $1°$ longitude box encompasses far less real estate near the North Pole than near the equator, because of the convergence of lines of equal ϕ to a point.

Now let's demonstrate that we can recover the expected value of 4π steradians for the entire sphere:

$$\int_{4\pi} d\omega = \int_0^{2\pi}\int_0^{\pi} \sin\theta\, d\theta\, d\phi = 2\pi \int_0^{\pi} \sin\theta\, d\theta = 4\pi. \qquad (2.50)$$

Note that the notation used in the left-most integral expresses the *abstract* idea that we are integrating over the full sphere (4π steradians). This notation makes no assumption about the coordinate system that we will use to actually perform the integration. The integral just to the right of it translates the abstract integration over

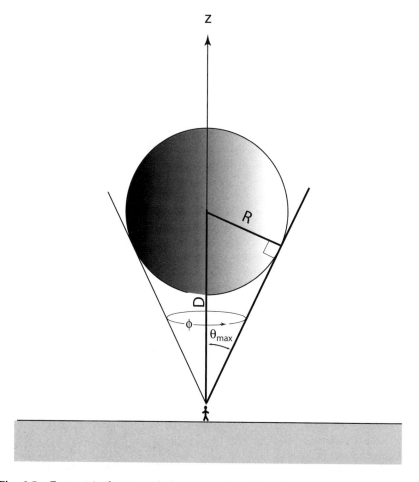

Fig. 2.5: Geometric framework for computing the solid angle subtended by a sphere of radius R whose center is a distance D from the observer.

all directions into a specific double integral using our coordinates θ and ϕ, based on (2.49). If we were to use a different coordinate system to describe directions, then the integrals on the right-hand side might take a different form, but the final result for this problem, if everything is done correctly, should still be 4π steradians!

Problem 2.11: Consider a cloud that, when viewed from a point on the surface, occupies the portion of the sky defined by $\pi/4 < \theta < \pi/2$ and $0 < \phi < \pi/8$.

(a) What is the solid angle subtended by the cloud?
(b) What percentage of the sky is covered by this cloud?

Problem 2.12: The moon is at a mean distance $D_m = 3.84 \times 10^5$ km from the earth; the Sun is at a mean distance $D_s = 1.496 \times 10^8$ km. The radius of the moon is $R_m = 1.74 \times 10^3$ km; the radius of the sun is $R_s = 6.96 \times 10^5$ km.

(a) Compute the angular diameter (in degrees) subtended by the sun and the moon. Refer to Fig. 2.5 for help visualizing the geometry of this problem. (b) Compute the solid angle subtended by the sun and the moon. (c) Which appears larger from Earth, and by what percentage do the two solid angles differ? (d) If the above values were constant, would it be possible to explain the occurrence of total solar eclipses?

Formal Definition of Intensity

Having defined solid angle, we are now in a position to attach a precise definition to the term radiant intensity. In words, *intensity* $I(\hat{\Omega})$ *is the flux* (measured on a surface normal to the beam) *per unit solid angle traveling in a particular direction* $\hat{\Omega}$. Visualize the above definition as follows:

- Looking in the direction $-\hat{\Omega}$, identify a very small element of the scene with solid angle $\delta\omega$.

- Measure, normal to the beam, the flux δF of radiation arriving just from that small region, while excluding all other contributions.

- The intensity in that direction is then given by

$$I(\hat{\Omega}) = \frac{\delta F}{\delta\omega} \, . \tag{2.51}$$

This recipe is strictly valid only when $\delta\omega$ is vanishingly small, but it's a reasonable approximation for finite solid angles as well, as long as the maximum arc subtended by the region in question is much less than one radian — say 5° or less — *and* as long as the intensity is uniform throughout the region.

Problem 2.13: The broadband flux of solar radiation that reaches the top of the atmosphere is approximately 1370 W m^{-2}, when measured on a plane normal to the beam. Combine this with the solid angle you derived in a previous problem to compute the average radiant intensity of the sun's surface.

Problem 2.14: A typical laser pointer used in lectures puts out 5 mW of power into a nearly parallel beam with a diameter of 5 mm. (a) What is the *flux density* normal to the beam, and how does it compare with the typical clear-sky solar flux (at ground level) on a surface normal to the beam of 1000 W m^{-2}? (b) If beam can be assumed to be confined to a cone of angular diameter 1 milliradian, what is the *intensity* of the beam in watts per steradian, and how does this compare with the intensity of sunlight computed from the above solar flux and an angular diameter of 0.5° for the sun's disk?

Conservation of Intensity

You have probably known since you were small that the ability of a light source to illuminate an object weakens rapidly with increasing distance. A flashlight illuminates a book under the bedcovers much more brightly than it does an animal lurking in those bushes at the edge of the campsite. Likewise, the earth is much more brightly illuminated by the sun than is Pluto.

You might hastily infer from these observations that the *intensity* of radiation associated with a given point at the source is also a function of the distance of the observer. If you were talking about the incident *flux*, you would be right. This is not the case for intensity however. On the contrary, *within a vacuum or other transparent medium, radiant intensity is conserved along any optical path.*[5]

To verify this principle in a simple case, tape a sheet of white paper to the wall at eye level. Look at it from a couple feet away; then back up and look at it from across the room. Although its apparent size (solid angle) changes with distance, its apparent brightness does not (assuming you didn't adjust the room lights!).

The same principle applies to optical systems such as lenses, mirrors, prisms, etc., as long as we ignore losses due to absorption and/or partial reflections (e.g., from the surface of lenses) *and* as long as we measure the intensity in the same medium (e.g., air) in all cases. A magnifying glass makes objects appear larger, but it has little effect on the object's brightness. The same is true of binoculars and telescopes.[6]

Intensity and Polarization[†]

For many applications, one need only keep track of the total *scalar* intensity I of a stream of radiation as defined above. However, we previously alluded to the polarization properties of EM radiation, and it is sometimes necessary to keep track of these as well. One reason might be a need for greater accuracy in radiative transfer calculations, as disregarding polarization almost always entails an approximation, especially when scattering by particles or surfaces is important. Another occasion arises when you are measuring radiation of one particular polarization (e.g, linear vertical or horizontal). This is often the case for microwave remote sensing instruments.

---

[5]The intensity *can* change when the radiation passes from one medium to another.

[6]But wait, you say. Telescopes definitely do make stars appear brighter: many that are invisible to the naked eye become clearly visible through a telescope. How can this behavior be reconciled with the previous assertions? The explanation is that stars subtend a angle far too small for the eye to resolve. As a result, the eye responds not to the intensity of the star but rather to the total flux integrated over a finite solid angle. That solid angle is determined by the eye's resolving power. Thus, moderately near-sighted individuals will see a few bright stars but will miss many more that are easily detectable by sharp-eyed people. A telescope increases the solid angle subtended by a star, and thus the total flux from that direction, making it more easily visible to everyone.

When polarization must be considered, we require a representation of intensity that is capable of providing complete information about the state of polarization. One such representation gives the intensity as a four-element vector

$$\mathbf{I} = \begin{pmatrix} I \\ Q \\ U \\ V \end{pmatrix}. \qquad (2.52)$$

The elements of this vector are called the *Stokes parameters*. The first element, I, is the same as the scalar intensity we have already discussed. The remaining elements Q, U, V contain information concerning the *degree* of polarization (recall that incoherent radiation can be polarized to any degree, whereas coherent radiation is always fully polarized), about the *preferred orientation* of the polarization, and about the *nature* of the polarization – circular, linear, or something in between. In particular, the *degree of polarization* is defined as $\sqrt{Q^2 + U^2 + V^2}/I$. The ratios $\sqrt{Q^2 + U^2}/I$ and V/I, respectively, are *the degree of linear polarization* and *the degree of circular polarization*.

Thus, for completely unpolarized radiation, $Q = U = V = 0$, and for fully polarized radiation

$$I^2 = Q^2 + U^2 + V^2. \qquad (2.53)$$

It is beyond the scope of this introductory text to give a detailed electromagnetic definition of each of the Stokes parameters.[7] However, some illustrative examples are given in Table 2.1.

How is the vector representation of intensity actually used? In the scalar case (i.e., when we're ignoring polarization), most interactions of radiation with matter can be described via the multiplication of the intensity by a scalar coefficient, which we will arbitrarily denote A. Thus,

$$I_{new} = A \cdot I_{old}. \qquad (2.54)$$

---

[7] A good overview is given in Section 2.3 of S94.

Table 2.1: Examples of Stokes parameter values.

Description	[I,Q,U,V]
Horizontally polarized	$[1,1,0,0]$
Vertically polarized	$[1,-1,0,0]$
Linearly polarized at +45°	$[1,0,1,0]$
Linearly polarized at −45°	$[1,0,-1,0]$
Right circularly polarized	$[1,0,0,1]$
Left circularly polarized	$[1,0,0,-1]$
Unpolarized	$[1,0,0,0]$

For example, if the process in question is a reflection from a surface, the coefficient A might represent a scalar reflectivity value ranging from 0 to 1.

In the fully polarized case, the scalar coefficient A is replaced by a 4×4 *Mueller matrix* **A**, so that the new intensity is described via the matrix operation

$$\mathbf{I}_{new} = \mathbf{A}\mathbf{I}_{old}. \tag{2.55}$$

Thus, the Mueller matrix describes not only how the overall intensity changes but also how the polarization changes. For example, an optical device represented by the following Mueller matrix **A** will transform a beam of radiation having arbitrary polarization into one that is 100% right-circularly polarized:

$$\mathbf{A} = \frac{1}{2}\begin{pmatrix} 1 & 1 & 0 & 0 \\ 0 & 0 & 0 & 0 \\ 0 & 0 & 0 & 0 \\ 1 & 1 & 0 & 0 \end{pmatrix}. \tag{2.56}$$

Problem 2.15: Demonstrate that (2.56) does what is claimed.

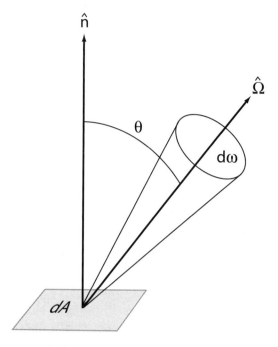

Fig. 2.6: The flux density of radiation carried by a beam in the direction $\hat{\Omega}$ through a surface element dA is proportional to $\cos\theta = \hat{n} \cdot \hat{\Omega}$.

2.7.3   Relationship between Flux and Intensity

We previously defined the flux F as the total power incident on a unit area of surface. We then defined intensity in terms of a flux contribution arriving from a very small element of solid angle $d\omega$ centered on a given direction of propagation $\hat{\Omega}$. It follows that the flux incident on, passing through, or emerging from an arbitrary surface is given by an integral over the relevant range of solid angle of the intensity.

Let us start by considering the flux emerging *upward* from a horizontal surface: it must be an integral of the intensity $I(\hat{\Omega})$ over all possible directions $\hat{\Omega}$ directed skyward; i.e., into the 2π steradians of solid angle corresponding to the upper hemisphere. There is one minor complication, however. Recall that intensity is defined in terms of flux per unit solid angle *normal to the beam*. For our horizontal surface, however, only one direction is normal; radiation from all other directions passes through the surface at an oblique angle (Fig.

2.6). Thus, we must weight the contributions to the flux by the cosine of the incidence angle relative to the normal vector $\hat{n}$. For the upward-directed flux $F^\uparrow$, we therefore have the following relationship:

$$F^\uparrow = \int_{2\pi} I^\uparrow(\hat{\Omega}) \hat{n} \cdot \hat{\Omega} \, d\omega. \tag{2.57}$$

The above expression is generic: it doesn't depend on one's choice of coordinate system. In practice, it is convenient to again introduce spherical polar coordinates, with the z-axis normal to the surface:

$$F^\uparrow = \int_0^{2\pi} \int_0^{\pi/2} I^\uparrow(\theta, \phi) \cos\theta \sin\theta \, d\theta d\phi \,, \tag{2.58}$$

where we have used (2.49) to express $d\omega$ in terms of θ and ϕ.

For the downward flux, we integrate over the lower hemisphere, so we have

$$F^\downarrow = -\int_0^{2\pi} \int_{\pi/2}^{\pi} I^\downarrow(\theta, \phi) \cos\theta \sin\theta \, d\theta d\phi \,. \tag{2.59}$$

Since I is always positive, the above definitions always yield positive values for $F^\uparrow$ and $F^\downarrow$.

Key fact: For the special case that the intensity is *isotropic* — that is, I is a constant for all directions in the hemisphere, then the above integrals can be evaluated to yield

$$F = \pi I \,. \tag{2.60}$$

Key fact: The *net flux* is defined as the difference between upward- and downward-directed fluxes:

$$F^{\text{net}} \equiv F^\uparrow - F^\downarrow \,, \tag{2.61}$$

which can be expanded as

$$F^{\text{net}} = \int_0^{2\pi} \int_0^{\pi} I(\theta, \phi) \cos\theta \sin\theta \, d\theta d\phi = \int_{4\pi} I(\hat{\Omega}) \hat{n} \cdot \hat{\Omega} \, d\omega. \tag{2.62}$$

Note, by the way, that the notation used throughout this subsection implies that we are relating a *broadband intensity* to a *broadband flux*. Identical relationships hold between the *monochromatic intensity* I_λ and the monochromatic fluxes $F_\lambda^\uparrow$ and $F_\lambda^\downarrow$.

Problem 2.16: If the intensity of radiation incident on a surface is uniform from all directions and denoted by the constant I, verify that the total flux is πI, as stated by (2.60). Note that this approximately describes the illumination of a horizontal surface under a heavily overcast sky. It also describes the relationship between the flux and intensity of radiation *leaving* a surface, if that surface is emitting radiation of uniform intensity in all directions.

Problem 2.17: As noted above, when the radiant intensity incident on a flat surface is isotropic with intensity I, the resulting flux is πI. The power intercepted by a circular flat plate of radius r is therefore $P = \pi^2 r^2 I$, assuming that it is illuminated from only one side. How much power is intercepted by a *sphere* of radius r exposed to the same source? Hint: There are various ways to reach the same conclusion, some of which are more cumbersome than necessary. Try to find a simple but compelling geometric argument.

Problem 2.18: Compute the flux from an overhead spherical sun, as seen from a planet in an orbit of radius D, given that the sun has radius R_s and a uniform intensity I_s. Make no assumptions about the size of D relative to R_s. Consider the radius of the planet itself to be negligible. Use two different methods for your calculation:

(a) Method 1: Integrate the intensity over the solid angle subtended by the sun, with the usual cosine-weighting relative to the local vertical. You will need to derive an exact expression for the solid angle subtended by the Sun's disk for arbitrary $D > R_s$ (see Fig. 2.5).

(b) Method 2: Compute the flux density emerging from the surface of the sun, translate that into a total power emitted by the sun, and then distribute that power over the surface of a sphere of radius D.

Do your two solutions agree?

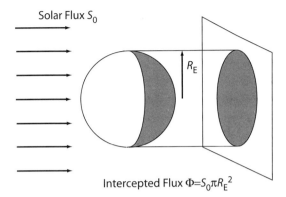

Solar Flux S_0

R_E

Intercepted Flux $\Phi = S_0 \pi R_E^2$

Fig. 2.7: The total flux of solar radiation intercepted by the earth is equal to the product of the incident flux density S_0 and the area of the earth's shadow.

2.8 Applications to Meteorology, Climatology, and Remote Sensing

Of fundamental importance to the global climate is the input of energy from the sun and its spatial and temporal distribution. This input is a function of two variables: 1) the flux of solar radiation incident on the top of the atmosphere, and 2) the fraction of that flux that is absorbed by either the surface or the atmosphere at each point in the earth-atmosphere system. The second of these depends in a complex way on distributions of clouds and absorbing gases in the atmosphere, as well as on the absorbing properties of the surface. These are all issues that will be taken up in the remainder of this book. The first variable, however, can already be understood in terms of the material presented in this chapter.

2.8.1 Global Insolation

The first question that may be asked is, how much *total* solar radiation Φ is incident on the earth's atmosphere, on average? This question is easily solved by computing how much of the Sun's output is intercepted by the earth's disk. That is, given that the mean solar flux at Earth's mean distance from the Sun is $S_0 = 1370$ W m^{-2}, what cross-sectional area is presented to that flux by the earth (i.e., how big of a shadow does the earth cast)? The answer of course[8] is $A = \pi R_E^2$, where the mean radius of the earth is $R_E = 6373$ km (Fig. 2.7). Thus

$$\Phi = S_0 \pi R_E^2 = 1.74 \times 10^{17} \text{ W} \qquad (2.63)$$

This result is consistent with a mean distance of the earth from the sun $(\overline{D}_s)$ of 1.496×10^8 km. The reality, however, is that the earth's orbit is slightly elliptical, with the D_s varying from 1.47×10^8 km near January 3 (perihelion) to 1.52×10^8 km on about July 5 (aphelion). Thus, the top-of-the-atmosphere (TOA) solar flux S varies seasonally from as little as 1330 W m^{-2} in July to as much as 1420 W m^{-2} in January.

Problem 2.19: Derive an expression for S as a function of S_0, $\overline{D}_s$, and D_s. Show that $\Delta S/S_0 \approx -2\Delta D_s/\overline{D}_s$. That is, a positive 1% change in D_s leads to a negative 2% change in S.

2.8.2   Regional and Seasonal Distribution of Insolation

At the distance of the earth from the sun, there is a more or less constant flux of solar radiation of $S_0 = 1370$ W m^{-2}. As noted above, there is actually some deviation from this value over the course of the year, owing to the slightly varying distance of the earth from the sun. Also, the power output P from the sun itself varies slightly over time, due to factors such as sunspot activity as well as other longer term variations that are neither well-measured nor well-understood.

Even ignoring minor variations in S_0 itself, it is clear that solar radiation is not uniformly incident on the earth. The night side of the earth receives no solar radiation at all. And even on the daylight side, the flux of solar radiation measured on a unit horizontal area at the top of the atmosphere depends on the angle of incidence of the sun. If the sun is directly overhead (solar zenith angle $\theta_s = 0$), then the flux is equal to S_0, but if $\theta_s > 0$, then a unit area normal to

---

[8]Strictly speaking, this is an approximation that is valid only because the earth's radius is far smaller than the radius of the earth's orbit.

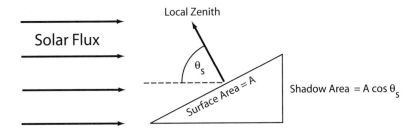

Fig. 2.8: The relationship between local solar zenith angle θ_s and insolation on a local horizontal plane.

the sun's rays projects onto a larger area on the earth's surface (Fig. 2.8). Thus, the solar flux measured on a unit horizontal area is given by

$$F = S_0 \cos \theta_s . \tag{2.64}$$

Now consider the *total* insolation [energy per unit area] at the top of the atmosphere at a single location over the course of a 24-hour period. This insolation is given by

$$W = \int_{t_{\text{sunrise}}}^{t_{\text{sunset}}} S_0 \cos \theta_s(t) \, dt. \tag{2.65}$$

As you can probably guess from this expression (and from everyday experience), W depends on two readily identifiable factors: (1) the length of the day $t_{\text{sunset}} - t_{\text{sunrise}}$, and (2) the average value of $\cos \theta_s(t)$ during the time the sun is up.

At the equator, the length of a day is 12 hours year-round, but the maximum elevation the sun reaches in the course of the day varies with the time of year. Twice a year, at the time of the vernal and autumnal equinox (approximately March 21 and September 21, respectively), the sun passes directly overhead at noon. At other times of year, the minimum zenith angle achieved in the course of the day is equal to the angle of tilt of the earth's axis toward or away from the sun, up to a maximum of 23° at the time of the summer and winter solstices (June 21 and December 21, respectively).

At latitudes poleward of 23°, the sun is never directly overhead, and the minimum zenith angle is always greater than zero. During the summer season, the sun can reach a point fairly high in the sky, whereas in the winter season, the maximum elevation angle is much lower. Moreover, the days are longer in the summer hemisphere than in the winter hemisphere. Indeed, poleward of the arctic or antarctic circles, there is a substantial period of time during the winter when the sun never comes up at all, while during the corresponding period of high summer, the sun never sets. At the poles themselves, the situation is very simple: the sun is up continuously for one half of the year, and the solar zenith angle θ_s is nearly constant over a 24-hour period.[9]

The combined effects of the length of day, of the variation in $\cos \theta_s$, and of the slight variation of the earth's distance from the sun on daily insolation (at the top of the atmosphere) are depicted in Fig. 2.9. Blacked-out areas depict dates and latitudes for which the sun never emerges above the horizon. The dashed line ("declination of the sun") indicates the dates/latitudes at which the noontime sun passes directly overhead. Not surprisingly, this curve coincides with the location of maximum daily insolation over most of the year. However, within a week or two of the summer solstice, the maximum daily insolation is found instead near the pole, where there is daylight for a full 24 hours *and* the sun is a relatively high 23° above the horizon for the entire day.

If you integrate the daily insolation at a given latitude over the entire annual cycle and then divide your result by the number of days in a year, you get the *daily average insolation*, as depicted by the heavy curve labeled "Annual" in Fig. 2.10. Also shown is the daily insolation for the two solstice dates.

In closing, I would like to remind you that the insolation discussed above describes only the amount of solar radiation incident at the top of the atmosphere. It is thus an *upper bound* on the amount of solar radiation that is available to be absorbed by the earth and atmosphere. In reality, a significant fraction of this radiation is immediately reflected back to space by clouds, aerosols, air molecules, and the underlying surface. A good part of the rest of this book is concerned with the processes that determine how much radiation is

---

[9]Atmospheric refraction allows the sun to be visible from a location on the earth's surface when it is actually about 0.5°, or approximately the diameter of the sun's disk, below the horizon. Thus, the sun rises somewhat sooner and sets somewhat later than would be predicted from geometric considerations alone. Therefore, the length of continuous daylight at the North Pole (for example) is actually somewhat longer than the expected six months.

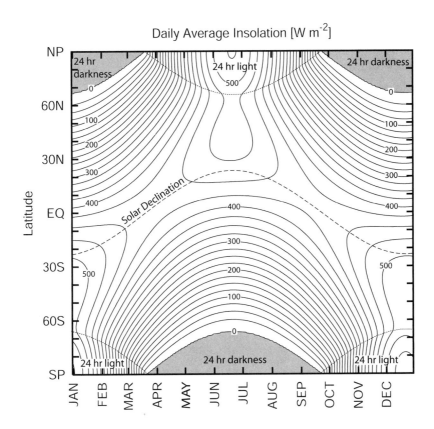

Fig. 2.9: Daily average solar flux at the top of the atmosphere, as a function of latitude and time of year. Contour values are given in units of W m^{-2}

.

absorbed and how much is reflected.

Problem 2.20:   Compute, and compare with Fig. 2.9, the daily average top-of-the-atmosphere insolation [W m^{-2}] for the following two cases: (a) the North Pole at the time of the Northern Hemisphere summer solstice; (b) the equator at the time of the equinox. Assume that the solar flux normal to the beam is a constant 1370 W m^{-2}, and note that the North Pole is inclined 23° toward the Sun at the time of the solstice.

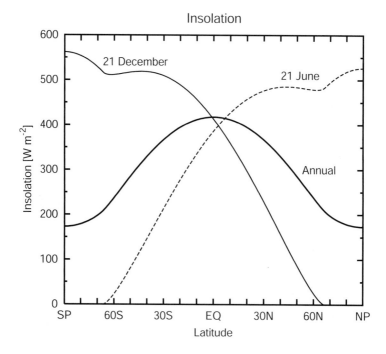

Fig. 2.10: Daily average solar flux at the top of the atmosphere as a function of latitude, for the two solstice dates and averaged over a year.

CHAPTER 3

The Electromagnetic Spectrum

In the previous chapter, we examined how electromagnetic radiation behaves on a purely physical level, without being concerned yet with its detailed interactions with matter. One important observation was that we can treat an arbitrary radiation field as a superposition of many "pure" sinusoidal oscillations. The clearest everyday example of this is the rainbow: white sunlight interacting with raindrops is decomposed into the constituent colors red through violet, each of which corresponds to a narrow range of frequencies. Radiation associated with a given frequency and trajectory in space may be analyzed completely independently of all the others.

We also saw that there is no fundamental constraint on the frequency that EM radiation can exhibit, as long as an oscillator with the right natural frequency and/or an energy source with the minimum required energy is present (recall from Section 2.6 that a single photon has a specific energy determined by its frequency and that an oscillator cannot emit less than that minimum amount).

In a vacuum, the frequency or wavelength of a photon is of little practical consequence, as it cannot be absorbed, scattered, reflected, or refracted but rather is condemned to continue propagating in a straight line forever, regardless. In the presence of matter however, the frequency becomes an all-important property and, to a very great degree, determines the photon's ultimate fate.

There are several reasons why frequency *does* matter in the atmosphere. First of all, as already mentioned several times, the energy of a photon is given by $E = h\nu$. The rate of absorption and emission of photons by the atmosphere is strongly dependent on the precise value of that energy. Among other things, a physical or chemical event requiring a minimum input of energy ΔE_{min} cannot be initiated by a photon with a frequency of less than $\nu_{min} = \Delta E_{min}/h$. Furthermore, the quantum mechanical behavior of matter at the molecular level imposes an even stronger constraint in many cases: to be absorbed, the energy of a photon must almost exactly match a certain well-defined set of values associated with allowable energy levels in that molecule. We will examine these issues in considerable detail in Chapter 9.

Another reason arises from the wave nature of radiation, which comes to the forefront when radiation is scattered or reflected by particles or surfaces. Such interactions arise primarily when the dimensions of a particle are comparable to or larger than the wavelength. Thus, radiation in the visible band is rather weakly scattered by air molecules but strongly scattered by cloud droplets. Longer wavelengths in the microwave band (e.g., radar) are negligibly scattered by cloud droplets but rather strongly by raindrops and hailstones. Longer wavelengths still (e.g., AM radio, with wavelengths of order 10^2 m) may propagate unimpeded through any kind of weather but may be diffracted around hills and reflected by deep layers of ionized gases in the extreme upper atmosphere.

3.1   Frequency, Wavelength and Wavenumber

The most fundamental characteristic of a harmonic electromagnetic field is its frequency $\nu = \omega/2\pi$, which has units of cycles per second, or Hertz (Hz). Regardless of where you are and what other processes affect it, radiation with frequency ν will always have that frequency until such time as it is absorbed and converted into another form of energy[1].

---

[1]This assumes that you, the observer, are at a fixed distance from the source. Otherwise the frequency will be shifted by the Doppler effect.

In practice, it is usually more convenient to specify the wavelength λ rather than the frequency ν. This is because the frequencies of interest to most atmospheric scientists tend to be numerically large and unwieldy. The two parameters are related by

$$c = \lambda \nu .$$
(3.1)

Note that this relationship is valid for the wavelength in a vacuum. Inside a medium like air or water, the phase speed of radiation is somewhat slower than c and the actual wavelength is correspondingly shorter. The dependence of the actual wavelength on the index of refraction of the medium is important for understanding some effects such as refraction. Normally, if we refer to wavelength without further qualification, we mean wavelength in a vacuum.

For atmospheric radiation, wavelength is most commonly expressed using one of the following units, whichever is most convenient: nanometers (nm = 10^{-9} m), micrometers or *microns* (μm = 10^{-6} m), or centimeters (cm = 10^{-2} m). Other units, such as the Angstrom (10^{-10} m) are no longer widely used by meteorologists.

The description preferred by some specialists is neither wavelength nor frequency but *wavenumber* $\tilde{\nu}$, which is just the reciprocal of wavelength:

$$\tilde{\nu} = \frac{1}{\lambda} = \frac{\nu}{c} .$$
(3.2)

Wavenumber is usually stated in units of inverse centimeters (cm^{-1}).

3.2 Major Spectral Bands

The electromagnetic spectrum spans an enormous range of frequencies, from essentially zero to extremely high frequencies associated with energetic photons released by nuclear reactions. As a matter of convention, the spectrum has been subdivided by scientists and engineers into a few discrete spectral *bands*. The frequency and wavelength boundaries of the major spectral bands are given in Table 3.1

Table 3.1: Regions of the electromagnetic spectrum

Region	Spectral range	Fraction of solar output	Remarks
X rays	$\lambda < 0.01~\mu$m		Photoionizes all species; absorbed in upper atmosphere
Extreme UV	$0.01 < \lambda < 0.1~\mu$m	3×10^{-6}	Photoionizes O_2 and N_2; absorbed above 90 km
Far UV	$0.1 < \lambda < 0.2~\mu$m	0.01%	Photodissociates O_2; absorbed above 50 km
UV-C	$0.2 < \lambda < 0.28~\mu$m	0.5%	Photodissociates O_2 and O_3; absorbed between 30 and 60 km
UV-B	$0.28 < \lambda < 0.32~\mu$m	1.3%	Mostly absorbed by O_3 in stratosphere; responsible for sunburn
UV-A	$0.32 < \lambda < 0.4~\mu$m	6.2%	Reaches surface
Visible	$0.4 < \lambda < 0.7~\mu$m	39%	Atmosphere mostly transparent
Near IR	$0.7 < \lambda < 4~\mu$m	52%	Partially absorbed, mainly by water vapor
Thermal IR	$4 < \lambda < 50~\mu$m	0.9%	Absorbed and emitted by water vapor, carbon dioxide, ozone, and other trace gases
Far IR	$0.05 < \lambda < 1$ mm		Absorbed by water vapor
Microwave	$\lambda > 1$ mm		Clouds semi-transparent

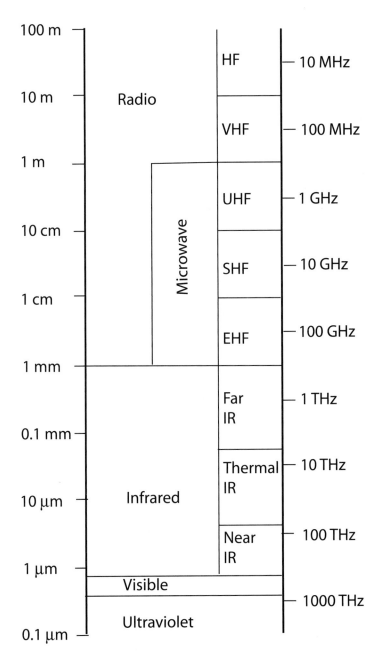

Fig. 3.1: The electromagnetic spectrum.

and Fig. 3.1. It is important to understand that there is nothing special about the precise frequencies defining the boundaries between bands; in most cases, these boundaries were decided more or less arbitrarily and have no real physical significance. There is for example no abrupt change in the behavior of radiation as one crosses from the microwave to the infrared band in the vicinity of 1 mm wavelength. The exception of course is the visible band, whose boundaries are defined by the range of wavelengths (approximately 0.4 to 0.7 μm) that the normal human eye can see. Other animal species might have defined this band differently. Many insects, for example, can see well into the ultraviolet band.

Note that there are three rather distinct ways in which a particular spectral band can make itself "interesting" to atmospheric scientists:

Diabatic heating/cooling - As pointed out in the introduction, radiative transfer is one of the most important mechanisms of heat exchange in the atmosphere, and is the *sole* mechanism for heat exchange between the earth and the rest of the universe. For reasons that will become clearer later, not all spectral bands contribute significantly in this category.

Photochemistry - Many of the chemical reactions that take place in the atmosphere, including those that produce smog, as well as some that help cleanse the air of pollutants, are driven by sunlight. In addition, the existence of the ozone layer is a direct result of photochemical processes. The photon energy $E = h\nu$ is a crucial factor in determining which spectral bands are "players" in atmospheric photochemistry.

Remote sensing - Any frequency of radiation that is absorbed, scattered or emitted by the atmosphere can potentially be exploited for satellite- or ground-based measurements of atmospheric properties, such as temperature, humidity, the concentration of trace constituents, and many other variables.

In this book, we shall restrict our attention to radiative processes relevant primarily to the troposphere and stratosphere. With this constraint in mind, we may now undertake a brief survey of the major spectral bands.

3.2.1 Gamma Rays and X-Rays

Gamma rays and X-rays, which are associated with wavelengths shorter than $\sim 10^{-2}$ μm, are usually produced by nuclear decay, nuclear fission and fusion, and other reactions involving energetic subatomic particles. The most energetic of photons, gamma and X-ray radiation can easily strip electrons from, or *ionize*, atoms and decompose chemical compounds. As such, ionizing radiation poses significant hazards to life. It is therefore fortunate that the strongest natural sources are extraterrestrial — so-called *cosmic rays* — and thus affect primarily the upper levels of the atmosphere. The intensity of gamma and X-ray radiation arriving at the top of the atmosphere is typically reduced by well over half for each 100 mb of atmosphere that it traverses, so that very little of this radiation makes it to the lowest levels. But airline passengers are exposed to nonnegligible levels of cosmic radiation.

In the lower troposphere, most natural radiation observed in this spectral band is traceable to radioactive materials in the earth's crust, such as uranium and its daughter isotopes. Although such sources are widely distributed, most are (thankfully) rather weak.

The gamma and X-ray bands are the only bands that have no major significance for any of the three processes identified in the previous section. Fluxes of radiation in these bands are not large enough to have a measurable effect on the heating or cooling of the lower and middle atmosphere. For various reasons, including the absence of strong natural terrestrial sources and the relatively strong attenuation of ultrashort wavelength radiation by the atmosphere, remote sensing of the troposphere and stratosphere is not a practical proposition in these bands. Finally, although these types of radiation can potentially participate in chemical reactions, their role is minor compared with that of ultraviolet radiation (see below). In the view of lack of strong relevance of this band to meteorology, we will not consider it further in this book.

3.2.2 Ultraviolet Band

The ultraviolet (UV) band occupies the range of wavelengths from approximately 0.01 μm on the X-ray side to approximately 0.4 μm on the visible-light side. The sun is the sole significant source of natural UV radiation in the atmosphere. However, the fraction of sunlight at the top of the atmosphere that falls in this band is small, only a few percent of the total power output. Nevertheless, this contribution is very important. The UV band is further divided into the following sub-bands:

UV-A extends from 0.4 down to 0.32 μm. Radiation in this sub-band is a significant component of sunlight, comprising close to 99% of the total solar UV radiation that reaches sea level. Although UV-A radiation is invisible to the human eye, it stimulates fluorescence (the emission of visible light) in some materials — e.g., "Day-Glo" markers, highway safety cones, and yellow tennis balls. So-called "black lights" used with fluorescent posters are artificial sources of UV-A radiation. Although the wavelengths are shorter, and therefore more energetic, than those of visible light, UV-A is still relatively innocuous with respect to living organisms. This is fortunate because the atmosphere is rather transparent to UV-A.

UV-B extends from 0.32 down to 0.280 μm. Because of its even shorter wavelength, its photons are energetic enough to initiate photochemical reactions, including injury of tissues (e.g., sunburn) and even damage to cellular DNA, leading to increased risk of skin cancer in exposed individuals. Fortunately, most UV-B (approximately 99%) is absorbed by ozone in the stratosphere. However, thinning of the ozone layer by human-manufactured chemicals is believed to be responsible for a significant increase in the amount of UV-B now reaching the surface.

UV-C extends from 0.280 to $\sim$0.1 μm. The most energetic UV sub-band, virtually all UV-C radiation is absorbed in the mesosphere and uppermost stratosphere, where much of its energy is expended on the dissociation of O_2 into atomic oxygen. The remainder is absorbed by ozone.

UV radiation is interesting in all three of the respects outlined earlier. As we have already mentioned, it is a major player in atmospheric photochemistry. Also, satellite remote sensing of ozone and other stratospheric constituents is possible in this band. Finally,

Table 3.2: Relationship between color and wavelength

Wavelength interval (μm)	Color
0.39–0.46	Violet
0.46–0.49	Dark Blue
0.49–0.51	Light Blue
0.51–0.55	Green
0.55–0.58	Yellow-Green
0.58–0.59	Yellow
0.59–0.62	Orange
0.62–0.76	Red

the absorption of solar UV radiation by ozone is a major diabatic heating term in the stratosphere and mesosphere.

3.2.3 Visible Band

The visible band extends from approximately 0.4 μm to 0.7 μm. In addition to its obvious importance for human vision, its significance for the atmosphere cannot be overstated, despite the fact that it occupies a surprisingly narrow slice of the EM spectrum.

First, through an interesting coincidence, *the visible band includes the wavelength of maximum emission of radiation by the sun.* (Fig. 3.2) In fact, close to half of the total power output of the sun falls in this narrow band.

Second, *the cloud-free atmosphere is remarkably transparent to all visible wavelengths.* We may take this for granted, but for no other major spectral band is the atmosphere as uniformly transparent (Fig. 3.3). This means that the absorption of visible solar radiation occurs primarily at the surface of the earth rather than within the atmosphere itself. Thus, the atmosphere is largely heated from below and only secondarily by direct absorption of solar radiation. The thermal structure of the atmosphere would likely be quite different if the atmosphere were less transparent to this component of the solar flux.

Clouds are remarkably reflective in the visible band. Again, this might seem obvious, but it's not true for many other spectral bands. The global distribution of cloud cover has a huge influ-

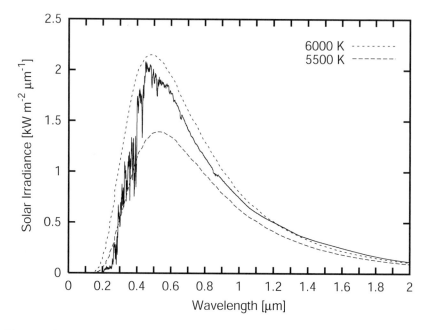

Fig. 3.2: Spectrum of solar radiation at the top of the atmosphere, at moderate spectral resolution. Dashed curves represent emission from an ideal blackbody at the indicated temperatures.

ence on the fraction of total solar radiation that gets absorbed by the earth-atmosphere system rather than being reflected back out to space.

Satellites with imaging capabilities in the visible band are able to easily detect and classify clouds. In the absence of clouds, visible imagers are able to map surface features, vegetation types, ocean color (related to biological productivity) and many other variables.

3.2.4   Infrared Band

The infrared (IR) band extends from wavelengths of approximately 0.7 μm up to approximately 1000 μm or 1 mm. This rather broad range (over three decades of wavelength) encompasses a rich variety of absorption and emission features in the atmosphere. IR radiation is enormously important as the means by which energy is exchanged between lower and upper levels of the atmosphere and between the earth-atmosphere system and outer space. Not only does

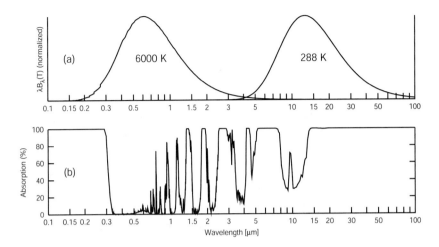

Fig. 3.3: Overview of the relationship between solar and terrestrial emission and the transmission properties the atmosphere. a) Normalized blackbody curves corresponding to the approximate temperature of the sun's photosphere (6000 K) and a typical terrestrial temperature of 288 K. b) A coarse-resolution depiction of the absorption spectrum of the cloud-free atmosphere.)

the steady-state climate of the earth depend heavily on the absorptive and emissive properties of the atmosphere in the IR band, but we now believe that the climate can change in response to human-induced increases in IR-absorbing trace constituents ("greenhouse gases") in the atmosphere, such as water vapor, carbon dioxide, methane, and chlorofluorocarbons (CFCs).

Because so many major and minor constituents of the atmosphere have distinctive (and often very strong) absorption features in the IR band, there are countless ways to exploit this band for remote sensing of temperature, water vapor, and trace constituents. On the other hand, the IR band is unimportant for atmospheric photochemistry, because photon energies are below the threshold required to dissociate most chemical compounds.

Atmospheric scientists tend to subdivide the IR band into three sub-bands: the *near IR* band, the *thermal IR* band, and the *far IR* band.

The near IR band is in one sense a continuation of the visible band, in that the primary source of this radiation in the atmosphere is the sun. It extends from 0.7 to 4 μm. Approximately half of the sun's output is found in this band, so that all but 1% of solar radiation incident on the top of the earth's atmosphere is accounted for by the UV, visible, and near IR bands together.

Unlike the case for the visible band, however, the atmosphere is not uniformly transparent to all near-IR wavelengths but rather exhibits a number of significant atmospheric absorption features. Thus, a moderate fraction of near-IR radiation from the sun is absorbed by the atmosphere in this band. For some wavelengths, e.g., near 1.3 μm, absorption is nearly total.

The range from 4 μm to 50 μm encompasses what we will refer to as the *thermal IR* band. Different sources quote various upper wavelength bounds on the thermal IR band, some as low as 15 μm. We have chosen the 50 μm bound because significant thermal energy exchanges via radiative transfer in the atmosphere occur up to approximately this limit. The thermal IR band is "where the action is" in view of both the magnitude of the energy exchanges and the enormous complexity of the atmospheric absorption spectra in this band. We will have much more to say about this band in later chapters.

For our purposes, the *far IR* band represents wavelengths between about 50 μm and 1000 μm (1 mm). Energy transfer in the atmosphere at these wavelengths is insignificant relative to that associated with the thermal IR, near IR, and visible bands. There are some potential applications of the far IR band to remote sensing, especially of cirrus clouds, but otherwise this region of the spectrum is relatively uninteresting to meteorologists.

3.2.5 Microwave and Radio Bands

Moving through the EM spectrum toward longer wavelengths (lower frequencies), one leaves the far IR band and enters the *microwave band* at a wavelength of about 1 mm, or at a frequency of about 300 GHz (GHz = gigahertz = 10^9 Hz). The lower bound (in frequency) is often taken to be around 3 GHz, or 10 cm wavelength. Thus, the microwave band encompasses two decades of frequency. At lower frequencies still, and continuing down to zero, we have the *radio band*. Note that both for historical reasons and because the numbers are low enough to be manageable, it is most common to use frequency rather than wavelength when describing microwave and radio band radiation.

From an engineering point of view, one of the distinguishing characteristics of the radio band is that the frequencies involved are low enough to be amenable to generation, amplification, and detection using traditional electronic components and circuits. By contrast, the much higher frequencies and shorter wavelengths of IR and visible radiation require mirrors, diffraction gratings, and/or lenses. The microwave band occupies a gray area, as many of the components in microwave circuits have a quasi-optical character — e.g., waveguides, resonant cavities, feedhorns, and parabolic reflectors.

The microwave band has risen greatly in prominence in recent years for its role in remote sensing of the atmosphere and surface. Radar, which was first developed during World War II, is now the principal means by which meteorologists monitor severe weather and study the dynamics of convective cloud systems. Satellites with sensors operating in the microwave band have proliferated since the mid-1970s and are now a very important component of our weather satellite programs, both for research and operationally.

The utility of the microwave band is greatly enhanced by the relative transparency of clouds, especially at frequencies well below 100 GHz. The properties of the surface and of the total atmospheric column — can be observed from space under all weather conditions except rainfall.

The radio band, which by some definitions includes the microwave band, continues down to zero frequency. Frequencies lower than around 3 GHz tend to interact very weakly with the atmosphere and therefore have only limited applicability to atmospheric remote sensing. Also, because of the long wavelengths involved, it is difficult to achieve good directionality with antennas of managable size (especially on satellites).

Two notable examples of remote sensing in the radio band do bear mentioning: 1) ground-based Doppler wind profilers operating near 915 MHz, which observe scattering from turbulence-induced fluctuations in atmospheric density and humidity, and 2) lightning detection systems, which are sensitive to low-frequency "static" emitted by lightning discharges. Apart from these cases, radio wavelengths are of very limited interest to meteorologists.

3.3   Solar and Terrestrial Radiation

In the previous section, we surveyed the entire electromagnetic spectrum with an eye toward outlining the relevance of each major band to atmospheric science. The two most important facts to emerge from this survey are the following:

- Over 99% of the energy radiated by the sun and incident on the top of the earth's atmosphere is accounted for by just three bands spanning wavelengths from 0.1 μm to 4 μm: the ultraviolet band contributes a few percent, with the remainder more or less evenly split between the visible band and the near-infrared band. We collectively refer to these bands as *solar* or *shortwave* radiation. Although solar emission in other bands may have some significance for remote sensing (e.g., sunglint from the ocean surface in the microwave band), it is insignificant for the energy budget of the atmosphere.

- Over 99% of the radiative energy emitted by the earth and atmosphere is found in the thermal infrared band from 4–100 μm. We will often refer to radiation in this band as *terrestrial* or *longwave* radiation. Emission in other bands (principally the far-IR and microwave bands) may be important for remote sensing but is essentially irrelevant for the atmospheric energy budget.

It is an interesting and convenient coincidence that a wavelength of approximately 4 μm cleanly separates the band containing most solar radiation from that containing most terrestrial emission (Fig. 3.3). For a narrow range of wavelengths in the vicinity of 4 μm, it may sometimes be necessary to consider both terrestrial and solar sources, but for most wavelengths it is just one or the other. The physical reasons for this separation will be addressed in Chapter 5; for now it is sufficient to point out that disparate temperatures of the sources (approximately 6000 K for the sun versus 250–300 K for the earth and atmosphere) are responsible.

Problem 3.1: For the given electromagnetic waves in a vacuum, compute the frequency ν in Hz, the wavenumber $\tilde{\nu}$ in cm^{-1}, and the wavelength λ in μm. Also identify the spectral band.

a) $\lambda = 0.0015$ cm, b) $\nu = 37$ GHz, c) $\tilde{\nu} = 600$ cm^{-1}, d) $\lambda = 300$ nm, e) $\nu = 3 \times 10^{14}$ Hz, f) $\tilde{\nu} = 10000$ cm^{-1}.

3.4 Applications to Meteorology, Climatology, and Remote Sensing

3.4.1 UV Radiation and Ozone

The Ozone Layer

The absorption of radiation by way of molecular photodissociation was briefly mentioned in Section 2.6. It turns out that this process has easily observable consequences for the atmosphere and, for that matter, for all of life on Earth. In particular, UV-C radiation is responsible for dissociating molecular oxygen, according to the reaction

$$O_2 + h\nu \ (\lambda < 0.2423 \ \mu m) \rightarrow O + O. \tag{3.3}$$

The large amount of molecular oxygen in the atmospheric column absorbs most solar radiation at wavelengths shorter than 0.24 μm by this mechanism.

The free oxygen atoms from the above reaction then can combine with O_2 to form ozone according to the reaction

$$O + O_2 + M \rightarrow O_3 + M, \tag{3.4}$$

where M is any third molecule or atom (required in order to carry away the energy released by the above reaction).

It is fortunate for us that this second reaction occurs, because ordinary oxygen by itself would continue to allow dangerous UV-C and UV-B radiation with wavelengths between 0.24 and 0.32 μm to reach the surface, posing a deadly hazard to life. But ozone happens to absorb strongly between about 0.2 and 0.31 μm via electronic transitions. It therefore "mops up" most of whatever UV-B and UV-C was not absorbed via (3.3). Of course it does little for UV-A radiation, with wavelengths longer than 0.32 μm. But radiation in this band is relatively innocuous, except perhaps when it is used to illuminate velvet blacklight posters of Elvis.

There remains a small sliver of the UV-B band between about 0.31 and 0.32 μm that manages to reach the surface without complete absorption; it is precisely this narrow sliver that is primarily responsible for sunburn. Lately, there has been considerable concern over observed declines in ozone layer density. If the decline continues, then the resulting widening of this narrow UV-B window could have serious consequences for life on Earth.

In the very process of absorbing harmful shortwave UV radiation, the ozone layer influences our environment in another very important way. The solar energy that is absorbed by ozone warms the atmosphere at those levels to a much higher temperature than would be the case without the presence of ozone. Have you ever wondered why temperature *increases* with height in the stratosphere, reaching a maximum at the stratopause before decreasing again in the mesophere? The ozone layer is responsible!

In an atmosphere without free oxygen, and therefore without ozone, the temperature structure would be much simpler: we'd have a *very* deep troposphere (temperature generally decreasing with height) transitioning directly to the thermosphere. The stratosphere and mesosphere would be missing. This is in fact what you find on Mars, whose atmosphere consists mainly of CO_2. On Earth, the temperature structure of the lower stratosphere serves as a very important "lid" on tropospheric convection and other circulations. If you already have some background in atmospheric dynamics, try to imagine how different our weather might be if the tropopause were near 50 km altitude rather than its present 5-15 km!

Photochemical Smog

We have just surveyed the role of oxygen and ozone in the middle atmosphere (stratosphere and mesosphere) in absorbing UV-C and UV-B radiation. The UV-C, we saw, is mostly absorbed by photodissociation of O_2; the UV-B was then mostly absorbed by the resulting O_3. This leaves mainly UV-A radiation to reach the troposphere.

Although less energetic than UV-B and UV-C radiation, UV-A radiation is a key player in tropospheric chemistry. Among other things, photochemical reactions involving organic molecules (e.g. unburned fuel vapors) and nitrogen oxides (produced by high temperatures in automobile engines) can lead to the formation of ozone in surface air. Although ozone in the stratosphere is highly desirable because of its UV-blocking characteristics, it is considered a serious pollutant in near-surface air where we live, because it is a strong chemical oxidant which attacks most organic substances, including the lining of your lungs. Ozone is thus one of the main ingredients of *photochemical smog*.

In its most basic form, the chemical sequence leading to ozone pollution goes like this:

1. Automobile engines and other industrial processes emit *primary pollutants*, which include unburned hydrocarbons (a.k.a. volatile organic compounds, or VOC) and nitrogen oxides — nitrogen monoxide (NO) and nitrogen dioxide (NO_2), collectively known as NO_x. The NO oxidizes, further increasing the NO_2 concentration.

2. The NO_2 is photolyzed (photodissociated) according to the reaction

$$NO_2 + h\nu \ (\lambda < 0.4 \ \mu m) \rightarrow NO + O^\star, \qquad (3.5)$$

   where $O^\star$ is a highly reactive free oxygen atom that immediately combines with an ordinary oxygen molecule to form one of several *secondary pollutants*[2], in this case ozone:

$$O_2 + O^\star + M \rightarrow O_3 \qquad (3.6)$$

3. A third reaction completes the cycle, bringing us back to our starting point:

$$O_3 + NO \rightarrow NO_2 + O_2 \qquad (3.7)$$

Graphically, the cycle is shown in Fig. 3.4. Although each pass through the cycle doesn't yield a net increase of ozone, the fact that

---

[2]Another major secondary pollutant, also produced by photochemical action on the primary emissions, is peroxyacetyl nitrate, or PAN.

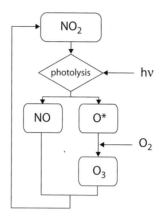

Fig. 3.4: Photolysis of NO_2 and generation of O_3.

there is (during the daytime) a continuous input of UV radiation implies that there will be constant generation of new ozone as earlier ozone molecules are destroyed, leading to a finite steady state concentration in the atmosphere. Although we won't go into the process here, one role of VOC molecules is to create additional sources of NO and NO_2, which increases the equilibrium concentration of O_3.

The location in the U.S. most stereotypically associated with photochemical smog is the Los Angeles basin, with its high quota of sunshine, high concentration of automobiles, and shallow pool of stagnant air hemmed in by mountains.

The Hydroxyl Radical

So far we have seen an example of a photochemical process that is "good" (ozone production in the stratosphere) and one that is "bad" (ozone production in the troposphere). UV-A and visible radiation are responsible for other photochemical processes in the troposphere besides smog, not all of which yield harmful byproducts. One in particular is quite beneficial: the production of short-lived hydroxyl (OH) radicals by the following pair of reactions:

$$O_3 + h\nu \ (\lambda < 0.34 \ \mu m) \rightarrow O_2 + O^\star \tag{3.8}$$

$$H_2O + O^\star \rightarrow 2OH \tag{3.9}$$

where the ozone in the first of these equations occurs at low levels even in unpolluted air. What is interesting about the hydroxyl radical is that it is highly reactive and acts to break down a wide range of undesirable pollutants in the atmosphere, such as carbon monoxide and methane. In fact, OH radicals are sometimes referred to as the atmosphere's "detergent." Without the daily action of hydroxyl radicals, the air would be much dirtier, on average, than it is.

Among the very few pollutants that are impervious to breakdown by OH radicals are the synthetic compounds known as chlorofluorocarbons (CFCs). These molecules are so exceptionally stable that they can persist in the atmosphere for as long as it takes — often a year or more — for them to get circulated from the troposphere into the stratosphere. Only there are CFC molecules exposed to enough UV-B and UV-C radiation to get broken down. Unfortunately, one byproduct of the photolysis is a free chlorine atom. A single Cl atom has the capacity to catalytically destroy many ozone molecules. Therefore, the release of CFCs into the atmosphere over the past few decades has led to a marked decrease in the steady state concentration of ozone in the stratosphere. This is especially the case in the polar regions during springtime, where complex chemical processes involving polar stratospheric cloud particles and sunlight greatly accelerates the destruction of ozone. As noted above, this thinning of the ozone layer is a point of great concern, due to the hazards of UV-B radiation to life. Fortunately, progress has been made in slowing the release of CFCs into the atmosphere, and the ozone layer is now expected to gradually recover over the next few decades.

CHAPTER 4

Reflection and Refraction in a Homogeneous Medium

In this chapter, we undertake our first quantitative examination of the interaction of radiation with matter. We will focus initially on the behavior of EM waves when they encounter, and propagate through, a *homogeneous* medium.

By "homogeneous," we mean a medium that is smooth and uniform on scales comparable to the wavelength of the radiation. Water, glass, air, red wine, maple syrup, liquid mercury, and solid gold are all effectively homogeneous with respect to radiation in the visible, infrared and microwave bands, because the size and spacing of the individual molecules and other irregularities are much smaller than the wavelength of the radiation. If this were not the case, then glass and water, for example, would have a cloudy or milky appearance rather than being perfectly transparent to the eye. In fact, milk looks "milky" precisely because of the presence of suspended particles that are larger than the wavelengths of visible light.

To radiation in the X-ray and gamma bands, these and all other substances appear quite lumpy, or *inhomogeneous*, because the wavelength of the radiation is comparable to or smaller than the spacing between the molecules. Likewise, centimeter- and meter-scale turbulent eddies and fluctuations in humidity may make even the atmosphere appear inhomogeneous with respect to radio and microwave radiation. On the other hand, consider a cloud that is made up of 10 μm-diameter water droplets: it behaves like a homogeneous medium with respect to the long wavelengths of microwave radiation even though it is quite inhomogeneous with respect to visible and infrared radiation.

At the microscopic level, interactions of radiation with even homogeneous media are quite complex, involving the constructive and destructive interference of waves scattered by the countless individual atoms or molecules in the medium. From a macroscopic point of view, however, all of this complexity is hidden in a single parameter, the complex index of refraction $N = n_r + n_i i$ of the medium. As discussed in Chapter 2, the real part n_r controls the effective phase speed of EM waves propagating through the medium while the imaginary part n_i describes the rate of absorption of the wave.

The phase speed of radiation in a medium may seem uninteresting to the uninitiated; after all, even in the densest medium, it's too fast to directly observe without highly specialized equipment. However, it is the sudden change in this phase speed at boundaries between media such as air and water that gives rise to the phenomena of *reflection* and *refraction*.

It is important to keep in mind that N is not a constant for any substance but rather depends strongly on wavelength and, to a lesser degree, temperature, pressure and other variables. It is the variation of n_r with wavelength in raindrops that gives rise to rainbows; it is a sharp variation of n_i with wavelength that makes wine red.

It is also worth pointing out in passing that, in any real material, n_r and n_i are not free to vary independently of one another but rather are tightly coupled to one another via the so-called *Kramer-Kronig* relations. Although the equations describing these relationships, and their physical interpretation, are beyond the scope of this book, suffice it to say that knowledge of the value of n_i over the full range of frequency is sufficient to compute n_r at any frequency, and vice versa. See BH83, Chapter 2 for a detailed discussion.

4.1   A Closer Look at N

4.1.1   The Real Part

Recall from Chapter 2 that, in a nonabsorbing medium, the imaginary part of the index of refraction $n_i = 0$ and $N = n_r$, where n_r is real and the phase speed c' in the medium is given by

$$c' = \frac{c}{n_r} , \qquad (4.1)$$

where c is the speed of light in a vacuum. For virtually all real substances $n_r > 1$, so that the phase speed of light in a physical medium is somewhat slower than that in a vacuum.

The values of n_r for both water and ice are given as functions of wavelength in the top panel of Fig. 4.1. In the visible band ($0.4 < \lambda < 0.7$), the value of n_r for water is approximately 1.33, though it is slightly larger for the shorter wavelengths (e.g. blue and violet) than for longer wavelengths (red and orange).

For air at standard temperature and pressure, $n_r \approx 1.0003$ in the visible band and is thus so close to unity that the difference between air and a vacuum may be ignored for some purposes. Nevertheless, the difference does sometimes matter: it is variations in n_r associated with changes in atmosphere density that give rise to mirages and the twinkling of stars, for example.

4.1.2   The Imaginary Part

When the imaginary part n_i of the index of refraction is nonzero, absorption of an EM wave occurs as it passes through the medium. In fact, n_i is sometimes referred to as the *absorption index*. Values of n_i for water and ice are shown as functions of wavelength in the bottom panel of Fig. 4.1. Note that n_i for both substances is extremely small in the visible band but increases sharply as you move into either the ultraviolet or infrared bands.

In Section 2.5, we found that the rate of power attenuation per unit distance is given by the *absorption coefficient* β_a (dimensions of inverse length), which is related to n_i by

$$\beta_a = \frac{4\pi n_i}{\lambda}, \tag{4.2}$$

where λ is the wavelength in a vacuum. It was shown that, for an initial intensity I_0 at position $x = 0$ within the medium and propagating in the x direction,

$$I(x) = I_0 e^{-\beta_a x}. \tag{4.3}$$

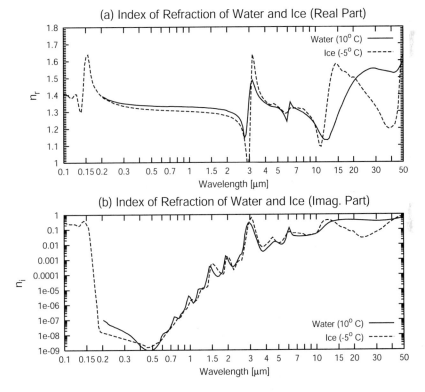

Fig. 4.1: The complex index of refraction of water (solid curves) and ice (dotted curves). (a) The real part, which largely influences the reflection and refraction properties of a medium. (b) The imaginary part, which determines absorption within the medium.

We can rewrite this as

$$t(x) \equiv \frac{I(x)}{I_0} = e^{-\beta_a x} , \qquad\qquad (4.4)$$

where the *transmittance t* is the fraction of radiation that survives the trip over the distance x. That fraction of the initial radiation not transmitted must have been absorbed and therefore converted to another form of energy, such as heat.

The above equation is the first instance we have encountered of a very important relationship called *Beer's law*.[1] It states that the intensity of a beam of monochromatic radiation falls off exponentially as it traverses a uniform medium. The *rate* at which it falls off is proportional to β_a.

It is important to note that even very small values of n_i can imply strong absorption within a medium. For example, if a 1 mm thick sheet of a material transmits only 1% of radiation having a wavelength of 0.5 μm, equations (4.2) and (4.3) imply $n_i = 1.8 \times 10^{-4}$.

We can also define a quantity called the *penetration depth*, which is the value of x for which $t(x) = e^{-1} \approx 37\%$. It is just the reciprocal of the absorption coefficient:

$$D \equiv \frac{1}{\beta_a} = \frac{\lambda}{4\pi n_i}. \qquad\qquad (4.5)$$

The penetration depth D for water and ice is shown as a function of wavelength in Fig. 4.2, based on (4.5) applied to the values of n_i shown in Fig. 4.1. Whereas D is on the order of tens of meters in the visible band, it rapidly falls to only millimeters or even micrometers in the thermal infrared band!

> **Problem 4.1:** Show that the total transmission t_{total} of radiation through two sheets of material stacked together is equal to the product of the individual transmittances t_1 and t_2. Ignore reflections.

---

[1]In fairness to other scientists who derived physically equivalent relationships, Beer's law is cited by some authors as the *Beer-Bouguer-Lambert law*. In this book, we will sacrifice fairness for convenience and opt for the traditional short form. Other authors avoid the thorny issue of attribution altogether and refer to it as *the extinction law*.

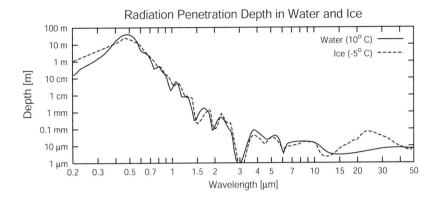

Fig. 4.2: The penetration depth of radiation in water and ice.

4.1.3   The Dielectric Constant[†]

In some situations, it is convenient to utilize the complex *dielectric constant* ϵ of a medium (also known as the *relative permittivity*) rather than the complex index of refraction N to describe the absorption and refraction properties of a substance at a particular wavelength. There is no need to be dismayed by the introduction of yet another parameter, as N and ϵ are very closely related.[2] In fact, for nonmagnetic materials ($\mu = \mu_0$),

$$\epsilon = \frac{\varepsilon}{\varepsilon_0} = N^2, \tag{4.6}$$

where the permittivity of the medium ε and the permittivity of free space ε_0 were previously introduced in connection with (2.36). Please keep in mind that, despite the name, the dielectric "constant" is really a *function* of frequency and, to a lesser extent, of variables like temperature and pressure.

Expanding in terms of the real and imaginary components, we find

$$\epsilon = (n_r + n_i i)^2 = n_r^2 + 2n_i n_r i - n_i^2, \tag{4.7}$$

so that the real and imaginary parts of ϵ are given by

$$\epsilon' = \mathrm{Re}\{\epsilon\} = n_r^2 - n_i^2, \qquad \epsilon'' = \mathrm{Im}\{\epsilon\} = 2n_r n_i. \tag{4.8}$$

---

[2]Specifically, $\epsilon \equiv \varepsilon/\varepsilon_0$, which appears in the definition of N given by (2.36).

Though requiring somewhat more involved algebra, one may find analogous expressions for n_r and n_i in terms of ϵ' and ϵ'':

$$n_r = \sqrt{\frac{\sqrt{\epsilon'^2 + \epsilon''^2} + \epsilon'}{2}} \tag{4.9}$$

$$n_i = \sqrt{\frac{\sqrt{\epsilon'^2 + \epsilon''^2} - \epsilon'}{2}} \tag{4.10}$$

Of course, in any programming environment (e.g., Fortran) that provides for manipulation of complex numbers, there is no need to bother with the above equations; rather, one just computes $N = \sqrt{\epsilon}$ or $\epsilon = N^2$.

I introduce the dielectric constant here because, for certain types of electrodynamic computations, it is more convenient than the index of refraction. The subject of the next section is a good example.

4.1.4   Optical Properties of Heterogeneous Mixtures[†]

At the beginning of this chapter, we stated that we would focus on radiative interactions with media that are homogeneous *on the scales of the wavelength of the radiation*. It is possible for even a decidedly heterogeneous mixture of different substances to satisfy this criterion if the particles of each material are much smaller than the wavelength.

For example, a layer of fallen snow consists of loosely aggregated ice crystals having dimensions of approximately 1 mm. Sunlight falling on snowpack has wavelengths small enough to be affected by the small-scale structure of the snow. If we look closely, we are able to resolve individual snow crystals with our eyes. But if microwave radiation having wavelengths of 10 cm or more encounters the same snowpack, it is no more influenced by the individual particles of snow than an ocean wave crashing on the beach "cares" that the beach is not a solid surface but rather made up of grains of sand. Thus, in the microwave band, the snowpack behaves more nearly like one that is homogeneous and therefore subject to the same principles discussed in this chapter. Likewise, even complex structures like falling snowflakes are sometimes be treated as equivalent homogeneous particles for the purpose of computing radar backscatter.

Several formulas have been derived for computing the *effective index of refraction or dielectric constant* of such mixtures. The precise form of these relationships depends on what assumptions are made concerning the structure of, and relationship between, the constituents. In a two-component mixture, one component may be viewed as the *matrix* and the other as disconnected *inclusions* embedded within that matrix. For example, a cloud is best viewed as water inclusions (droplets) embedded in a matrix of air, whereas foam patches on a stormy ocean surface consist of air inclusions (bubbles) in a matrix of sea water. In other cases, such as snowpack, it may be difficult to decide whether the ice should be considered the matrix or the inclusion, because neither the air nor the ice tends to exist in isolated, disconnected pockets.

One common formula used for computing effective dielectric constants of heterogeneous mixtures is the Maxwell Garnett formula

$$\epsilon_{av} = \epsilon_m \left[1 + \frac{3f \left(\frac{\epsilon - \epsilon_m}{\epsilon + 2\epsilon_m} \right)}{1 - f \left(\frac{\epsilon - \epsilon_m}{\epsilon + 2\epsilon_m} \right)} \right], \tag{4.11}$$

where ϵ_m and ϵ are the dielectric constants of the matrix and the inclusions, respectively, and f is the volume fraction occupied by the inclusions.

Another widely used relationship is that of Bruggeman:

$$f_1 \frac{\epsilon_1 - \epsilon_{av}}{\epsilon_1 + 2\epsilon_{av}} + (1 - f_1) \frac{\epsilon_2 - \epsilon_{av}}{\epsilon_2 + 2\epsilon_{av}} = 0, \tag{4.12}$$

where ϵ_1 and ϵ_2 are the dielectric constants of the two components, and f_1 is the volume fraction occupied by component 1. Note that this formula treats both components symmetrically; it does not distinguish between matrix and inclusion.

It is straightforward to extend either of the above formulas to mixtures of three or more components. This is desirable in the treatment of radar backscatter by melting snowflakes, for example, which may be regarded as mixtures of air, ice, and liquid water. In the case of the Maxwell Garnett formula, one first computes ϵ_{av} for two components, choosing one to be matrix and the other inclusion. The result may then be combined with a third component by applying (4.11) a second time. Unfortunately, there are 12 distinct possibilities for the order in which three components are combined, and each may yield decidedly different values of ϵ_{av} for the mixture! Even the Bruggeman formula, which does not distinguish between matrix and inclusion, yields slightly different results depending on the order in which the constituents are included.

In general, the Bruggeman formula tends to produce results that fall between the extremes of the various Maxwell Garnett combinations. Unfortunately, it is not obvious in most cases which, if any, of the many possibilities is "best."

Ultimately, any formula for the effective dielectric constant of a heterogeneous mixture is derived based on approximations or assumptions that may or may not be valid for the case under consideration. Wherever possible, the chosen method should be validated for the application in question by comparing predictions with actual measurements.

4.2   Refraction and Reflection

When an EM wave encounters a planar boundary between two homogeneous media having different indices of refraction, some of the energy of the wave is *reflected*, while the remainder passes through the boundary into the second medium (Fig. 4.3b, Fig. 4.4). In addition, the direction of the transmitted wave in medium 2 may be altered from the original direction in medium 1, a phenomenon known as *refraction* (Fig. 4.3a). The nature of both reflection and refraction at an interface between two homogeneous media follows directly from Maxwell's equations, combined with appropriate continuity constraints imposed at the boundary, and is covered extensively in other texts. We will not repeat the derivations here but simply summarize the key results.

4.2.1   Angle of Reflection

Consider an EM wave incident on a plane interface between two media. If the local normal unit vector is $\hat{n}$ and the direction of the incident ray is $\hat{\Omega}_i$, then the reflected ray $\hat{\Omega}_r$ lies in the same plane as $\hat{n}$ and $\hat{\Omega}_i$ but on the opposite side from $\hat{\Omega}_i$. Furthermore, the angle

a) Refraction

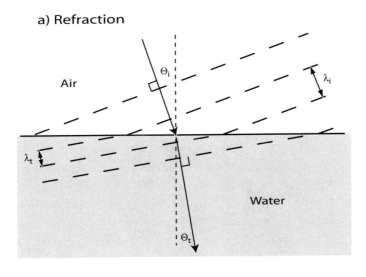

b) Reflection

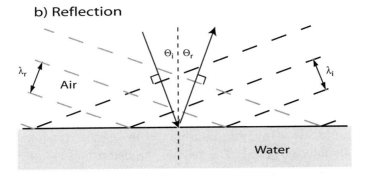

Fig. 4.3: Geometry of (a) refraction and (b) reflection of plane waves at an air-water interface.

Θ_r between $\hat{\Omega}_r$ and $\hat{n}$ equals the angle of incidence Θ_i defined by $\hat{n}$ and $\hat{\Omega}_i$.

In simple terms, a ray of light (or other EM radiation) reflects from a smooth surface much like an ideal elastic ball thrown at the floor: the component of its motion perpendicular to the surface abruptly reverses, while the component parallel to the surface remains unchanged. Reflection obeying this rule is termed *specular reflection*. The basic requirement in order for reflection to be specular is that any irregularities on the surface must be much smaller than the incident wavelength. In the visible band, this is generally

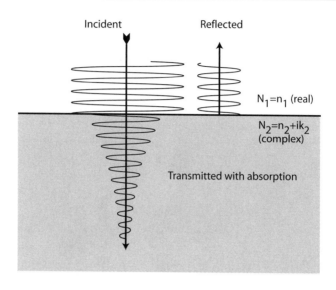

Fig. 4.4: Reflection and transmission of normally incident radiation.

true of glass, polished metals, most liquids (including water), and many plastic materials.

4.2.2   Angle of Refraction

When an incident ray of radiation falls on a smooth surface, reflection is usually not total. The part of the beam that is not reflected passes into the second medium. In general, the transmitted ray changes direction according to Snell's Law

$$\frac{\sin \Theta_t}{N_1} = \frac{\sin \Theta_i}{N_2} \, , \qquad (4.13)$$

where N_1 and N_2 are the indices of refraction of the first and second medium, respectively, and Θ_t is the angle of the transmitted ray $\hat{\Omega}_t$ relative to $\hat{n}$. Although N_1 and/or N_2 may be complex, the above law is most easily interpreted when the both are real, or nearly so (i.e., weak absorption).

    Case 1: $\Theta_i = \Theta_t = 0$. If a ray is normally incident on a surface, there is no change of direction as it enters the second medium.

Case 2: $\Theta_i > 0$; $N_2 > N_1$. A ray incident obliquely on a medium with larger index of refraction will bend *toward* the local normal; i.e., $\Theta_t < \Theta_i$. This situation describes sunlight falling on a smooth water surface, such as the surface of a pond or the exterior surface of a raindrop.

Case 3: $\Theta_i > 0$; $N_2 < N_1$. A ray incident obliquely on a medium with smaller index of refraction will bend *away* from normal; i.e., $\Theta_t > \Theta_i$. This situation arises, for example, when a ray of sunlight that has already entered a raindrop attempts to exit on the far side.

Case 3 above includes an interesting and important special case. Consider the possibility that

$$\Theta_i > \Theta_0 , \tag{4.14}$$

where the *critical angle* is defined as

$$\Theta_0 \equiv \arcsin \left(\frac{N_2}{N_1} \right) , \tag{4.15}$$

provided that $N_2 < N_1$. But (4.13) would then imply $\sin \Theta_t$ greater than one, a mathematical impossibility! The way out of this apparent paradox is to recognize that waves incident on the interface at an angle greater than the critical angle simply cannot pass through the interface at all but rather experience *total reflection*.

This is a good opportunity, by the way, to point out that the path taken by a beam of light is invariant with respect to reversal of direction. Viewed one way, Θ_0 defines the threshold for total internal reflection within the denser medium; viewed another, it describes the maximum possible value of Θ_t when light is externally incident on the medium at the largest possible angle ($\Theta_i = 90°$).

In the visible band, $N_1 \approx 1.33$ for water and $N_2 \approx 1$ for air; hence, in water, $\Theta_0 \approx 49°$.

Problem 4.2: Show that, for real N, Snell's Law (4.13) can be derived geometrically by requiring that the intersection of wave fronts with a planar boundary between two media match on both sides of the boundary (see Fig. 4.3).

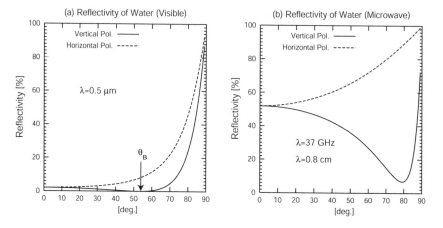

Fig. 4.5: Examples of the specular reflectivity of water as a function of incidence angle. (a) Visible band. (b) Microwave band.

4.2.3   Reflectivity

We have just addressed three aspects of how EM waves are affected by a planar interface between two homogeneous media: 1) the *angle of reflection* ($\Theta_i = \Theta_r$), 2) the *angle of refraction* (Snell's Law), and 3) the *critical angle for total reflection*. We now turn to the following slightly more complicated question: given that a beam of radiation is incident on a surface at an angle $\Theta_i < \Theta_0$, *what fraction of the beam is reflected?*

As before, the answer follows from the equations for a plane EM wave, with suitable constraints on the continuity of the magnetic and electric fields at the boundary. Also as before, we will not reproduce the derivation here but rather summarize the key results, in the form of the *Fresnel relations*:

$$R_p = \left| \frac{\cos\Theta_t - m\cos\Theta_i}{\cos\Theta_t + m\cos\Theta_i} \right|^2 , \tag{4.16}$$

$$R_s = \left| \frac{\cos\Theta_i - m\cos\Theta_t}{\cos\Theta_i + m\cos\Theta_t} \right|^2 , \tag{4.17}$$

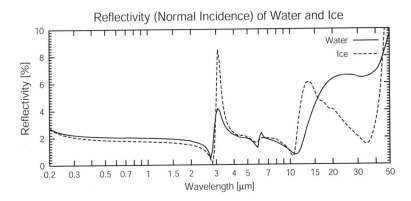

Fig. 4.6: The reflectivity (in air) of water and ice at normal incidence, based on (4.21) applied to the complex indices of refraction plotted in Fig. 4.1.

where Snell's Law can be manipulated to yield

$$\cos \Theta_t = \sqrt{1 - \left(\frac{\sin \Theta_i}{m}\right)^2},$$ (4.18)

and the complex *relative index of refraction m* is defined as

$$m = \frac{N_2}{N_1}.$$ (4.19)

R_p and R_s are *reflectivities*. They give the fraction of an incident beam of radiation that is reflected from a smooth interface, given the local angle of incidence Θ_i and the relative index of refraction m.

But why do we have *two* expressions for reflectivity? It turns out that this is one of those cases when the *polarization* of the incident radiation matters. R_p defines the reflectivity when the electric field vector is parallel to the plane of incidence; R_s is valid when the electric field vector is perpendicular to the plane of incidence. Since any EM wave can be decomposed into parallel and perpendicular polarized components, the total reflectivity can always be found by taking an appropriate average of R_p and R_s. For example, if the incident radiation happens to be unpolarized, then parallel and perpendicular polarizations are present in equal amounts, in which case the total reflectivity is given by

$$R = \frac{1}{2}(R_s + R_p) .$$

(4.20)

Note, however, that the reflected radiation is, in general, no longer unpolarized, so it can be dangerous to disregard polarization when considering the net outcome of multiple reflections from surfaces.

For the special case that $\Theta_i = 0$, both (4.16) and (4.17) collapse to the following single expression for the *reflectivity at normal incidence*:

$$R_{\text{normal}} = \left| \frac{m-1}{m+1} \right|^2 .$$

(4.21)

At normal incidence, there is no physically important distinction between the two polarizations, hence the need for only one formula.

In atmospheric applications, smooth reflecting surfaces are often horizontal, the most common example being a water surface, such as the ocean or a lake. In this case, parallel polarization is often known as *vertical polarization,* and perpendicular polarization equates to *horizontal polarization.* The corresponding reflectivities are then written as R_v and R_h. This terminology is common in the field of microwave remote sensing, where the rather large difference between R_v and R_h is of great practical importance. Figure 4.5a gives examples of R_v and R_h as functions of incidence angle for water in the visible band. The following features are of particular interest:

- In general, the reflectivity is quite low (2%) for light at near-normal incidence ($\Theta_i \approx 0$) but increases sharply to 100% for near-grazing angles ($\Theta_i \rightarrow 90°$). In other words, a smooth water surface is a rather poor reflector of sunlight at high noon but an excellent reflector of the setting sun. This is of course consistent with everyday experience.

- Except at near-grazing and near-normal incidence, the reflectivity for vertical polarization is much lower than that for horizontal polarization. It is this fact that led to the development of polarizing sunglasses, which block the largely horizontally polarized glare from water and other reflecting surfaces while transmitting vertically polarized light from other sources.

- There is a single angle Θ_B, known as the *Brewster angle*, at which the reflectivity for vertically polarized radiation vanishes completely, implying that *only* the horizontally polarized component of incident light survives reflection at that angle. By setting the numerator in (4.16) equal to zero and solving for $\sin \Theta_i$, we find that

$$\Theta_B = \arcsin \sqrt{\frac{m^2}{m^2 + 1}} \, . \tag{4.22}$$

For water in the visible band, the $\Theta_B = 53°$.

All of the above features can be found in the reflectivities of most nonconducting materials; i.e., those for which n_i is zero or at least very small. Larger values of the real part of m lead to greater overall reflectivities, larger values for the Brewster angle Θ_B, and smaller values for the critical angle for total internal reflection Θ_0. Diamonds, with their unusually large $N = 2.42$, owe their alluring sparkle to all three properties.

Problem 4.3: For (a) glass with $N = 1.5$ and (b) a diamond with $N = 2.42$, find the values of the reflectivity at normal incidence, and the critical angle for total internal reflection Θ_0. In both cases, assume that the external medium is air, with $N \approx 1.0$. Compare your results with their counterparts for water.

In the case of conducting materials, e.g., metals, as well as liquid water at microwave frequencies (Fig. 4.5b), the imaginary part of m is significantly greater than zero and also contributes to increased reflectivity. However, although the vertically polarized reflectivity still has a minimum at some angle Θ_B, that minimum is no longer zero. Therefore, (4.22) cannot be used to find Θ_B in such cases.

4.3 Applications to Meteorology, Climatology, and Remote Sensing

4.3.1 Rainbows and Halos

Geometric Optics

In the previous section, we tacitly assumed that we were dealing with EM waves incident on a *planar* (flat) boundary between two homogeneous media. However, the above rules for reflection and refraction can be applied not only to planar boundaries, but to any surface whose radius of curvature is much greater than the wavelength of the radiation. In this case, the angles Θ_i, Θ_t, Θ_r, Θ_0, etc., are measured relative to the local normal where the ray intercepts the surface. With this generalization, we have the ability to analyze the scattering and absorption properties of a variety of atmospheric hydrometeors via the straightforward technique of *ray tracing*, also known as *geometric optics*.

Unfortunately, most particles in the atmosphere are not much larger, and may even be smaller, than the wavelength of interest. This is true for air molecules, aerosols and cloud droplets in the visible and infrared bands and even raindrops in the microwave band. Geometric optics cannot be used for these cases; rather, more sophisticated solutions to the wave equation must be derived. These solutions and their interpretation will be outlined in Chapter 12.

Nevertheless, there are a number of interesting cases for which the particle size *is* much larger than the wavelength. This condition applies for example to the scattering of visible sunlight ($\lambda < 0.7 \, \mu$m) by large cloud ice particles ($>50 \, \mu$m) and raindrops ($100 \, \mu$m $< r <$ 3 mm). In fact, a number of common optical phenomena, such as rainbows, halos, and parhelia (sundogs) can be explained by geometric optics, simply by considering how rays of light refract and reflect as they encounter the surface of the particle.

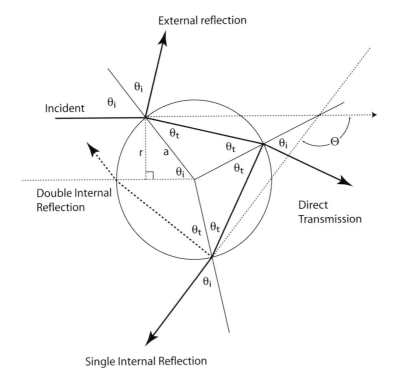

Fig. 4.7: Ray tracing geometry for a spherical water droplet of radius a, for a ray incident at distance r from a parallel line passing through the drop center. θ_i and θ_t denote the incident and transmitted angles relative to the local normal and are related by Snell's law. Θ is the angle of scattering relative to the original direction of the ray, in this case for a ray that has undergone a single internal reflection.

The Rainbow

To a reasonable approximation, a falling raindrop is spherical. If a spherical droplet is uniformly illuminated, then the geometry of the path of each incident ray depends only on $x \equiv r/a$, where r is the distance of the incident ray from the center axis of the drop, and a is the radius of the drop (Fig. 4.7). So $x = 0$ corresponds to a ray that is incident "dead center," while $x = 1$ corresponds to a ray that barely grazes the edge of the sphere.

Now let's follow the path of a single incident ray after it intercepts the drop:

1. A fraction of the energy in the ray will be reflected upon its

first encounter with the surface of the drop. If the incident radiation is unpolarized, then that fraction will be given by the average of the Fresnel relations (4.16) and (4.17), evaluated for the local angle of incidence θ_i. Fig. 4.5 reveals that this fraction is typically only a few percent, except when the ray strikes the sphere at a near-grazing angle.

2. Whatever is not reflected is transmitted into the drop and refracted to an angle θ_t relative to the local normal, as required by Snell's Law.

3. The above ray now encounters the back side of the drop, where a small fraction (a few percent) is reflected internally, as determined again by the Fresnel relations. The remainder exits the drop again at an angle θ_i relative to the local normal.

4. That portion of the original ray that was internally reflected now encounters the surface from the inside again. As before, a fraction is reflected internally (now for a second time), while the remainder is transmitted to the exterior. It is the part that escapes at this point that is responsible for the primary rainbow.

5. The above process is repeated for each additional internal reflection. However, after only two internal reflections, very little of the original energy in the incident ray remains inside the drop. The part that exits the drop after exactly two internal reflections is responsible for the secondary rainbow.

As noted above, the primary rainbow is associated with radiation that undergoes a single internal reflection before exiting the droplet again, so let's take a closer look at that case. Figure 4.8a depicts the full range of possible paths for rays undergoing a single internal reflection. If the incident ray encounters the droplet dead center ($x = 0$), it of course gets reflected exactly backward from the rear surface of the drop, so the scattered direction for that ray is 180°. A ray that encounters the droplet just slightly off-axis will undergo a slight degree of refraction, reflect off the rear surface at a slightly non-normal angle, and ultimately exit the drop at an angle near to, but not quite equal to, 180°.

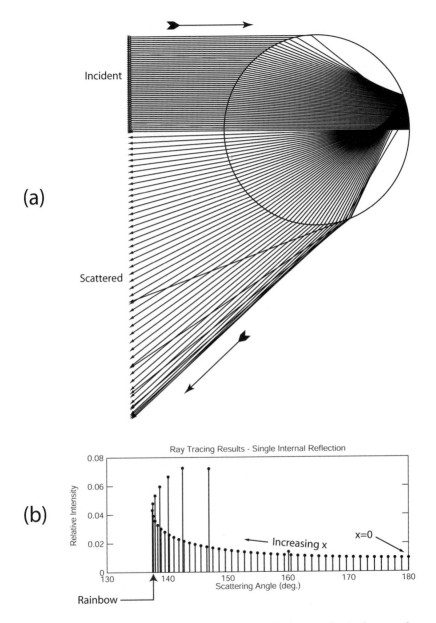

Fig. 4.8: Illustration of the ray-tracing method applied to a spherical water drop. (a) Diagram tracing the rays that undergo a single internal reflection, assuming uniform incident illumination. (b) Angles and relative intensities of the scattered rays.

Starting at $\Theta = 180°$ on the right edge of the plot in panel (b), we see how Θ for each subsequent ray (increasing x) initially decreases at a fairly steady rate. Also shown is the relative intensity of the exiting ray, based on the fraction that "survives" this particular path according to the Fresnel relations. The overall intensity in a particular direction is proportional to the intensity of the individual rays times the density of rays per increment of Θ.

Although the trend initially is toward ever-smaller Θ, there comes a point where Θ reaches a minimum, which we'll call Θ_0, and starts increasing again. For water, which has an index of refraction of approximately 1.33 in the visible band, $\Theta_0 \approx 137°$.

Because the reversal is gradual, there is a fairly significant range of x for which the scattered rays all bunch up rather close to Θ_0. It is this "focusing" of energy on a narrow range of Θ that gives rise to the bright ring that we call a rainbow. Of course, a rainbow is only visible when a rainshower is illuminated by a directional source of bright light — e.g., sunlight.

The precise value of Θ_0 depends of course on the index of refraction: increasing n_r has the effect of increasing Θ_0. A rainbow exhibits the characteristic separation of colors for which it is best known because n_r for water increases slightly from the red end to the violet end of the visible spectrum (Fig. 4.1).

As already mentioned, a similar process is behind the much weaker secondary rainbow, which arises from two internal reflections. The scattering angle for the second rainbow is approximately 130°, which puts it about 7° outside the primary rainbow, when you are viewing it with the sun at your back.

Halos and Related Optical Phenomena

Ray tracing can also be used to explain optical features like *halos*, which are bright rings that appear around the sun in conjunction with a thin cirrostratus cloud layer, and *parhelia* (or sundogs), which are bright iridescent spots positioned on either side of the sun, usually in connection with cirrus clouds, when the sun is fairly low in the sky. In both cases, the most common angle separating the halo or parhelion from the sun is 22°. This scattering angle is associated with refraction (without internal reflection) through two faces of a hexagonal ice crystal whose extensions form a 60° angle.

In contrast to the case for the rainbow, ray tracing analysis of various optical phenomena associated with ice crystals is complicated by the fact that they are not spherical. Therefore, results for all possible orientations of the crystal must be obtained and then averaged together. Halos are associated with randomly oriented crystals, but most other optical phenomena in cirrus clouds, including sundogs, require ice crystals falling with a preferred orientation.

A more complete discussion of the optics of rainbows and haloes may be found in BH83, section 7.2 and 7.3, and L02, section 5.3.

CHAPTER 5

Radiative Properties of Natural Surfaces

In the previous chapter, we looked at what happens when radiation encounters a smooth surface separating two homogeneous media, such as air and water. We saw that a handful of relatively simple formulas are able to describe all important aspects of this interaction, including the angles of reflection ($\Theta_r = \Theta_i$) and refraction (Snell's law) and the fraction and polarization of the radiation that is reflected (the Fresnel relationships).

The above relationships are sufficient to understand a handful of significant radiative phenomena in the atmosphere – the existence of rainbows, halos, and parhelia, or the glint of the setting sun off a calm water surface. Unfortunately, most surfaces encountered in nature are not so simple. Most land surfaces are covered by soil, sand, vegetation, rough rocks, or snowpack, none of which are either smooth or homogeneous. Water surfaces are usually roughened substantially by wind waves, so that even though the laws of specular reflection apply, at least approximately, at each individual point on the surface, the pattern of reflected sunlight is considerably more diffuse and complex when viewed over a larger area.

Most natural surfaces do not lend themselves to a precise theoretical treatment. Therefore, we must be satisfied with characterizing their radiative properties in a more empirical way; e.g. via

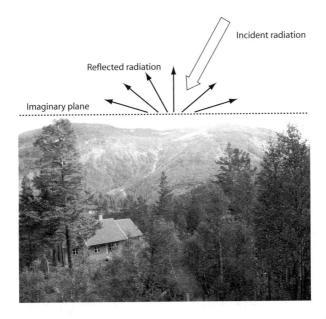

Fig. 5.1: Example of how one treats an irregular surface as an equivalent plane surface.

direct measurements of how much radiation they reflect and absorb at various wavelengths and in what direction(s) the radiation is reflected as a function of the incidence angle.

5.1 Natural Surfaces Idealized as Planar Boundaries

As already pointed out, most natural surfaces cannot be viewed as planar boundaries but rather are highly irregular and inhomogeneous. As seen from very high altitude, a forest may appear as a fairly smooth green surface, but up close, it is anything but smooth. Rather, it is a messy mix of foliage, branches, trunks, shrubs, dead leaves, soil and (mostly) air filling a layer some 10 or more meters thick.

For the purposes of our discussions to follow, however, we can pretend that a forest is indeed a flat surface by imagining a transparent horizontal plane just above the highest treetops and ignoring the details of what happens to radiation *below* that plane (Fig. 5.1).

All we really need to know, from an atmospheric perspective, is that when radiation (e.g., sunlight), incident from above, passes downward through that imaginary surface, some fraction of it is never seen again. We can safely assume that that fraction was absorbed and converted to heat or some other form of energy. The fraction of the incident radiation not absorbed reemerges (by what detailed mechanism we need not inquire) in various directions and contributes to "upwelling" radiation illuminating the atmosphere from below.

The above simplified picture is particularly useful when we're willing to limit our attention to the *average* radiative effects of forests and other natural "surfaces" over fairly large areas. Cloud layers may also sometimes be viewed in this simplified way, if we're willing to overlook the details of what happens *inside* the cloud layer and focus only on the upwelling and downwelling radiation through an imaginary horizontal plane just above cloud top or just below cloud base.

I should mention one caveat before you embrace this approach too firmly: when considering *emission* of radiation from a complex medium (as we will in later chapters), it is really only safe to treat it as an equivalent "surface" if there is also a single more-or-less unique temperature that can be ascribed to every participating point in the scene.

5.2   Absorptivity and Reflectivity

When radiation is incident on the earth's surface, some fraction is reflected and the remainder absorbed. The fraction absorbed we call the *absorptivity*, while the fraction reflected is the *reflectivity*.

We will use the symbols a and r for absorptivity and reflectivity, respectively. Obviously neither quantity can be less than zero nor greater than one.

In general a and r depend on the wavelength λ. A surface that is highly reflective at one wavelength ($r \sim 1$) may be highly absorbing at another ($r \sim 0$). For example, grass and other vegetation appears green because it reflects green, yellow, and blue wavelengths more strongly than red and orange. Often we will make the wavelength dependence explicit by adding a subscript λ, unless there is no possibility of confusion.

In addition, both of these quantities usually depend on the direction $\hat{\Omega} = (\theta, \phi)$ of the incident radiation. For example, in Chapter 4 we saw that the reflectivity (in the visible band) of a smooth water surface varies from a rather small value of 2% at normal incidence ($\theta = 0$) to nearly 100% at grazing angles ($\theta \to 90°$).

For any given wavelength and direction of incident radiation, it is clear that the reflectivity and absorptivity must sum to unity:

$$a_\lambda(\theta, \phi) + r_\lambda(\theta, \phi) = 1 . \tag{5.1}$$

Note that many natural surfaces are *azimuthally isotropic*, meaning they reflect about the same amount of radiation regardless of whether the sun (for example) shines on them from the east, south, west, or some other direction. In that case, the dependence on ϕ may disappear from the above equations.

Furthermore, in the case of many rough surfaces, such as forests, grasslands, ploughed fields, etc., even the dependence on θ may be weak, in which case we might choose (as an approximation) to ignore the directional dependence altogether. One could then relate the reflected monochromatic flux $F_{\lambda, r}$ to the incident flux $F_{\lambda, 0}$ as follows:

$$F_{\lambda, r} = r_\lambda F_{\lambda, 0} . \tag{5.2}$$

It follows that the power per unit area (per unit wavelength) absorbed by the surface is

$$F_{\lambda, 0} - F_{\lambda, r} = (1 - r_\lambda) F_{\lambda, 0} = a_\lambda F_{\lambda, 0} . \tag{5.3}$$

5.2.1 Examples of Reflectivity Spectra

Fig. 5.2 gives examples of how reflectivity typically varies as a function of wavelength for a few natural surface types. Not surprisingly, fresh snow has a very high reflectivity (85%–95%) throughout

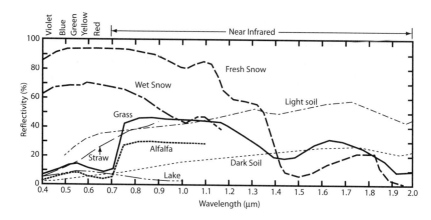

Fig. 5.2: Typical shortwave reflectivity of various natural surface types as a function of wavelength.

the visible band, whereas the reflectivity of fresh vegetation, soil, and bodies of water is generally very low ($< 15\%$). There is a pronounced peak in reflectivity near 0.55 μm for fresh grass and alfalfa which, not surprising, corresponds to the green portion of the visible spectrum and is due to chlorophyll. Dry straw, on the other hand, exhibits no such peak and is considerably brighter overall, though with a bias toward the orange and red end of the spectrum.

An important point to take from this diagram is that there may be relatively little relation between the reflectivity of a surface type in the visible part of the spectrum and that in the near-IR band. For example, at 1 μm, grass is nearly as reflective as wet snow. And both fresh and wet snow are far less reflective in the near-IR band — especially beyond about 1.3 μm, than they are in the visible. These differences can become even more extreme as one continues into the thermal IR band (not shown) where many natural surface types, including fresh snow, have reflectivities of less than 5%.

5.2.2 The Graybody Approximation

As we have just seen, the absorptivity and reflectivity of a surface depends on the exact wavelength being considered. Often, however, it is useful, especially in introductory treatments of radiation such as this one, to disregard the details of this dependence and to pretend that the surface is "gray" over some rather broad range of wavelengths. That is to say, we specify a single average absorptivity that is taken to be representative of the entire band. This is known as the *graybody* approximation.

For example, if the total incident flux of radiation between two widely separated wavelengths is denoted F_i, and the reflected flux within the same range of wavelengths is F_r, then the effective graybody reflectivity is defined as

$$\bar{r} \equiv \frac{F_r}{F_i},$$ (5.4)

and the corresponding graybody absorptivity is $\bar{a} = 1 - \bar{r}$.

A word of caution: $\bar{r}$ and $\bar{a}$ do, in general, depend on the spectral details of the incident radiation, so it usually makes sense to use the graybody approximation only when those details are reasonably constant. For example, the spectrum of solar radiation reaching the surface does not change drastically from one day to the next, so it is reasonable to use the graybody approximation to describe the reflection and absorption of the incident solar flux.

A common application of the graybody approximation is to assign one constant absorptivity a_{sw} to the entire shortwave, or solar, band, and another constant absorptivity a_{lw} to the longwave, or thermal IR, band. For most terrestrial surfaces, a_{lw} is close to unity, whereas a_{sw} can be highly variable, from close to zero in the case of deep snow to close to unity in the case of forests and bodies of water.

The complement of the shortwave absorptivity a_{sw} is of course the shortwave reflectivity $r_{sw} = 1 - a_{sw}$, also commonly known as the shortwave *albedo*. Examples of albedos for common surfaces are given in Table 5.1.

The value of this kind of partitioning between longwave and shortwave absorptivities and reflectivites will become more apparent when we consider simple radiative energy budgets for the surface and atmosphere later on.

Table 5.1: Shortwave (solar) reflectivity (in percent) of various surfaces.

Fresh, dry snow	70–90
Old, melting snow	35–65
Sand, desert	25–40
Dry vegetation	20–30
Deciduous Forest	15–25
Grass	15–25
Ocean surface (low sun)	10–70
Bare soil	10–25
Coniferous Forest	10–15
Ocean surface (high sun)	<10

5.3 Angular Distribution of Reflected Radiation

Early in this chapter (Section 5.2), I introduced the concept of *reflectivity*, which describes the fraction of incident radiation that is reflected from a surface. Among other things, I pointed out that the reflectivity and absorptivity of an opaque surface must sum to unity; that is, all incident radiation must be either reflected or absorbed:

$$a_\lambda + r_\lambda = 1 . \tag{5.5}$$

This seems straightforward enough, and you might assume that there's little more to be said. But we have not yet explained *what happens* to the radiation that is reflected from a surface. That is to say, given r_λ, we know how *much* radiation is reflected, but we don't yet know where it goes.

5.3.1 Specular and Lambertian Reflection

In Chapter 4 we discussed reflection from a very smooth boundary between two homogeneous media. In this special case, which is called *specular reflection*, the reflected angle Θ_r (relative to the local normal) is just equal to the incident angle Θ_i. Furthermore, the reflectivity is then given by the Fresnel relationships (4.16) and (4.17).

Surfaces encountered in nature are not so simple. About the only place where you sometimes find true specular reflection on the scales important to us is from the mirror-like surface of a very smooth body of water, such as a pond or lake on a completely calm day. Under those conditions, the reflection of the sun and other objects is very sharp and clear.

More commonly however, the surface of open bodies of water are at least somewhat roughened by ripples or waves generated by the wind, so that light from the sun is not reflected in a single direction but rather is scattered in a variety of different directions, depending on the local slope where each light ray from the sun encounters the surface. For a lightly roughened water surface, most of the radiation is scattered in a fairly narrow cone of angles surrounding the specular direction. Thus, the reflection of the sun is still identifiable to the eye (or a radiometer) as a relatively concentrated bright spot, but it appears blurred in comparison to the sun itself. The rougher the surface, the greater the blurring, until the reflected radiation is scattered almost uniformly in all directions, irrespective of the direction of incidence.

Apart from bodies of water, the vast majority of surfaces encountered outdoors, as viewed from a significant altitude, are very rough. A forest or a corn field observed from an airplane tends to look more or less uniformly bright when illuminated by the sun, regardless of which direction you are looking. At least, there is no pronounced "hot spot" in the direction where you would expect the specular reflection of the sun to be.

As a crude approximation, one often assumes the flux of upward reflected radiation is equally distributed over all angles, irrespective of the direction of the source. Reflection obeying this rule is called *Lambertian* . Lambertian reflection is thus the exact opposite of specular reflection, since in the latter case all reflected radiation emerges in a single well-defined direction.

> **Problem 5.1:** Wall paint is sold in several varieties, including *glossy, semigloss,* and *flat.* The distinction between these lies in the angular pattern of reflected radiation. Which of these do you think would be best described by the Lambertian model of reflection?

For any kind of reflection, the upward reflected flux F_r is equal

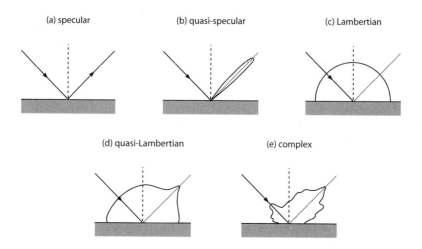

Fig. 5.3: Examples of various types of surface reflection, presented in the form of polar plots in which the distance of the curve to the reflection point on the surface represents the relative intensity of reflected radiation in that direction.

to the reflectivity r times the incident flux F_i:

$$F_r = rF_i \ . \tag{5.6}$$

In the Lambertian case, the intensity I_r of the reflected radiation is by definition independent of direction, so that $F_r = \pi I_r$. Thus we can express the reflected intensity $I^\uparrow$ in terms of the incident flux by simply dividing by π (see Section 2.16):

$$I^\uparrow = \frac{rF_i}{\pi} \ . \tag{5.7}$$

If the incident flux is entirely due to the direct rays of the sun positioned in the sky at an angle θ_i from zenith, we further have

$$I^\uparrow = \frac{rS_0 \cos\theta_i}{\pi} \ , \tag{5.8}$$

where S_0 is the solar flux normal to the beam.

The angular distribution of reflection from most natural surfaces is generally neither specular nor perfectly Lambertian. Indeed, it generally has no simple mathematical form at all but rather must be determined empirically from suitable measurements. Fig. 5.3

schematically depicts some reflection patterns that might be encountered in nature, just to give you an idea of what is possible. It is not uncommon for observed reflection patterns to combine specular- and Lambertian-like features, since there is often both a strong peak in the specular direction as well as a more diffuse component spread out more uniformly over all angles.

5.3.2 Reflection in the General Case[†]

In the previous section, we considered two important limiting cases: 1) specular reflection, wherein the direction of the reflected radiation is uniquely determined by the incident direction, and 2) Lambertian reflection, wherein the angular distribution of reflected radiation is uniform and therefore completely independent of the incident direction. Both cases are simple to deal with both conceptually and computationally. Radiation and remote sensing specialists therefore tend to fall back on one or the other simplifying assumption whenever they can get away with it.

Sometimes, however, they cannot, and a more sophisticated way of describing surface reflection is needed. In general, the intensity of reflected radiation is a continuously varying function of both the incident direction $\hat{\Omega}_i = (\theta_i, \phi_i)$ and the reflected direction $\hat{\Omega}_r = (\theta_r, \phi_r)$. Radiation specialists define the *bidirectional reflection function* $\rho(\theta_i, \phi_i; \theta_r, \phi_r)$, or *BDRF*,[1] such that

$$I^{\uparrow}(\theta_r, \phi_r) = \rho(\theta_i, \phi_i; \theta_r, \phi_r) S_0 \cos \theta_i , \qquad (5.9)$$

where S_0 is the solar flux normal to the beam.

The above relationship assumes direct illumination of the surface by the sun at position (θ_i, ϕ_i) in the sky. Of course, it is not uncommon for illumination to come from more than one direction. For example, on an overcast day, the downward illumination comes more or less equally from all directions. In this case, it is necessary to generalize the above relationship so as to integrate the contributions from all directions:

$$I^{\uparrow}(\hat{\Omega}_r) = \int_{2\pi} \rho(\hat{\Omega}_i; \hat{\Omega}_r) I^{\downarrow}(\hat{\Omega}_i) \hat{n} \cdot \hat{\Omega}_i \, d\omega_i , \qquad (5.10)$$

---

[1]Some authors prefer *bidirectional reflection distribution function,* or *BRDF.*

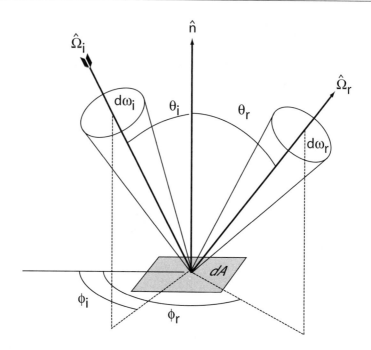

Fig. 5.4: Geometry and relevant variables for the definition of the BDRF.

where $\hat{n}$ is the vertical unit vector, so that $\hat{n} \cdot \hat{\Omega}_i = \cos \theta_i$.

Recall that the integral as written above represents a generic integration over solid angle covering the entire upper hemisphere of 2π steradians. Rewriting the above as an explicit integration over the two polar coordinates θ and ϕ, we have

$$I^\uparrow(\theta_r, \phi_r) = \int_0^{2\pi} \int_0^{\pi/2} \rho(\theta_i, \phi_i; \theta_r, \phi_r) I^\downarrow(\theta_i, \phi_i) \cos \theta_i \sin \theta_i \, d\theta_i d\phi_i \; . \tag{5.11}$$

As a special case, consider what happens if $\rho(\theta_i, \phi_i; \theta_r, \phi_r) = \rho_L$, where ρ_L is a constant. In that case, ρ_L can be taken out of the integral above, leaving

$$I^\uparrow = \rho_L \int_0^{2\pi} \int_0^{\pi/2} I^\downarrow(\theta_i, \phi_i) \cos \theta_i \sin \theta_i \, d\theta_i d\phi_i \; . \tag{5.12}$$

Note that the right hand side, and therefore $I^\uparrow$, no longer depends on (θ_r, ϕ_r), so we evidently have Lambertian reflection. Also, by comparing the remaining integral with (2.59), we realize that it represents the incident flux of radiation F_i, so that

$$I^\uparrow = \rho_L F_i . \tag{5.13}$$

If we multiply both sides of the above equation by π, we get an expression for the reflected flux (since $I^\uparrow$ is isotropic). From (5.2), we then conclude that

$$r = \pi \rho_L , \tag{5.14}$$

where r is the total (nondirectional) reflectivity of the Lambertian surface.

Let us now generalize to find the reflectivity $r(\hat{\Omega}_i)$ corresponding to an arbitrary BDRF. For simplicity, we again consider the relationship between the reflected flux F_r and the incident flux $F_i = S_0 \cos \theta_i$ due to a columnated beam originating from a zenith angle θ_i:

$$F_r = r(\hat{\Omega}_i) S_0 \cos \theta_i . \tag{5.15}$$

The reflected flux F_r can in turn be expressed in terms of an integral over the hemisphere of the upward reflected intensity $I^\uparrow$:

$$F_r = \int_{2\pi} I^\uparrow(\hat{\Omega}) \cos \theta \, d\omega = \int_{2\pi} \rho(\hat{\Omega}_i; \hat{\Omega}_r) S_0 \cos \theta_i \cos \theta_r \, d\omega_r , \tag{5.16}$$

where we have substituted (5.9) into the integral. Setting (5.15) equal to (5.16) and dividing out the incident flux terms yields

$$r(\hat{\Omega}) = \int_{2\pi} \rho(\hat{\Omega}; \hat{\Omega}_r) \cos \theta_r \, d\omega_r . \tag{5.17}$$

5.4 Applications to Meteorology, Climatology, and Remote Sensing

5.4.1 Solar Heating of Surfaces

The shortwave albedo of a surface has a large effect on the direct heating of the surface by sunlight and, ultimately, on the heating of air in contact with that surface. A field of freshly plowed bare soil (albedo $\sim$10%) will absorb almost 30% more solar radiation than a field of dry wheat (albedo ~30%) and nine times as much as a layer of fresh dry snow (albedo ~90%).

Whatever solar radiation is absorbed usually has the immediate effect of heating the surface. But much of that heat is eventually transferred to the atmosphere by way of (1) direct thermal conduction (*sensible heat flux*), (2) evaporation of surface moisture (*latent heat flux*), and/or (3) net longwave flux. Which one of these transfer mechanisms dominates depends on both atmospheric and surface conditions. A warm, humid atmosphere will tend to minimize the net loss of longwave radiation from the surface. A moist or vegetated surface will tend to transfer a proportionally larger fraction of its energy to the atmosphere in the form of latent heat.

If you have two dry, relatively bare land areas side by side with sharply differing albedos, then the darker surface, and therefore the air immediately above that surface, will be heated more rapidly by the absorption of solar radiation. If there is little wind, the sharp temperature difference that develops over time will trigger microscale circulations, as the warmer air over the darker surface rises in the form of a thermal updraft and is replaced by relatively cooler air flowing horizontally from the lighter surface. The latter air, of course, must be replaced by sinking air from above. Experienced glider pilots know how to exploit variations in land surface albedo so as to find the thermal updrafts that can help keep them aloft.

Problem 5.2: A field of snow that is just starting to melt is a special case, in that absorbed solar radiation will contribute primarily to a further phase change (solid to liquid) at a constant temperature of 0°C. Assume that the shortwave albedo of wet snow is 60% and that the solar flux reaching the surface on a particular sunny day is 500 W m^{-2}. The latent heat of fusion of ice L_f is 3.3×10^5 J/kg and you can assume that the density ρ_{ws} of wet snow stays constant (assuming all excess meltwater drains away) at around 200 kg m^{-3}. At what rate, in centimeters per hour, is the snow pack depleted by direct solar heating?

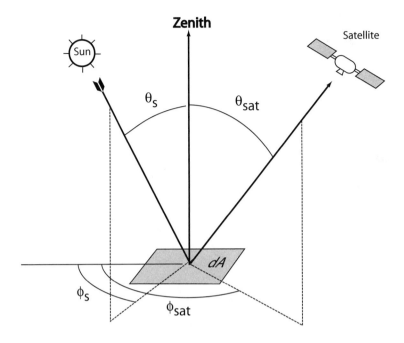

Fig. 5.5: Relationship between incident and reflected solar radiation, as seen by a satellite sensor.

5.4.2 Satellite Imaging at Visible and Near-IR Wavelengths

One of the simplest and most familiar applications of remote sensing is embodied in visible ("VIS") images captured by sensors on board both geostationary and polar orbiting meteorological satellites. Conceptually (though not technologically), these images are similar to an ordinary black and white photograph taken from the (admittedly less than ordinary) vantage point of outer space. As long as the satellite sensor is viewing the sunlit side of the earth, visible images allow you to easily distinguish regions of high reflectivity (clouds, snow cover, sea ice, desert sand) and low reflectivity (vegetated ground, water, soil).

The very first meteorological satellite images (beginning in April 1960) were of this type. In fact, they were little more than television pictures taken from space. Nevertheless, they provided the first clear pictures of the large scale organization and evolution of clouds and storm systems. While careful analysis of surface weather

Fig. 5.6: A visible image of the Eastern Pacific and west coast of North America taken by the GOES-West geostationary weather satellite.

observations had previously hinted at these structures, the network of observing stations was (and remains) too sparse to resolve more than grossest features, especially over sparsely populated areas.

Problem 5.3: An example of a visible image from a geostationary satellite is given in Fig. 5.6.

(a) Based on this image, characterize the relative reflectivities of the various geographical and meteorological features that you see.

(b) The apparent brightness of the clouds diminishes steadily toward the western edge of the image. Why?

Quantitative utilization of VIS imagery – i.e., the conversion of measured radiances to estimates of specific physical properties, such as albedo, snow depth, etc., is also possible but requires considerably more care. In particular, you need an instrument that is well calibrated, so that radiance measurements are reliable and accurate in an absolute sense, not just a relative one. Also, you have to carefully account for the variable angle and intensity of solar illumination.

Recall from (5.9) that the reflected intensity $I^\uparrow$ viewed by the satellite depends on the viewing direction (θ_r, ϕ_r), on the direction of incidence (θ_i, ϕ_i), and on the bidirectional reflectance function (BDRF) $\rho(\theta_i, \phi_i; \theta_r, \phi_r)$. While the various directions can be easily calculated, given the satellite's position, the scene location on the earth's surface, and the sun position (Fig. 5.5), the details of the BDRF are highly variable and, for many natural surfaces, are poorly known.

It is therefore not possible to reliably estimate the overall albedo of a surface from a radiance measurement made in only one direction and with one direction of solar illumination. Thus, a high radiant intensity observed by a satellite sensor at a particular point on the surface could imply either a) a high-albedo surface, such as snow, or b) a lower-albedo surface for which the BDRF happens to be sending a large fraction of the total reflected radiation in the direction of the satellite. Sun glint from a water surface is a good example of the second case: the *overall* albedo of water is quite low, but the reflected image of the sun can be very bright if you happen to be looking in exactly the right direction.

Problem 5.4: A certain meteorological satellite crosses the equator at a longitude of $\phi_{sat} = 50°W$ and time 1200 Greenwich Mean Time (GMT) on March 21, at which time the sun is overhead at the intersection of the equator and the Greenwich Meridian. At what geographic location is an imager on board the satellite most likely to observe sun glint? The satellite has an altitude above the surface of $H = 1000$ km, and the sun can be regarded as being infinitely far away from the earth (i.e., rays from the sun are parallel). The radius of the earth is $R_E = 6373$ km. *Hint:* First find the trigonometric equation that must be satisfied by the longitude of the sun glint. There is no simple closed-form solution to this equation, so you'll need to use successive approximation to find a *numerical* solution accurate to at least the nearest degree.

Some satellite sensors have channels at two or more visible

and/or near-IR wavelengths. Since the shape of the BDRF of most surfaces doesn't differ much between two nearby wavelengths, the *ratio* of the observed intensities doesn't depend too much on either the BDRF itself or the angle of solar illumination. This makes it possible to assess the color of a scene without too much ambiguity. Common applications include 1) land use classification, 2) assessment of phytoplankton concentration in coastal waters, and 3) characterization of vegetation extent and density. Of course, all of these techniques are subject to the adverse effects of atmospheric haze and clouds.

Problem 5.5:   A particular satellite sensor is being designed to measure the reflectivities r_1 and r_2 of a scene corresponding to two wavelengths λ_1 and λ_2. Based on Fig. 5.2, choose λ_1 and λ_2 so as to optimize the ability of the satellite to discriminate different scene types. Start by drawing a diagram with r_1 as the horizontal axis and r_2 as the vertical axis. Plot points corresponding to each surface type, and label the points. Try to develop a simple mathematical *algorithm* (e.g., a series of tests based on inequalities) that would allow you to correctly classify the surface as *snow, soil, growing vegetation, dry vegetation,* or *water,* based on observations of r_1 and r_2. You might want to consider reflectivity *differences* and/or reflectivity *ratios,* as well as individual channel reflectivities, as possible variables in your tests. Whatever criteria you develop, depict them graphically as curves separating surface types on your plot of r_1 vs r_2. Note that if you choose your two wavelengths so that any two differing surface types are too closely spaced on your plot, the risk of misclassification greatly increases when you apply your algorithm to real-world data. Hint: There is no single "correct" solution to this problem – be creative!

CHAPTER 6

Thermal Emission

Up to this point, we have considered only the *absorption, transmission,* and *reflection* of radiation incident externally on a medium. These interactions are sufficient for characterizing the disposition of shortwave (solar) radiation within the atmosphere, because its principal source, the sun, is external to the earth-atmosphere system. By contrast, the principal source of longwave radiation is thermal *emission* by the earth and atmosphere itself. Emission is the process by which some of the internal energy of a material is converted into radiant energy. This energy may either get reabsorbed at another location in the atmosphere or else escape to space, whereupon it is permanently lost, at least from the perspective of earthbound observers.

Normally, we are oblivious to the fact that we are constantly bathed in, and absorb, longwave radiation that is emitted by our surroundings, nor do we give much thought to the fact that our own bodies also lose heat energy via emission of radiation. One reason that we don't notice this is that the temperature of our skin and that of our surroundings is usually not too different; hence there is a near-balance between the heat we lose via radiation and that we absorb from our surroundings. Also, if there is any air movement at all (as is usually the case outdoors) then we tend to be more conscious of heat exchange with the air in direct contact with our skin, due to conduction, than that due to radiation.

The existence of thermally emitted radiation becomes more apparent to us when the temperature differences are larger. A wood-burning stove radiates heat that you can feel on your face from across a room. A car parked under a clear sky during the fall or winter can rapidly cool to the point that frost forms on the windshield, even if the free air temperature remains a few degrees above freezing. If an object becomes sufficiently hot, thermal emission may be great enough at the shorter wavelengths so as to be visible to the eye. The glowing embers in a fireplace or barbecue grill are one example; the white-hot filament of an incandescent light bulb is another.

It is possible to derive the relationship between temperature and thermal emission from first principles, based on the laws of quantum mechanics and statistical thermodynamics.[1] In keeping with the title of this book, we will instead go straight to the bottom line, explaining the general characteristics of thermal emission and giving you the tools to perform radiative calculations of the type most relevant to meteorologists.

Here, in words, are the key facts about thermal emission of radiation that you should be very comfortable working with by the time you finish this chapter. We will elaborate on these points, and provide the relevant formulas, in the subsequent subsections.

- An object having temperature T will generally emit radiation at all possible wavelengths. However, for any particular wavelength λ, there is a hard upper bound on the amount of that radiation. The function of T and λ that gives that upper bound is called *Planck's function*. The shape of Planck's function for several representative temperatures in the atmosphere is shown in Fig. 6.3. The mathematical details will be given shortly.

- For any given (absolute) temperature, Planck's Function has its peak at a wavelength that is inversely proportional to that temperature, a fact that is embodied in *Wien's Displacement*

---

[1]See for example Appendix A of L02.

Law. Thus, peak emission from a cool object, like the earth, occurs at much longer wavelengths than that from a very hot object, like the sun.

- By integrating Planck's Function over all possible wavelengths, you get the *Stefan-Boltzmann law*, which states that the theoretical maximum amount of total (broadband) radiation that can be emitted by an object is proportional to the fourth power of its absolute temperature. Thus, doubling the temperature of an object leads to sixteen-fold increase in the maximum amount of radiation it can theoretically emit.

- Within any given band of wavelengths, a good absorber is also a good emitter. This fact is embodied in *Kirchhoff's law*. Thus, a perfect reflector (nonabsorber) emits no thermal radiation. A perfect absorber emits the theoretical maximum amount of thermal radiation, as described by Planck's Function.

I urge you to spend some time thinking about the above four points and committing them to memory. Once you have an intuitive grasp of these basic facts, your brain will be more receptive to precise mathematical re-statements of the same facts. You will also be less likely to use the mathematical formulas "blindly" in possibly inappropriate ways.

6.1 Blackbody Radiation

I just made several references to the "theoretical maximum amount of radiation" that can be emitted by an object. I also pointed out that a good absorber is a good emitter. In order for thermal emission from an object to actually achieve the "theoretical maximum," it must be a perfect emitter, which is to say, a perfect absorber.

An object that absorbs radiation perfectly is called a *blackbody*. In other words, it is a graybody for which the absorptivity $a = 1$. As such, it is an idealization that is seldom exactly realized in nature. Nevertheless, it is surprisingly easy to approximate a blackbody as follows:

Take a large, empty cardboard packing box (say, two feet on a side) and tape it closed on all sides. Then punch a small hole — one

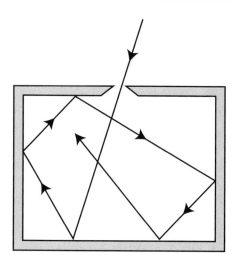

Fig. 6.1: Schematic depiction of the fate of a photon that enters a hollow cavity through a small hole. With each additional reflection from the wall of the cavity, its chance of surviving without absorption steadily decreases. A blackbody cavity can therefore easily be constructed such that only a negligible fraction of photons incident on the hole ever emerge again.

cm diameter will do — in one side. That hole is now a pretty good approximation of a blackbody over a wide range of wavelengths. If you shine a flashlight beam on it, virtually all of the light will disappear into the hole and never reemerge. In other words, the effective absorptivity of the hole is very close to unity. Why is this?

Consider the fate of a photon fired into the hole. First, it strikes the opposite surface inside the box (Fig. 6.1). At that point, its chance of getting absorbed is equal to the absorptivity of the cardboard. Let's assume that that absorptivity is 0.5, in which case there is a fifty-fifty chance of the photon getting absorbed. Even if it is not absorbed, the chance is very small that it will bounce directly out the same small hole that it came in through. Rather, it will encounter another interior side of the box, with another fifty-fifty chance of getting absorbed. Its total survival probability is now only one in four. Now consider a trajectory that allows the photon to exit the hole after reflecting off an interior wall of the box N times. The probability of the photon surviving that entire trajectory and exiting the hole is $(1 - a)^N$, where a is the absorptivity. If $a = 0.5$, as assumed above, N could be as small as seven and still imply less than a one-percent probability of a photon re-emerging from the hole. If the hole is small and the box is large, the expected value of N can be quite large. Also, if you paint the inside of the box black, then a approaches one, pushing the value of $(1 - a)^N$ even closer to zero. In short, it is not difficult to make the absorptivity of the hole in the box almost arbitrarily close to unity.

Now that we have a blackbody, what can we do with it? For one thing, we can measure the characteristics of the radiation *emitted* by the blackbody. At room temperature, this radiation lies primarily in the thermal infrared band and is therefore invisible to the eye. But if the box were made of something heat resistant, like iron, you could heat it to the point that visible light was emitted from the hole. If you increased the temperature of the cavity gradually up to several thousand degrees, you would first see a dark red glow, then more orange and yellow, and all the while the overall brightness would increase. At extremely high temperatures (several thousand K and higher) , the emitted light becomes white and, eventually, bluish white. Such high temperatures are found in nature only on the surface of the sun and stars.

Problem 6.1: An *infrared thermometer* allows the temperature of objects to be measured at a distance, assuming that they emit radiation more or less like blackbodies. Based on this description, would you infer that the instrument is designed to measure infrared *flux* or *intensity*? Why?

6.1.1 Planck's Function

The intensity of radiation emitted by a blackbody is given by Planck's Function $B(T)$. It takes slightly different forms depending on whether it is written as a function of wavelength λ, frequency ν or wavenumber $\tilde{\nu}$. When it is given as a function of wavelength, it is

$$B_\lambda(T) = \frac{2hc^2}{\lambda^5 \left(e^{hc/k_B \lambda T} - 1 \right)} , \qquad (6.1)$$

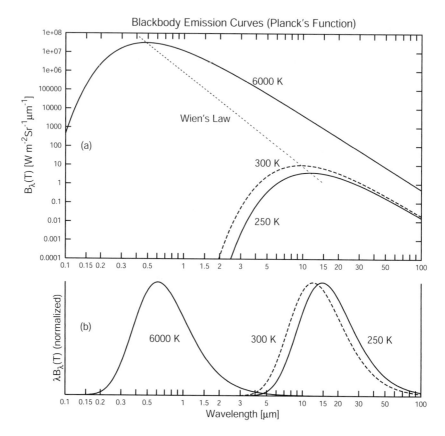

Fig. 6.2: Blackbody emission curves at temperatures typical of the sun and of the earth and atmosphere. (a) The actual value of Planck's function, plotted on a logarithmic vertical axis. The diagonal dashed line corresponds to Wien's law (6.3). (b) Normalized depictions of the same functions as in (a), so that the areas under each curve are equal. Note that the vertical axis in this case is linear.

where $c = 2.998 \times 10^8$ m s^{-1} is the speed of light, $h = 6.626 \times 10^{-34}$J s is Planck's constant, and $k_B = 1.381 \times 10^{-23}$ J/K is Boltzmann's constant.

The interpretation of this function is as follows:

$$B_\lambda(T)\, d\lambda = \begin{bmatrix} \text{total intensity of emitted radiation con-} \\ \text{tributed by the wavelength interval} \\ [\lambda, \lambda + d\lambda] \end{bmatrix}. \quad (6.2)$$

The physical dimensions of B_λ are thus those of intensity (power per unit area per unit solid angle) per unit wavelength; in common

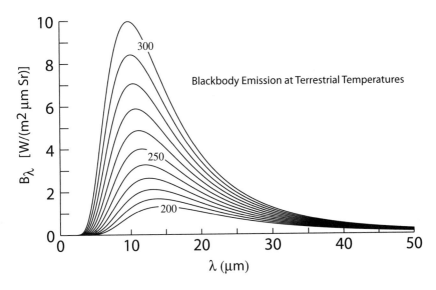

Fig. 6.3: The Planck (blackbody) function B_λ at temperatures typical of those found in the atmosphere.

units: $\text{W m}^{-2}\mu\text{m}^{-1}\text{sr}^{-1}$.

Note that this interpretation is consistent with a point I made earlier: if you allow $d\lambda$ to go to zero, then the emitted radiation in the interval $[\lambda, \lambda + d\lambda]$ also goes to zero. Thus, a hypothetical (and unrealizable) detector that only could measure radiation at exactly one wavelength would detect no radiation at all. Consequently, any real detector used in atmospheric remote sensing has a finite spectral "bandwidth" that describes the range of wavelengths to which it responds. The greater the bandwidth, the more total radiant power the sensor receives and the greater its overall sensitivity, all other factors being equal.

Problem 6.2: Sometimes Planck's function $B(T)$ may be expressed as a function of frequency ν or wavenumber $\tilde{\nu}$ instead of wavelength λ. Given that $B_\lambda(T)\, d\lambda$ must equal $B_\nu(T)\, d\nu$ when $d\nu$ and $d\lambda$ correspond to the same narrow interval of the spectrum, find the correct expression for B_ν as a function of ν only.

Examples of $B_\lambda(T)$ are shown for various temperatures in Figs.

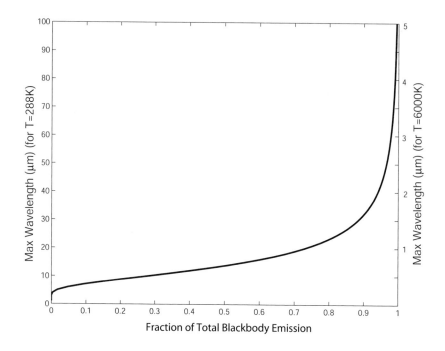

Fig. 6.4: The fraction of total blackbody emission contributed by wavelengths λ smaller than the threshold value indicated on the vertical axes. The horizontal axis gives the value of $\pi[\int_0^\lambda B_\lambda(T)\,d\lambda]/(\sigma T^4)$. The left axis corresponds to a blackbody with $T = 288$ K; the right axis corresponds to $T = 6000$ K. *(Figure courtesy of S. Ackerman, with modifications)*

6.2a and 6.3. Planck's function is seen to have its peak at a wavelength that is inversely proportional to absolute temperature (see Wien's Displacement Law, below). At any given wavelength, emission increases monotonically with increasing temperature. Emission is not symmetrically distributed about this peak; rather, the function drops off sharply at the short wavelength end of the spectrum while trailing off much more slowly toward long wavelengths.

6.1.2 Wien's Displacement Law

The wavelength $\lambda_{\max}$ of the peak of the Planck function — i.e., that of maximum emission from by a blackbody of temperature T is given by *Wien's Displacement Law*:

$$\lambda_{max} = \frac{k_W}{T} \, , \qquad (6.3)$$

where the constant $k_W = 2897 \ \mu m \ K$. Thus, peak emission from a blackbody with a temperature of 6000 K, similar to that of the sun, occurs at a wavelength of $\lambda_{max} = 0.48 \ \mu m$, whereas typical atmospheric temperatures in the range 200K–300K yield peak emission in the range 9.6–14.4 μm.

Problem 6.3: a) Derive an approximate value of Wien's constant k_W. Start with an approximate form of (6.1) that is valid when $\exp(hc/k_B\lambda T) \gg 1$. Then use standard calculus techniques to find the position of the maximum. Once you have found your expression for λ_{max}, verify that the approximation you used is always valid near that wavelength.

b) Show that the intensity at the peak of the Planck function is proportional to the fifth power of temperature.

Problem 6.4: Regardless of whether an emitter is a perfect blackbody or not, one may define the *color temperature* of the emitter in terms of its wavelength of maximum emission, according to Wien's law. The wavelength of maximum emission from the sun is approximately 0.475 μm. Determine its color temperature.

Problem 6.5: The filament of an incandescent light bulb typically has a temperature of 2,850 K. (a) Find λ_{max}. (b) Is this wavelength within the visible band? (c) Plot B_λ for this temperature, using linear axes. Either graphically or numerically, estimate the fraction of the total emission from an incandescent light bulb that falls within the visible portion of the spectrum (i.e., between 0.4 and 0.7 μm). (d) If the bulb consumes 60 W of electrical power, what is the *maximum* amount of visible light it produces, in watts?

6.1.3　Stefan-Boltzmann Law

Planck's function gives the *monochromatic intensity* emitted by a blackbody. Of fundamental interest for energy transfer within the atmosphere, and between the atmosphere and outer space, is the *broadband flux* emitted by a blackbody. This flux is obtained by integrating Planck's function over all wavelengths and over the 2π steradians of solid angle of one hemisphere. For uniform intensity, the latter integration entails nothing more than multiplication by a factor π; hence the desired blackbody flux is

$$F_{BB}(T) = \pi \int_0^\infty B_\lambda(T)\, d\lambda \ . \tag{6.4}$$

When expression (6.1) for B_λ is substituted and the integral evaluated analytically, the above integral reduces to the *Stefan-Boltzmann law*

$$\boxed{F_{BB}(T) = \sigma T^4 \ ,} \tag{6.5}$$

where

$$\sigma = \frac{2\pi^5 k_B^4}{15 c^2 h^3} \approx 5.67 \times 10^{-8} \frac{W}{m^2 K^4} \ . \tag{6.6}$$

Problem 6.6:　Given the following information, use the Stefan-Boltzmann relationship to compute the effective emitting temperature of the Sun: Solar constant at top of Earth's atmosphere $S_0 = 1370$ W m^{-2}; mean radius of Earth's orbit 1.496×10^8 km; radius of the Sun's photosphere 6.96×10^5 km. (Note that this value differs somewhat from the color temperature of the Sun derived in an earlier problem.)

Problem 6.7:　Perform the analytic integration of B_λ that yields the Stefan-Boltzmann relationship. Hint: Use the substitution $x = hc/k_B \lambda T$, and note that $\int_0^\infty [x^3/(e^x - 1)]\,dx = \pi^4/15$.

6.1.4   Rayleigh-Jeans Approximation

If you are concerned with microwave remote sensing of the atmosphere, then the wavelengths of interest to you are quite long —
$\lambda \sim 1$ mm or longer. In the limit of large wavelength,

$$B_\lambda(T) \approx \frac{2ck_B}{\lambda^4} T , \qquad (6.7)$$

in which case blackbody emission is seen to be proportional to absolute temperature. This so-called *Rayleigh-Jeans approximation* significantly simplifies some kinds of radiative transfer calculations and
sensor calibration relationships in the microwave band.

> **Problem 6.8:**   Derive the Rayleigh-Jeans approximation (6.7) by ex-
> panding $\exp(hc/k_B\lambda T)$ in (6.1) as a power series and discarding
> quadratic and higher order terms. State what specific condition must
> be satisfied in order for the approximation to be valid. For the case
> that $T = 300$ K, determine the minimum wavelength for which the
> Rayleigh-Jeans approximation is valid to better than 1%.

6.2   Emissivity

Planck's function $B_\lambda(T)$ describes thermal emission from a blackbody which, as already noted, corresponds to the theoretical maximum possible emission from any real object. As such, it is an idealization. In calculations, one must therefore account for the degree
to which real surfaces deviate from the ideal of a blackbody. We
therefore introduce the concept of *emissivity*, which is nothing more
than the ratio of what *is* emitted by a given surface to what *would be*
emitted if it were a blackbody.

There are two cases of particular interest: 1) the emissivity at a
single wavelength, and 2) emissivity over a broad range of wavelengths. The first case is most interesting in remote sensing applications, in which case we are primarily concerned with intensities, not
fluxes. The second is generally of greatest concern for energy transfer calculations, in which case we care more about fluxes than intensities. The definitions that follow reflect these biases. You should be

Table 6.1: Typical infrared emissivities (in percent) of various surfaces.

Water	92–96
Fresh, dry snow	82–99.5
Ice	96
Sand, dry	84–90
Soil, moist	95–98
Soil, dry plowed	90
Desert	90-91
Forest and shrubs	90
Skin, human	95
Concrete	71–88
Polished aluminum	1–5

aware, however, that analogous, but slightly different definitions arise in other contexts.

6.2.1 Monochromatic Emissivity

Consider a surface that emits *less* radiation at a given wavelength λ and temperature T than that predicted by the Planck Function. If the actual intensity of the emission is I_λ, then the *monochromatic emissivity* of the surface is defined as

$$\varepsilon_\lambda \equiv \frac{I_\lambda}{B_\lambda(T)} . \qquad (6.8)$$

Note that ε_λ might be a function of other variables, such as T, θ, and/or ϕ. In general $0 \leq \varepsilon_\lambda \leq 1$. When $\varepsilon_\lambda = 1$, the surface is effectively a blackbody at that wavelength.

6.2.2 Graybody Emissivity

By analogy to the monochromatic emissivity above, one may define a *graybody emissivity* ε as the ratio of the observed broadband flux F emitted by a surface to that predicted by the Stefan-Boltzmann relationship:

$$\varepsilon \equiv \frac{F}{\sigma T^4} \cdot \qquad (6.9)$$

Strictly speaking, no surface is truly "gray" over the full EM spectrum. Therefore, the use of a graybody emissivity (or absorptivity) in calculations invariably entails an approximation. It is nevertheless a convenient and useful simplification, especially for the types of problems encountered in an introductory survey of atmospheric radiation.

Sometimes, it is useful to apply the concept of graybody emissivity to a more limited range of wavelength $[\lambda_1, \lambda_2]$, in which case

$$\varepsilon(\lambda_1, \lambda_2) \equiv \frac{F(\lambda_1, \lambda_2)}{F_B(\lambda_1, \lambda_2)}, \qquad (6.10)$$

where $F(\lambda_1, \lambda_2)$ is the actual flux emitted by the surface integrated between λ_1 and λ_2, and

$$F_B(\lambda_1, \lambda_2) \equiv \pi \int_{\lambda_1}^{\lambda_2} B_\lambda(T) \, d\lambda . \qquad (6.11)$$

For example, one might reasonably attempt to characterize the emissivity of a surface in just the thermal IR band for the purpose of simple radiative balance calculations. Examples of IR emissivities are given in Table 6.1.

6.2.3 Kirchhoff's Law

I already alluded to the strong connection between how well a surface absorbs radiation at a given wavelength and how well it emits at the same wavelength. It's easy enough to confirm this experimentally by taking a light colored stone and a dark colored stone and heating them both in a furnace to the same high temperature. Turn out the lights and observe the red glow from each stone: the glow from the light stone will be much dimmer than that from the dark stone. In fact, if the stone were perfectly white (nonabsorbing), you would not be able to get it to glow at all, no matter how hot you heated it.

In quantitative terms, the relationship between absorptivity a and emissivity ε is embodied succinctly in *Kirchhoff's Law*, which states that

$$\varepsilon_\lambda(\theta, \phi) = a_\lambda(\theta, \phi) . \qquad (6.12)$$

Note that this equivalence is strictly valid only for monochromatic radiation at a given wavelength λ and when the viewing directions θ and ϕ are specified, unless a (and therefore ε) are independent of these parameters over some range.

I will not devote space to the derivation of Kirchhoff's Law; suffice it to say that if it did *not* hold, then it would be possible to construct a system in which there is a spontaneous net flow of energy from a colder object to a warmer object, in violation of the Second Law of Thermodynamics.

It is common and convenient to apply Kirchhoff's Law not only to *monochromatic, directional* emissivities and absorptivities, but also to *graybody, flux* emissivities and absorptivities specified for some extended wavelength range. Keep in mind, however, that this is always an approximation — and sometimes a poor one — for any real surface. This is because real surfaces generally have absorptivities that depend on both wavelength and direction. Thus the total absorption depends on the angular and spectral distribution of the incident radiation, whereas the total emission in the same wavelength range does not.

Caveat: Local Thermodynamic Equilibrium

For all common applications in atmospheric radiation, Kirchhoff's Law can be taken as an absolute. It is therefore only for the sake of completeness that I point out that Kirchhoff's Law only applies to systems in *local thermodynamic equilibrium* (LTE).[2] This condition applies, for example, when the molecules in a substance exchange energy with each other (e.g., through collisions) much more rapidly than they do with the radiation field or other sources of energy. LTE, and thus Kirchhoff's Law, breaks down at extremely high altitudes in the atmosphere, where collisions between molecules are

---

[2]See GY89 (pp. 30–32) for a more advanced treatment of this topic.

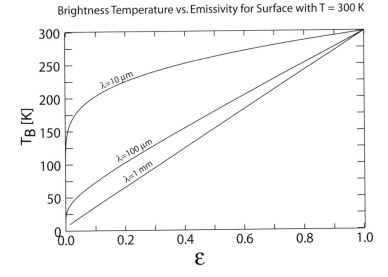

Fig. 6.5: Relationship between emissivity ε and brightness temperature T_B for a surface with a physical temperature of 300 K, at three different wavelengths.

rare. LTE also breaks down in systems like lasers, fluorescent light bulbs, gas-discharge tubes, and light-emitting diodes (LEDs), where the average electronic energy levels of the molecules may be artificially "pumped up" by various means to levels far higher than that expected from the thermodynamic temperature of the molecules. The emission from such systems is therefore far greater than that expected from a blackbody (indeed, that's why these devices are useful!) and therefore does not obey either Planck's Law or Kirchhoff's Law. Examples of non-LTE emission in the atmosphere include lightning discharges and the aurora (e.g. "northern lights.").

6.2.4 Brightness Temperature

Planck's function describes a unique, one-to-one relationship between the intensity of radiation emitted by a blackbody at a given wavelength and the blackbody's temperature. That is to say, if you know the intensity I_λ of radiation emitted by a blackbody, then you can find its temperature T, and vice versa. In view of this correspondence, you can convert *any* monochromatic intensity, regardless of source, to an equivalent blackbody temperature, or *brightness tem-*

perature:

$$T_B \equiv B_\lambda^{-1}(I_\lambda) , \qquad (6.13)$$

where B_λ^{-1} is the inverse of the Planck function applied to the observed radiance.

The concept of brightness temperature is extremely useful in remote sensing at infrared and microwave wavelengths. For example, at thermal IR wavelengths, most land and water surfaces and dense cloud layers have an emissivity $\varepsilon \approx 1$. Viewed through a transparent atmosphere, the brightness temperature of these surfaces is therefore very close to their actual physical temperature.

Problem 6.9: A satellite viewing a surface location under cloud-free conditions measures a 12 μm radiance of 6.2 W m$^{-2}\mu$m^{-1}sr^{-1}. (a) Compute the brightness temperature T_B. (b) Compute the actual temperature, assuming that the atmosphere is completely transparent, and that the surface in question is known to have an emissivity of 0.9 at this wavelength. (c) Is the ratio of the brightness temperature to the actual temperature equal to the emissivity?

At microwave wavelengths, on the other hand, the emissivity of some surfaces (especially water and glacial ice) is substantially less than unity, in which case the brightness temperature may be substantially less than the physical temperature. Nevertheless, the Rayleigh-Jeans approximation which is valid for microwave wavelengths (see Section 6.1.4) implies a direct proportionality between intensity I_λ and brightness temperature T_B. Therefore T_B remains a very convenient substitute for I_λ in radiative transfer calculations used in microwave remote sensing.

Problem 6.10: Repeat the previous problem, only for a wavelength of 1 cm and an intensity of 2.103×10^{-10} W m$^{-2}\mu$m^{-1}sr^{-1}. How does your answer to part (c) change?

Problem 6.11: On a particular day, a land surface has a physical temperature of 300 K. It is observed by a satellite that has both an infrared radiometer channel at 11 μm and a microwave radiometer channel at 19 GHz. In both cases, the emissivity ε of the surface is 0.95. (a) What brightness temperatures are recorded by the infrared and microwave radiometers? (b) Given that the true emissivity of a land surface scene is usually unknowable to better than a few percent, for which of the two bands is it safer to use the brightness temperature as a rough estimate of the true physical temperature of the surface?

In some wavelength bands, the cloud-free atmosphere is far from transparent. In this case, the brightness temperature observed from space can no longer be interpreted in terms of the apparent physical temperature of a surface but rather as a weighted average of all of the atmospheric temperatures encountered along the line-

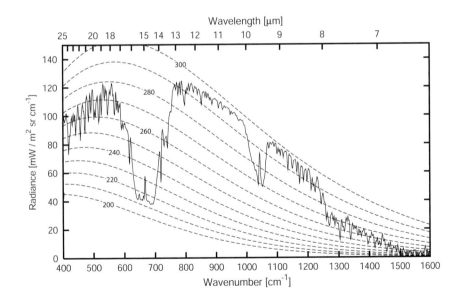

Fig. 6.6: Example of an actual infrared emission spectrum observed by the Nimbus 4 satellite over a point in the tropical Pacific Ocean. Dashed curves represent blackbody radiances at the indicated temperatures in Kelvin. *(IRIS data courtesy of the Goddard EOS Distributed Active Archive Center (DAAC) and instrument team leader Dr. Rudolf A. Hanel.)*

of-sight. The more opaque the atmosphere, the greater the altitude of the maximum atmospheric contribution to the observed T_B. This principle is at the foundation of satellite techniques for estimating atmospheric temperature profiles from space. We will discuss this problem in greater detail in a later chapter.

Problem 6.12:   The irregular solid curve in Fig. 6.6 depicts an actual satellite-derived spectrum of radiant intensity when the satellite passed over a particular ocean location on a cloudless day. The smooth curves represent Planck's function curves for various temperatures. (a) Estimate the brightness temperature at 11 μm. (b) Estimate the brightness temperature at 15 μm. (c) For which of these two wavelengths would you guess that you are looking primarily at emission from the surface? (d) For the wavelength that is *not* seeing the surface, make a rough estimate of the approximate altitude in the atmosphere that corresponds to the observed brightness temperature, assuming a standard lapse rate of 6.5 K/km.

6.3   When Does Thermal Emission Matter?

We have seen that all surfaces reflect and absorb radiation. We have also seen that all matter in local thermal equilibrium emits thermal radiation according to its emissivity and Planck's function. Common experience, however, tells us that thermal emission by the earth or atmosphere isn't always worth worrying about. For example, it is clear that all natural light visible to the naked eye normally originates from extraterrestrial sources (lightning, volcanoes, and fireflies excepted!); otherwise it would not be dark at night after the sun goes down.

   An important question, therefore, is when one can and can't ignore thermal emission from the earth and atmosphere. The simplistic answer is that, for wavelengths shorter than a certain value, the contribution of incident and reflected solar radiation to the total radiation field far exceeds the contribution due to direct thermal emission. For slightly longer wavelengths, one might need to consider both solar radiation and thermal emission from the earth-atmosphere system itself. For even longer wavelengths, one may often (though not always) ignore the solar component relative to the thermally emitted component.

How short must the wavelength be in order for thermal emission to be unimportant? A common (but somewhat misleading) way to answer that question is to compare the distributions of radiation emitted by a blackbody for two temperatures: that of the sun (approximately 6000 K) and a much cooler temperature characteristic of the earth and atmosphere (200–300 K). If the Planck function is normalized so as to have the same area under the curve (Fig. 6.2b), we see that there is surprisingly little overlap between the two areas of significant emission. In fact, a threshold of $\lambda \approx 4$ μm does a very nice job of separating solar emission from terrestrial emission, with more than 99% of solar emission taking place at wavelengths shorter than 4 μm and more than 99% of terrestrial emission taking place at longer wavelengths (Fig. 6.4). According to this analysis, therefore, one might neglect the sun as a source of atmospheric radiation much longer than 4 μm wavelength, and one may neglect terrestrial emission at wavelengths much shorter than this value.

In reality, the above argument glosses over some important facts. To begin with, while Fig. 6.2b does a nice job of showing the *relative* spectral distribution of emission for terrestrial and solar sources, recall that we normalized the curves so that the areas would be equal! If we had not done this, we would have seen that, for any given wavelength, emission from a blackbody with the temperature of the sun is *far greater* than that of a much cooler terrestrial source.

Problem 6.13: Use Planck's function to compute the ratio of blackbody emission at 6000 K to that at 255 K, for a wavelength of 12 μm, which is firmly in the thermal IR part of the spectrum.

A more convincing assessment of the relative importance of the two sources requires us to consider the following: 1) whether it is the flux or the intensity at a given wavelength that is of interest; 2) if the latter, then which direction is being viewed; and 3) if the direction being viewed is not directly toward the sun, then what are the relevant reflective properties of the surface and atmosphere.

Notwithstanding the above caution, it turns out that 4 μm is indeed a reasonable threshold for separating thermal from solar sources, as long as one views it only as a rough guide. A clear exception to this rule, however, occurs for satellite sensors that happen to be looking in the direction of the reflection of the sun from a smooth surface. Under certain conditions (e.g., over water), the intensity of this *sun glint* can be quite significant relative to thermal emission, even at microwave wavelengths, and can be an important source of error for remote sensing methods that do not account for it.

> **Problem 6.14:** Calculate the upward flux of reflected solar radiation at 12 μm, assuming an overhead sun (temperature 6000 K, solid angle $\Delta\omega = 6.8 \times 10^{-5}$ sr) and a surface (flux) reflectivity $r_\lambda = 0.1$. Find the ratio of the above flux to that due to terrestrial emission at a temperature of 300 K.

6.4   Applications to Meteorology, Climatology, and Remote Sensing

Even though we have not yet delved into the interaction of radiation with the atmosphere, the relationships we defined or derived in this chapter for surfaces (either real or imaginary) already give us powerful tools for analyzing some aspects of the radiation budget of the earth and atmosphere, as well as for understanding simple remote sensing applications.

Common to most of the analyses to follow is the application of the graybody approximation separately to shortwave and longwave fluxes. That is, we assume that a single absorptivity a_{sw} (equal to one minus the shortwave albedo A, if a surface) applies to all shortwave radiation and another, a_{lw}, applies to all longwave radiation. According to Kirchhoff's law, the longwave emissivity $\varepsilon = a_{lw}$, so emitted longwave fluxes may be computed as $\varepsilon\sigma T^4$. Furthermore, it is often reasonable to assume that $\varepsilon \approx 1$ in the longwave band. Emission in the shortwave band is neglected altogether.

Given the above, the condition for *radiative equilibrium* is simply that all fluxes balance at each point in the system. And if the system is *not* in equilibrium, the radiative imbalance may be interpreted as a heating or cooling rate. You may be surprised by the wide variety of problems that can be tackled at least qualitatively using the simple approach just outlined. We will start with the simplest systems (e.g., a single surface) and work our way up to a coupled surface-atmosphere model that, while crude, at least hints at some important features of the radiative interaction between the two.

Problem 6.15: A typical surface area for the human body around 2 m^2. (a) If we assume that bare skin temperature is $32°C$(note that skin temperature is usually somewhat cooler than the body's core temperature of $37°C$), then about how many watts of thermal radiation are emitted by the body, assuming an emissivity of 0.97? (b) If the person in question is surrounding by an environment emitting radiation at a temperature of $20°C$ (approximately room temperature), how much *net* heat loss occurs due to radiation alone? (c) Express your result for (b) in dietary calories per day (one "dietary calory" equals one kilocalory = 4180 Joules). (d) The average adult is known to require 2000–3000 kcal per day to cover the body's total expenditure of energy, which includes metabolic needs as well as physical heat losses due to radiation, conduction, and evaporation. Critique the stated and unstated assumptions in this problem in light of this new information.

6.4.1 Radiative Equilibrium in a Vacuum

The moon has no ocean or atmosphere and therefore no efficient mechanism for the lateral redistribution of heat. Furthermore, only a relatively shallow layer of the moon's soil plays a role in the storage and release of heat energy. To a good approximation therefore, the *equilibrium temperature* at a point on the moon's surface is determined by a balance between shortwave radiation absorbed from the sun and longwave radiation emitted to space. Assuming the albedo of the surface doesn't change, the local rate of shortwave absorption is a function only of the solar zenith angle. The emitted longwave radiation, on the other hand, increases sharply with increasing temperature according to the Stefan-Boltzmann relationship (6.5).

Therefore, if the emitted LW radiation is less than the absorbed SW radiation, the temperature of the surface will increase. The increase will continue until the LW emission has increased to the point where it balances the SW absorption. Likewise, if the outgoing LW emission exceeds the SW absorption, the temperature will cool until the two are again in balance. The criterion for radiative equilibrium is therefore

$$(1 - A)S_0 \cos \theta = \varepsilon \sigma T^4 , \tag{6.14}$$

where A is the shortwave albedo of the surface, θ is the zenith angle of the sun, and ε is the longwave emissivity. Solving for T yields the equilibrium temperature

$$T_E = \left[\frac{S_0(1 - A) \cos \theta}{\varepsilon \sigma} \right]^{1/4} . \tag{6.15}$$

Problem 6.16: Assuming an albedo $A = 0.10$, an emissivity $\varepsilon = 1$, and solar constant $S_0 = 1370$ W m^{-2}, plot the equilibrium temperature T_E as a function of solar zenith angle $0 \leq \theta < 90°$.

Equation (6.15) assumes, of course, that the surface of the moon has indefinitely long to equilibrate, a condition that is not met in practice. It also assumes that there is no other source of shortwave radiation. In reality, reflected sunlight from the earth, as well as a minor contribution from starlight, ensures that the radiative equilibrium temperature is greater than absolute zero even during the lunar night.

Problem 6.17: (a) Derive an expression for the net flux F_{net} at the surface of the moon as a function of the actual temperature T and the other parameters appearing in (6.15). (b) Find the numerical value of F_{net} for $A = 0.10$, $\theta = 45°$, $T = 300$ K, and $\varepsilon = 1$.

Now consider a small, perfectly black spherical object in outer space with radius r and exposed to direct solar radiation in the amount of S_0 (i.e., the object is at the same distance from the sun as the earth). We can derive the equilibrium temperature T_E of the object by requiring a balance between incoming solar and outgoing

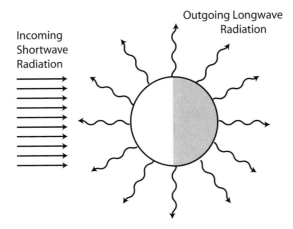

Fig. 6.7: Relationship between incoming solar radiation and outgoing thermal infrared radiation for a spherical object.

longwave radiation. The first is given by the area of the shadow of the object (i.e., its cross-sectional area) times the solar flux:

$$\Phi_{SW} = S_0 \pi r^2 . \tag{6.16}$$

The second is given by the Stefan-Boltzmann relationship times the surface area:

$$\Phi_{LW} = 4\pi r^2 \sigma T_E^4 . \tag{6.17}$$

Setting the two fluxes equal to each other and simplifying yields

$$S_0 = 4\sigma T_E^4, \quad \text{or} \tag{6.18}$$

$$T_E = \left[\frac{S_0}{4\sigma} \right]^{\frac{1}{4}} . \tag{6.19}$$

Substituting $S_0 = 1370$ W m^{-2} and $\sigma = 5.67 \times 10^{-8}$ W/(m^{2}K^4) yields $T_E = 279$ K.

Problem 6.18: Consider a spherical object like the one discussed above, with radius $r = 10$ cm and heat capacity C of 1×10^4 J/K.
(a) Find an expression for the heating rate dT/dt as a function of T, when $T \neq T_E$.

(b) Assume that after the temperature reaches equilibrium, the incident solar radiation is suddenly shut off – for example, the object passes into the shadow of a planet. Use your solution to the previous part to find the temperature T of the object as a function of time t. Ignore the effects of finite thermal conductivity.

(c) From your solution to (b), determine the time that it takes for the object to cool to 100 K, 10 K, and 1 K.

Problem 6.19: (a) Generalize the solution for T_E found above for a black sphere to one with shortwave albedo A and longwave emissivity ε.

(b) Compute the numerical value of T_E for $A = 0.10$ and $\varepsilon = 0.95$.

(c) If your solution to (a) is correct, you should find that $T_E \to \infty$ when $\varepsilon \to 0$. This would seem to imply that an object that is highly reflective of longwave radiation (and therefore has low ε) but strongly absorbs shortwave radiation could theoretically be heated to an arbitrarily large temperature in a vacuum simply by exposing it to radiation from the sun. Since the temperature of the sun itself is finite ($T \approx 6000$ K), this result would seem to violate the Second Law of Thermodynamics. Identify the logical flaw in this analysis. *Hint:* Consider the implications of Wien's Law for this problem.

6.4.2 Top-of-the-Atmosphere Global Radiation Balance

The earth is a much more complex system than either the moon or the spherical solid object considered in the previous system. Among other things, the atmosphere and ocean facilitate the rapid lateral transport of heat. Furthermore, the atmosphere itself both emits and absorbs solar and longwave radiation. The radiation balance at the surface of the earth cannot be considered independently of that of the atmosphere. For both reasons, one cannot use a simple radiative equilibrium of the type we have discussed so far as a criterion for estimating *local surface* temperatures. Nevertheless, the principle of balance between *globally averaged* absorbed solar radiation and outgoing longwave radiation (OLR) must still apply *at the top of the atmosphere* in order for the global climate to be more or less in a steady state over decades or centuries.

Just as we did for the sphere earlier, we compute the total absorbed solar flux (in watts) as the product of the area of the shadow cast by the earth, the solar constant S_0, and one minus the observed average *planetary albedo* A_p of approximately 30%, which takes into account the important contribution of clouds as well as surface albedo.

The total flux of outgoing longwave radiation must equal the absorbed shortwave flux (Fig. 6.7). Although this OLR does not represent emission from a simple surface with a single unique temperature, it is nevertheless useful to express the average OLR in terms of an *effective emitting temperature*, assuming pure blackbody emission (i.e., $\varepsilon = 1$):

$$T_{\text{eff}} = \left[\frac{S_0(1 - A_p)}{4\sigma} \right]^{1/4} . \tag{6.20}$$

Substituting the appropriate numerical values for the earth yields $T_{\text{eff}} = 255$ K.

Note that this value for T_{eff} is about 33 K colder than the observed global average surface temperature of approximately 288 K. Recall, however, that the OLR seen from space originates not just from the surface but also from various levels within the atmosphere itself, most of which is substantially colder than the surface. Therefore our calculated value of T_{eff} is not inconsistent with reality, as long as we recognize that our simple criterion for radiative balance at the top of the atmosphere doesn't give us any basis for determining the vertical distribution of temperature *within* the atmosphere.

Problem 6.20: The following table gives the albedos and distances from the sun of various planets:

Planet	Distance from sun (AU)	Albedo
Mercury	0.39	0.11
Venus	0.72	0.65
Earth	1.00	0.30
Mars	1.52	0.15
Jupiter	5.20	0.52
Neptune	30.0	0.41
Pluto	40.0	0.30

(a) Assuming that the sun is the sole energy source, compute the effective emitting temperatures of each planet.

(b) The *observed* effective emitting temperature of Jupiter is actually 140 K. The difference is apparently due to an internal heat source somewhere deep within Jupiter's atmosphere. Determine the magnitude of the source in units of W m^{-2}.

Problem 6.21: If there were no meridional heat transport via the fluid motions of the oceans and atmosphere, the mean temperature at a given latitude would be determined by a local balance between absorbed solar radiation and outgoing longwave radiation. Assuming that the zonally averaged absorbed solar radiation remained at the level indicated in Fig. 1.1 (this unrealistically assumes that feedbacks due to changing cloud, ice, and vegetation cover are inoperative), use the Stefan-Boltzmann relationship to estimate the effective mean emitting temperature (as seen from the top of the atmosphere) that would prevail at the poles and at the equator. Then add 33°C to estimate the corresponding surface temperatures (this again unrealistically assumes that mean lapse rate and atmospheric opacity would not change from current values).

Problem 6.22: A meteorological satellite in a polar orbit is typically found at an altitude of around 1000 km above the earth's surface. A geostationary satellite, on the other hand, orbits at an altitude of 35,800 km. (a) For each type of satellite, compute the longwave flux from the earth experienced at the satellite's orbit, as measured by a flat plate directly facing the satellite subpoint. Assume a uniform effective emitting temperature of 255 K for the earth.

Problem 6.23: Suppose that the sun were hotter (and therefore bluer) than it is, so that wavelength of maximum emission were 0.400 μm instead of 0.475 μm. Find the resulting change in the equilibrium emitting temperature of the Earth, assuming that the albedo stays the same. For simplicity, assume here that the sun's emission obeys Planck's function. Hint: Start by combining (6.3) and (6.5) in order to find the ratio of the new solar constant to the present value S_0. Then use this to derive a simple expression for the new equilibrium temperature as a function of the present value and the two wavelengths.

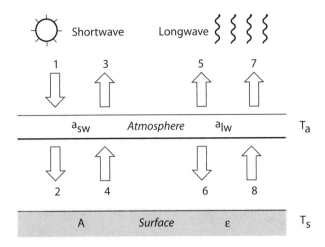

Fig. 6.8: Schematic depiction of the radiative coupling between the surface and a thin isothermal atmosphere.

6.4.3 Simple Radiative Models of the Atmosphere

Single Layer, Nonreflecting Atmosphere

Let us now consider a system consisting of an opaque surface and an overlying atmosphere that we will model as a single thin translucent sheet having uniform temperature. The temperature of the surface is denoted T_s and that of the atmosphere T_a. The surface has longwave emissivity $\varepsilon = 1$ and shortwave albedo A. The atmosphere has corresponding absorptivities a_{lw} and a_{sw} (for the time being, we will assume that the atmosphere only absorbs but does not scatter or reflect either shortwave or longwave radiation). Finally, at the top of the atmosphere, the globally averaged incident shortwave flux from the sun is $S = S_0/4$.

With the aid of the parameters given above, we can now begin to construct expressions for the upwelling and downwelling shortwave and longwave fluxes at the top of the atmosphere and between the atmosphere and the surface. Fig. 6.8 depicts the various components of these fluxes, and their physical interpretation is given here:

F_1	incident shortwave flux from the sun
F_2	transmitted portion of F_1
F_3	transmitted portion of F_4
F_4	shortwave flux reflected by the surface
F_5	longwave emission upward by atmosphere
F_6	longwave emission downward by atmosphere
F_7	transmitted portion of F_8
F_8	longwave emission by surface

Note that if we did not specify ahead of time that $\varepsilon = 1$, we would have also had to include terms that describe the upward reflection of F_6 from the surface.

We can write expressions for each of the flux terms using the parameters specified at the beginning of this section and the basic principles introduced earlier in this chapter. *Make sure you understand how each of the following expressions was obtained!*

$$F_1 = S , \tag{6.21}$$

$$F_2 = (1 - a_{sw})F_1 = (1 - a_{sw})S , \tag{6.22}$$

$$F_3 = (1 - a_{sw})F_4 = A(1 - a_{sw})^2 S , \tag{6.23}$$

$$F_4 = AF_2 = A(1 - a_{sw})S . \tag{6.24}$$

In the following two expressions, we are invoking Kirchhoff's Law, which tells us that the longwave emissivity of the layer is the same as its absorptivity:

$$F_5 = a_{lw}\sigma T_a^4 , \tag{6.25}$$

$$F_6 = F_5 = a_{lw}\sigma T_a^4 , \tag{6.26}$$

$$F_7 = (1 - a_{lw})F_8 = (1 - a_{lw})\sigma T_s^4 , \tag{6.27}$$

$$F_8 = \varepsilon\sigma T_s^4 = \sigma T_s^4 . \tag{6.28}$$

The condition for radiative equilibrium is that the net fluxes (shortwave and longwave combined) at the top of the atmosphere and between the surface and the atmosphere are both zero. If this were not the case, then either the atmosphere or the surface, or both, would experience a net gain or loss of energy over time, leading to heating or cooling.

If we take the fluxes in the above table to be positive quantities, we thus have the following two conditions for radiative equilibrium:

$$F_{\text{net,top}} = F_3 + F_5 + F_7 - F_1 = 0 , \tag{6.29}$$

$$F_{\text{net,sfc}} = F_4 + F_8 - F_2 - F_6 = 0 . \tag{6.30}$$

Substituting our previous expressions for each flux term yields

$$A(1 - a_{\text{sw}})^2 S + a_{\text{lw}}\sigma T_a^4 + (1 - a_{\text{lw}})\sigma T_s^4 - S = 0 , \tag{6.31}$$

$$A(1 - a_{\text{sw}})S + \sigma T_s^4 - (1 - a_{\text{sw}})S - a_{\text{lw}}\sigma T_a^4 = 0 , \tag{6.32}$$

which we rearrange to give

$$(1 - a_{\text{lw}})\sigma T_s^4 + a_{\text{lw}}\sigma T_a^4 = S[1 - A(1 - a_{\text{sw}})^2] , \tag{6.33}$$

$$\sigma T_s^4 - a_{\text{lw}}\sigma T_a^4 = (1 - A)(1 - a_{\text{sw}})S . \tag{6.34}$$

Note that if we define $x = \sigma T_s^4$ and $y = \sigma T_a^4$, then we have a pair of coupled linear equations in the two unknowns x and y. We can first solve these for x and y and then divide by σ and take the fourth root to get T_s and T_a:

$$T_s = \left\{ \frac{S}{\sigma}[1 - (1 - a_{\text{sw}})A]\left(\frac{2 - a_{\text{sw}}}{2 - a_{\text{lw}}}\right) \right\}^{\frac{1}{4}} , \tag{6.35}$$

$$T_a = \left\{ \frac{S}{\sigma}\left[\frac{(1 - A)(1 - a_{\text{sw}})a_{\text{lw}} + [1 + (1 - a_{\text{sw}})A]a_{\text{sw}}}{(2 - a_{\text{lw}})a_{\text{lw}}} \right] \right\}^{\frac{1}{4}} . \tag{6.36}$$

These expressions look complicated, but if we focus just on T_s and consider a couple of limiting cases, we can quickly get some useful insight into the role of the atmosphere in controlling global surface temperature.

The simplest case is when $a_{\text{lw}} = 0$ and $a_{\text{sw}} = 0$. This is equivalent to saying that there is no atmosphere at all, because it is completely invisible as far as both shortwave and longwave radiation is concerned. In fact, if you substitute these values and $S = S_0/4$ into (6.35) and simplify, you immediately recover (6.20), which is what you would expect.

Now consider the case that the surface is completely black (i.e., $A = 0$), while a_{lw} and a_{sw} may each be nonzero. We then have

$$T_s = \left[\frac{S_0}{4\sigma} \left(\frac{2 - a_{sw}}{2 - a_{lw}} \right) \right]^{\frac{1}{4}}. \qquad (6.37)$$

This relationship is interesting, because it tells us that if $a_{lw} > a_{sw}$, then the surface temperature in our simple system will be warmer than would be the case without an atmosphere ($a_{lw} = a_{sw} = 0$) or, for that matter, any case where $a_{lw} = a_{sw}$.

In fact, our atmosphere is relatively transparent to shortwave radiation from the sun, while being comparatively absorbing at thermal IR wavelengths. We can approximate the earth's atmosphere by choosing $a_{sw} = 0.1$ and $a_{lw} = 0.8$. Thus, we expect the surface temperature of the earth to be substantially warmed by the absorption and re-emission of longwave radiation by the atmosphere. This warming effect due to the presence of an atmosphere is commonly known as the *Greenhouse effect*.

The above analysis assumes that the atmosphere either transmits or absorbs all of the solar radiation that is incident on it. It therefore cannot be used directly to obtain a realistic estimate of the equilibrium surface temperature of the earth. However, we can compensate for the loss of radiation due to reflection by clouds etc. by replacing S with $S(1 - A_p)$, where $A_p = 0.30$ is the observed planetary albedo utilized earlier in our calculation from (6.20). We are in effect pretending that all the solar radiation reflected to space by clouds etc. experiences this reflection at the top of the atmosphere, before having any opportunity to be absorbed by the surface or atmosphere. With this simplifying assumption, we obtain a new surface equilibrium temperature of 286 K, as contrasted with 255 K obtained earlier for the earth with the same planetary albedo but no atmosphere. In view of the crudeness of our model, this is surprisingly close to what is actually observed!

One of the chief concerns of climate scientists today is that, by adding carbon dioxide and other "greenhouse gases" that are transparent to shortwave radiation but strongly absorb longwave radiation, humankind is inexorably increasing the value of a_{lw} and thereby shifting the radiative equilibrium of the globe to warmer temperatures.

Of course, a far more elaborate computer model of the earth and atmosphere, one that incorporates fluid motions, cloud and water vapor feedbacks and other complex processes, is required in order to study this problem in any detail. The most sophisticated such models are called *general circulation models* (GCMs) and are the best tools we have today for understanding climate and climate change. Even now, however, a fully comprehensive treatment of radiation and other physical processes remains too complex a problem for the most powerful computers to tackle for the entire atmosphere at once. GCMs therefore continue to rely on grossly simplified representations of some of these processes, with the attendant risk of error in the models' predictions. Finding ways to improve the accuracy of radiative and other physical parameterizations within the constraints of the available computing power is a major focus of current research in atmospheric science.

Problem 6.24: In the example above, we set the surface albedo A to zero and then reduced the assumed global insolation S by 30% in order to crudely account for the solar radiation that was reflected rather than absorbed by the earth-atmosphere system. We could have equally well left $S = S_0/4$ and then chosen a larger A such that exactly $1 - A_p = 70\%$ of the solar radiation was absorbed by either the surface or the atmosphere.

(a) Using this revised approach, find an expression for the appropriate choice of A in terms of A_p and a_{sw}.

(b) Calculate the numerical value of A, given $A_p = 0.30$ and $a_{sw} = 0.1$.

(c) Calculate the resulting T_s, given the above parameters and $a_{lw} = 0.8$.

Problem 6.25:   Imagine an atmosphere of n layers in which each layer is transparent to shortwave radiation but opaque ($\varepsilon = 1$) in the longwave band. Show that the radiative equilibrium surface temperature in this system is

$$T_0 = T_n(n+1)^{\frac{1}{4}}$$

where T_n is the temperature of the topmost layer.

6.4.4   Nighttime Radiative Cooling

In the previous section, we discussed the criteria for radiative equilibrium in a simple two-level model, based on an assumed balance between the *long-term globally averaged* LW fluxes and the *long-term globally averaged* SW flux from the sun. Of course, the solar input at any location is not constant with time but varies from zero at night to a maximum at around noon, as well as varying with latitude and season. Also both SW and LW fluxes at the surface vary sharply with temperature, humidity, and cloud cover. Although it remains a very crude representation of reality, we can nevertheless invoke our two-level model to learn a few things about *short-term, local* radiative processes.

In particular, let us examine the basis for the well-known rule of thumb that dew or frost is far more likely to occur on clear nights than cloudy nights. Both dew and frost occur when the surface cools to below the dewpoint or frostpoint temperature of the air, while the air above the surface may remain at a significantly warmer temperature. The latter observation rules out direct thermal conduction (through physical contact of the air with the surface) as the reason for the cooling of the surface, as heat always conducts from warm to cold. The only other obvious candidate is radiation.

Because we are addressing a night-time situation, we don't need to worry about SW fluxes. Furthermore, we're not interested in establishing the criteria for radiative equilibrium but rather in estimating the surface cooling rate under conditions of disequilibrium. We therefore need only consider flux components 6 and 8 in Fig. 6.8, which we will refer to simply as $F^\downarrow$ and $F^\uparrow$ for the purposes of this discussion:

$$F^\downarrow = a_{\mathrm{lw}} \sigma T_a^4 , \tag{6.38}$$

$$F^\uparrow = \varepsilon \sigma T_s^4 = \sigma T_s^4 , \tag{6.39}$$

where, as before, we are taking the LW surface emissivity $\varepsilon \approx 1$.

The cooling rate of the ground is proportional to the net flux

$$F^{\mathrm{net}} = F^\uparrow - F^\downarrow = \sigma T_s^4 - a_{\mathrm{lw}} \sigma T_a^4 , \tag{6.40}$$

or

$$F^{\mathrm{net}} = \sigma (T_s^4 - a_{\mathrm{lw}} T_a^4) . \tag{6.41}$$

The effective value of a_{lw} for the cloud-free atmosphere ranges from approximately 0.7 in the wintertime arctic to approximately 0.95 in the tropics. This variation is driven primarily by the humidity of the atmosphere, as water vapor is a strong absorber of radiation over much of the thermal IR band. The corresponding range of effective atmospheric temperature T_a is 235 K (arctic winter) to 290 K (tropical), yielding typical clear-sky downwelling longwave fluxes $F^\downarrow$ ranging from a minimum near ~120 W m^{-2} to a maximum of ~380 W m^{-2}.

For a midlatitude winter situation, we may use $a_{\mathrm{lw}} = 0.8$ and $T_a = 260$ K, and take the initial surface temperature to be $T_s = 275$ K. Plugging these values into (6.41) yields a positive (upward) net flux of 117 W m^{-2}. On level ground with no wind, very little of this heat loss from the ground is shared with the overlying air, so the surface temperature of the ground falls rapidly.

A crude estimate of the rate of the temperature fall may be had by noting that heat conduction in soil is rather slow, so that only the top few centimeters of soil experience the fluctuation of temperature associated with the diurnal (day-night) cycle. If we somewhat arbitrarily choose an effective depth over which to average the cooling as $\Delta Z = 5$ cm, and use a typical soil heat capacity (per volume) of $C \approx 2 \times 10^6$ J m^{-3}K^{-1}, then we have

$$\frac{dT}{dt} \approx \frac{-F^{\mathrm{net}}}{C \Delta Z} \approx -4.2 \, \frac{\mathrm{K}}{\mathrm{hr}} . \tag{6.42}$$

You can see that it will not take long for the ground temperature to drop below freezing and, presumably, below the frost point of the overlying air, at which point frost will start to deposit (or sublime) directly onto the surface.

The above calculation assumed a cloud-free atmosphere. What happens when we introduce a low-level opaque cloud deck whose temperature is only a few degrees below that of the surface? Taking $a_{lw} = 1$ and $T_a = 270$ K, we now find a net surface flux of only 22 W m^{-2}, or less than a fifth of value for a clear sky. The cooling rate of the surface is reduced by the same ratio and is now only 0.8 K/hr. What a difference a cloud makes!

Of course, other processes, such as surface latent and sensible heat fluxes, while small (unless there is a significant breeze!), partially offset the radiational cooling predicted by the above simple analysis. Nevertheless, you should now be persuaded that radiation can have observable meteorological effects even on rather short time scales.

6.4.5   Radiative Cooling at Cloud Top

A similar analysis can be applied to the top of a continuous cloud layer, such as the low-level marine stratocumulus clouds that are common within midlatitude and subtropical high pressure zones over relatively cool ocean areas, such as the Eastern Pacific near California and Peru or in the vicinity of the Azores near North Africa and the Iberian Peninsula.

Although the processes involved in the steady-state maintenance of these persistent cloud sheets is complex and includes turbulent fluxes of sensible heat and moisture, it is at least possible to evaluate the potential role of radiative fluxes as one component in the overall balance.

To begin with, because the cloud layer is opaque to LW radiation and does not reflect appreciably at these wavelengths, we can consider it as having two radiating "surfaces", each with emissivity $\varepsilon \approx 1$. The base height Z_{base} for marine stratocumulus clouds is commonly near 300 m altitude, below which the air follows a dry adiabatic temperature profile of 9.8 K/km. This implies a temperature difference between cloud base and the ocean surface of only 3 K. Taking the surface temperature to be $T_s = 288$ K, we have

$T_{base} = 285$ K and a net LW flux at cloud base of

$$F_{net,base} < \sigma(T_s^4 - T_{base}^4) \approx 16 \text{ W m}^{-2}. \qquad (6.43)$$

The use of the '<' sign is intended to indicate that the above is an *upper bound* on the net flux at cloud base, because not all the radiation reaching cloud base originates at the surface; some is emitted at higher, slightly cooler altitudes on account of the high opacity of the atmosphere at some wavelengths.

Within the cloud, the moist adiabatic lapse rate of approximately 6 K/km prevails. Therefore, at cloud top, typically near 1 km altitude, the temperature is approximately 4 K colder than at cloud base, yielding $T_{top} \approx 281$ K. Because marine stratocumulus clouds typically occur in regions of high pressure and therefore subsiding air aloft, the atmosphere above cloud top is often warm but very dry. The downward flux of radiation from the overlying atmosphere may therefore be estimated as $a_{lw}\sigma T_a^4$, where we assume $T_a \approx 280$ K and $a_{lw} \approx 0.8$:

$$F_{net,top} \approx \sigma(T_{top}^4 - a_{lw}T_a^4) \approx 75 \text{ W m}^{-2}. \qquad (6.44)$$

In summary, we have substantial radiative cooling (~ 75 W m^{-2}) at cloud top but relatively weak radiative warming (~ 16 W m^{-2}) at cloud base. There is therefore net radiative cooling of ~ 59 W m^{-2} for the cloud layer as a whole. Note, by the way, that any time you cool a layer of air from above, you increase the lapse rate. Once the lapse rate exceeds the applicable adiabatic lapse rate (in this case the moist adiabatic lapse rate), you destabilize the layer, leading to vertical overturning. The same applies to warming from below. Consequently, the net radiative cooling experienced by the cloud ends up being distributed pretty much throughout the entire atmospheric boundary layer (or mixed layer), which extends from the surface to cloud top. In the present example, this represents ~ 59 W m^{-2} of cooling distributed over a 1 km depth of air. We can compute the cooling rate as

$$\frac{dT}{dt}_{rad} \approx \frac{F_{net,base} - F_{net,top}}{c_p\rho\Delta z} \approx -4.2 \text{ K/day}, \qquad (6.45)$$

where $c_p = 1004$ J kg^{-1} K^{-1} is the heat capacity at constant pressure of air, $\rho \approx 1.2$ kg m^{-3} is the density of air near the surface, and $\Delta z = 1$ km.

In reality, we know that the temperature in the marine boundary layer is close to a steady state, implying that there must be compensating inputs of energy in the form of surface latent and sensible heat fluxes and turbulent fluxes at cloud top. In fact, the convective overturning that results from cloud-top radiative cooling is responsible for mixing between the cloud and the warmer, drier overlying air, which plays an important role in the overall mass and energy balance of the boundary layer. Also, it is responsible for the fact that stratocumulus cloud layers viewed from above usually have the appearance of rolls and "cells" rather than appearing as featureless, flat sheets of cloud.

6.4.6   IR Imaging from Space

For some ranges of wavelength in the thermal IR and microwave bands, the cloud-free atmosphere is rather transparent. We refer to such a region as a *spectral window*. Within the thermal IR band, the most important spectral window encompasses wavelengths in the vicinity of 11 μm.

Almost all operational weather satellites are equipped with at least one imaging channel in this window, typically with surface spatial resolutions of approximately 4 km at nadir. An example of a standard satellite 10.7 μm image from a geostationary satellite is shown in Fig. 6.9. Similar products are also available from most polar orbiting weather satellites.

Because the atmospheric gases themselves are nearly transparent (apart from a slight degree of absorption by water vapor), conventional satellite IR imagery typically records thermal emission from the surface and from the tops of any clouds present. It is convenient to express IR radiance observations at brightness temperatures (see Section 6.2.4). The brightness temperature of a scene with emissivity ε and temperature T is given by

$$T_B = B_\lambda^{-1}[\varepsilon B_\lambda(T)] . \qquad (6.46)$$

When $\varepsilon \approx 1$, the above reduces to $T_B \approx T$. Since land and water surfaces, most clouds (excepting thin cirrus), and even snow-covered land surfaces are rather black ($\varepsilon \approx 1$) at thermal IR wavelengths, the observed brightness temperature is in fact a reasonably good measure of the physical temperature.

Fig. 6.9: A 10.7 μm image of the Eastern Pacific and west coast of North America taken by the GOES-West geostationary weather satellite.

IR imagery from satellites is most often depicted using white or light gray for the coldest brightness temperatures and black or dark gray for the warmest brightness temperatures. Thus, hot land surfaces ($T \approx 310$ K or more) during the summer (especially daytime) appear black, and cold land surfaces during the winter ($T < 250$ K) appear medium gray.

The coldest scenes of all, however, are often associated not with the surface but rather with high cirrus clouds and deep thunderstorms, whose temperature at cloud top may occasionally be colder than 200 K ($-73°$C). The strong brightness temperature contrast between deep thunderstorms and surrounding shallower, and therefore warmer cloud tops makes IR imagery particularly useful for operational detection of developing severe weather and even for estimating probable rainfall amounts. In this respect, satellite IR imagery is complementary to VIS imagery, which depicts *all* clouds as relatively bright features, regardless of cloud-top height. Also, IR imagers are not constrained by the availability of sunlight but yield high quality images of cloud systems both day and night.

Problem 6.26:   An IR imager observes a cloud layer with $T_B = 240\ K$. The cloud radiates as a blackbody and the surface air temperature near that location is known to be 15°C.
(a) Assuming a standard atmospheric lapse rate of $\Gamma = 6.5$ K/km, estimate the height of the cloud layer top.
(b) Assuming the cloud top is a blackbody over the entire LW band, compute the upward flux of longwave radiation (OLR) that would be observed by an aircraft flying directly over the cloud.

If you view a movie loop of GOES IR imagery covering a full day or longer, you can see not only the evolution of cloud patterns associated with extratropical cyclones, thunderstorms, etc., but also the evolution in surface temperature. It is not uncommon to see the land surface temperature vary sharply between day and night, while ocean surfaces remain at relatively constant temperature over long periods.

Problem 6.27:   Examine Fig. 6.9 for clues as to the most likely season and/or time of day when the image was taken. Explain your reasoning.

IR imagery is currently the primary basis for mapping global sea surface temperatures (SSTs) at high precision (approaching 0.1 K), allowing the depiction of the Gulf Stream and other features of importance for climate and weather forecasting, as well as for fisheries and for physical oceanographic studies. In particular, the well-known El Niño phenomenon, which dramatically influences large-scale weather patterns around much of the world, is manifested in the form of a dramatic warming of SSTs over the Eastern Tropical Pacific ocean. *In situ* measurements of SST by buoys and ships are rather sparse in this region, so IR imagery is the principal method today for monitoring the onset and evolution of El Niño.

Keep in mind, however, that accurate IR observations of surface temperature are only possible in cloud-free areas and with careful attention to the correction of minor atmospheric effects, mostly due to water vapor. One way to isolate, and correct, contamination due to water vapor is to utilize two channels at nearby wavelengths but with differing sensitivity to absorption by water vapor. The difference in brightness temperature between the two images is then an indicator of how much water vapor is present. In fact, one common form of this so-called *split window* technique entails the simultaneous retrieval of both SST and total column water vapor, also known as *precipitable water*. Both variables are of great interest to meteorologists, though for different reasons.

When even thin or broken clouds are present, which is true a majority of the time at many locations around the globe, IR imagers can no longer accurately measure surface properties. When surface measurements are required in the presence of clouds, we turn to the microwave band.

6.4.7 Microwave Imaging from Space

Passive microwave remote sensing is in many respects similar to IR remote sensing, in that a satellite sensor views naturally emitted radiation from the earth and atmosphere.[3] Especially at wavelengths greater than 3 cm (frequencies less than 10 GHz), atmospheric effects are fairly small, and the primary variable observed in this case is thermal emission from the earth's surface. There are several important differences from IR imagery that are worth briefly noting.

For one thing, it takes a rather heavy cloud to seriously interfere with a microwave imager's ability to observe the surface, in contrast to IR imagers, which are foiled by even thin clouds. In fact, at low microwave frequencies, only a cloud that is actually producing rainfall presents a serious obstacle.

Also, in contrast to the IR band, the microwave emissivities of natural surfaces are often considerably less than unity and may in fact vary wildly from one scene to the next. In particular, ocean

---

[3]*Active* remote sensing is also employed in the microwave band but entails the measurement of backscattered radiation from an artificial source. Radar is the best-known example.

surface emissivities may be as small as 0.25–0.7, whereas land surface emissivities are typically in the range 0.8–0.95. This variation in surface emissivity makes it much more difficult (though not impossible) to use microwave imagery for accurately estimating surface temperature, but greatly facilitates the determination of other surface properties.

A particularly convenient property of the microwave band is the validity of the Rayleigh-Jeans approximation introduced in Section 6.1.4. Because of the accurate proportionality between blackbody radiance and temperature in the microwave band, the slightly cumbersome relationship between T, ε, and T_B represented by (6.46) simplifies down to just

$$T_B = \varepsilon T . \tag{6.47}$$

Elsewhere in this book, we tend to neglect the polarization properties of radiation. But polarization cannot be ignored for microwave remote sensing. In particular, the ocean surface emissivity is markedly higher for vertical polarization than for horizontal polarization when the ocean is viewed at an oblique angle. In fact, if the water surface is perfectly smooth, the reflectivity r, and thus the emissivity $\varepsilon = 1 - r$, is given by the Fresnel relations discussed in Chapter 4. Fig. 4.5b showed the Fresnel reflectivity of water for a microwave frequency of 37 GHz. For a satellite sensor viewing a water surface at a typical angle from vertical (i.e. *nadir angle*) of ~50°, the horizontally polarized emissivity $\varepsilon_h \approx 0.35$ while the vertically polarized emissivity $\varepsilon_v \approx 0.65$. Thus, for the same physical temperature of $T = 283$ K, the brightness temperature of emission from the ocean surface is approximately 100 K for horizontal polarization and close to 185 K for vertical polarization, an 85 K difference.

Things get even more interesting when you consider that the microwave emissivity of the ocean surface is not a constant at any given frequency but depends (albeit fairly weakly) on the sea surface temperature T_s (via changes in the complex index of refraction N of seawater) and on the degree of roughening and foam coverage associated with a given near-surface wind speed U. Thus, the observed brightness temperature can be represented as

$$T_{B,p} \approx \varepsilon_p(T_s, U)T_s + \Delta_{\text{atmos}} , \tag{6.48}$$

where p represents the polarization (V or H) and Δ_{atmos} represents an atmospheric correction, which is usually small (<10 K) at low microwave frequencies.

The typical increase of T_B in response to increasing ocean surface wind speed is of the order of 1 K per m/s for horizontal polarization, which is easily measurable. The net sensitivity of T_B to changing sea surface temperature, on the other hand, can be very small or even be negative at some frequencies. This is because ε tends to decrease with increasing T_s.

By making observations at multiple microwave frequencies and/or polarizations, and provided a reasonably accurate model for $\varepsilon_p(T_s, U)$ and Δ_{atmos} is available, it is possible to infer sea surface temperature T_s to an accuracy of a few tenths of a degree and near-surface wind speed U to better than ± 2 m/s.

Over land, it is more difficult to express the relationship between microwave T_B and surface properties in a concise way. As a general rule, the surface emissivity is rather high over most land surfaces but fluctuates markedly with soil type, soil wetness, and vegetation density. All of these variables can be estimated with varying degrees of success using satellite microwave imagers. In addition, the presence of snow can markedly depress brightness temperatures at higher microwave frequencies, making it possible to use microwave imagers to monitor snow extent and depth over remote areas of the globe even under cloudy skies.[4]

A significant drawback to the microwave band for remote sensing is that the longer wavelength limits the "sharpness," or resolution, with which a satellite sensor can observe the earth. While an IR imager can easily resolve details as small as 4 km from even a geostationary satellite at an altitude of around 36,000 km, a current-generation microwave imager in low earth orbit (typical altitude 800–1000 km) can resolve SST patterns down to only about 30-50 km.

---

[4]In addition to the surface properties just discussed, certain atmospheric properties, such as total column water vapor, total column cloud water, and surface rain rate, can also be retrieved over ocean using microwave imaging channels at about 18 GHz and higher. For these channels, the atmospheric contribution to emission seen from space is nonnegligible and depends strongly on the above variables.

Problem 6.28: Note: The computational labor required by this problem can be greatly reduced with the help of a short computer program, preferably using a language that recognizes complex variables and operations.

At the frequencies observed by the Advanced Scanning Microwave Radiometer (AMSR), sea water has the following complex index of refraction:

Frequency (GHz)	Refractive Index 10°C	Refractive Index 20°C
6.93	$8.095 + 2.371i$	$8.211 + 2.144i$
10.65	$7.431 + 2.708i$	$7.745 + 2.416i$
18.70	$6.164 + 2.980i$	$6.712 + 2.819i$
23.8	$5.566 + 2.958i$	$6.151 + 2.901i$
36.5	$4.575 + 2.721i$	$5.123 + 2.831i$
89.0	$3.115 + 1.842i$	$3.433 + 2.083i$

(a) Ignoring atmospheric effects, compute the brightness temperature T_B (in Kelvin) of the smooth ocean surface for each combination of temperature, frequency, and polarization (vertical and horizontal), assuming an incidence angle of 55° and using the Rayleigh-Jeans approximation.

(b) Determine the average sensitivity of each of the 12 channels (6V, 6H, 10V, 10H, etc.) to changes in sea surface temperature T_s, expressed as $\Delta T_B / \Delta T_s$ within the above temperature range. Which channel(s) do you think would be most useful for estimating sea surface temperature from space, keeping in mind that atmospheric variability also becomes a significant source of error at frequencies of 23.8 GHz and above?

CHAPTER 7

Up to this point, our discussion of the interaction of radiation with matter has focused mainly on reflection, refraction, absorption, and emission by *surfaces*, either real or "virtual" (note that in the last chapter we crudely treated the atmosphere as a translucent, gray, isothermal "surface" for the purpose of some simple radiation budget calculations).

Only in Section 2.5 did we briefly consider the absorption of a monochromatic EM wave propagating *through* a homogeneous medium whose index of refraction N included a nonzero imaginary part. I pointed out that, in this homogeneous absorbing medium, the intensity I_λ falls off exponentially with distance:

$$I_\lambda(x) = I_{\lambda,0} \exp(-\beta_a x), \qquad (7.1)$$

where β_a is an absorption coefficient that depends on the physical medium and on the wavelength of the radiation.

We are now ready to generalize this result to the atmosphere. Specifically, we will have to adjust (7.1) to allow for two minor complications:

1. The fact that a beam of radiation can be attenuated not only by *absorption* (i.e., conversion of the energy of the radiation to

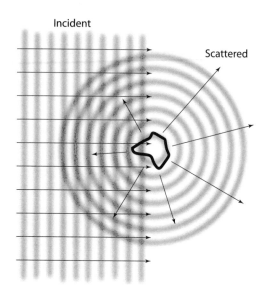

Fig. 7.1: Scattering of an incident wave by a particle.

heat or chemical energy) but also by *scattering* (redirection of radiation out of the original direction of propagation, usually due to interactions with particles; Fig. 7.1). This will require us to define a more general *extinction coefficient* to replace the absorption coefficient β_a appearing above.

2. The likelihood that the strength of the absorption or scattering will vary significantly along the path, so that our mathematical starting point must be the differential equivalent to (7.1), in which we initially consider the change of intensity of the radiation as it traverses an infinitesimal distance ds, over which the extinction coefficient can be assumed constant.

In addition to the above two *minor* complications, there is one more *major* complication that I will defer until a later chapter: the fact that radiation can be scattered from other directions *into* the direction of propagation, thereby enhancing its intensity. But for now we will continue to focus strictly on line-of-sight transmission and depletion of radiation, which can be understood entirely in terms of *local* properties encountered along that line of sight.

Let us start by illustrating the first of the above points with the help of a classic classroom demonstration[1] in which the instructor places three transparent Petri dishes partly filled with water onto an overhead projector and projects their silhouettes onto the screen. Because the water and the dishes are transparent, nearly all the light from the projector passes through unattenuated, so that the shadows cast by the dishes are barely perceptible.

Into one of the dishes the instructor then introduces a few drops of India ink; into another, a tablespoon or so of milk (Fig. 7.2a). Those two dishes now cast strong shadows, indicating that the light from the projector has been significantly *attenuated* or *extinguished* (Fig. 7.2b). The mechanisms for the extinction are quite different, however. In the case of the black ink, the energy carried by the light is largely absorbed and, presumably, converted to heat. In the case of the white milk, the light lost from the original beam is not absorbed but merely *scattered* out of its original direction of propagation and into all other directions.

Here are two ways to convince yourself of the truth of the above statement:

---

[1]C. Bohren, 1987: *Clouds in a Glass of Beer*. Wiley, New York

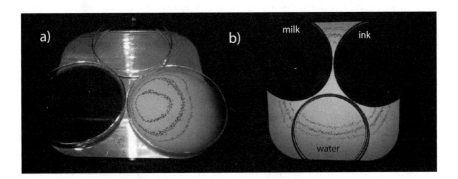

Fig. 7.2: Demonstration of radiative extinction using an overhead projector. (a) Three dishes of liquid, as positioned on the light source of the projector. The clear liquid is water, the black liquid is diluted ink (an absorbing medium), and the white liquid is diluted milk (a scattering medium). (b) The projected images of the three dishes. The dark shadows for milk and ink demonstrate that absorption and scattering are equally effective at depleting transmitted radiation.

- View the dishes from the side against a dark background: the milk "lights up" strongly against this background due to the illumination from the projector bulb, while the ink does so only weakly if at all. This suggests that light from the original beam is being redirected toward your eye in the first case but not the second.

- Place the bulbs of two identical thermometers in the ink and milk dishes and monitor the temperature change with time. The temperature of the dish with the ink will rise faster than that with the milk, indicating a greater rate of absorption of energy from the light beam.

Despite the difference in the *mechanisms* by which the original light beam is depleted, or extinguished, common sense tells us that the *rate* of depletion in either case should be proportional to the intensity of the incident radiation. In other words, if the illumination is zero (the projector is shut off), the depletion is zero as well (you can't take away energy from a nonexistent beam!). If one doubles the intensity of the illumination, the rate of absorption (in the case of the ink) or scattering (in the case of the milk) is doubled as well.

Both of these expectations (which are easily confirmed experimentally) are consistent with a relationship of the form of (7.1), provided that we replace the absorption coefficient β_a with an extinction coefficient β_e that accounts for depletion due to either scattering or absorption or, more likely, a combination of both. We're also asserting (without proof), by the way, that we can successfully adapt this relationship to an *inhomogeneous* medium (such as a cloud), as long as we restrict our attention to the extinction of the *original direct beam* and ignore any enhancement via the scattering of radiation from other directions *into* the line of sight.

Now consider what happens if you add a drop or two of India ink to the Petri dish containing the milk solution. If any significant fraction of the light had succeeded in passing through the dish before, it is now further reduced by the addition of the ink. Moreover, it is now clear that some fraction of the light that is extinguished is being absorbed while the remainder is scattered. That is, the solution is now neither white nor black, but gray.

7.1 Extinction, Scattering and Absorption Coefficients

One may characterize the relative contributions of scattering and absorption to the total extinction by considering the extinction coefficient to be the sum of an absorption coefficient and a scattering coefficient:

$$\beta_e = \beta_a + \beta_s \, . \tag{7.2}$$

In the case of the milk solution, $\beta_a \approx 0$, so that $\beta_e \approx \beta_s$. For the ink solution, $\beta_s \approx 0$ so that $\beta_e \approx \beta_a$. Note, by the way, that all three of these parameters have physical dimensions of inverse length.

To more conveniently characterize the relative importance of scattering versus absorption in a medium, radiative transfer specialists have introduced an important quantity called the *single scatter albedo*, which is defined as follows:

$$\tilde{\omega} = \frac{\beta_s}{\beta_e} = \frac{\beta_s}{\beta_s + \beta_a} \, . \tag{7.3}$$

The value of $\tilde{\omega}$ ranges from zero in a purely absorbing medium to one in a purely scattering medium. From an optical standpoint at least, the fundamental difference between milk and India ink, therefore, is that $\tilde{\omega} \approx 1$ for milk whereas $\tilde{\omega} \approx 0$ for the ink. A mixture of milk and ink would have a value of the single scatter albedo somewhere in between.

At this point it is worth reminding you that the quantities discussed in this chapter have values that are usually very specific to the wavelength being considered. Milk and India ink are somewhat unusual in that β_e, $\tilde{\omega}$, etc., are more or less constant across the entire visible band. If that were not the case, they would have a perceptible color other than white, gray, or black.

Problem 7.1: Based on what you know about their appearance, attempt to characterize the apparent spectral dependence of β_e and $\tilde{\omega}$ for the following substances: red wine, chocolate milk, a cloud,

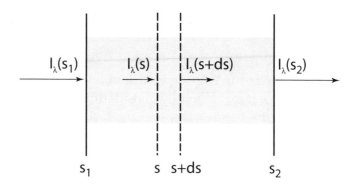

Fig. 7.3: Depletion of radiation over an infinitesimal path ds within an extinguishing medium.

a plume of exhaust from a diesel truck, the cloud-free atmosphere (based on the color of the setting sun).

7.2 Extinction Over a Finite Path

7.2.1 Fundamental Relationships

Let us now consider how to adapt (7.1) to a radiative path over which the extinction coefficient varies with location, since this is the situation we encounter in the atmosphere. We do not want to limit our attention to radiative paths aligned with the x-axis, so we generalize by replacing x with the geometric distance s along a ray in any arbitrary direction (Fig. 7.3). We further consider the attenuation of radiation over an infinitesimal path ds, which is chosen to be small enough so that (a) the extinction coefficient β_e is effectively constant within the interval, and (b) the incident radiation is attenuated by an infinitesimal amount dI_λ. We can then write

$$dI_\lambda \equiv I_\lambda(s+ds) - I_\lambda(s) = -I_\lambda(s)\beta_e(s)\,ds, \tag{7.4}$$

which we can rewrite as

$$\frac{dI_\lambda}{I_\lambda} \equiv d\log I_\lambda = -\beta_e\,ds. \tag{7.5}$$

In other words, the infinitesimal decrease in intensity dI_λ, expressed as a fraction of the incident intensity I_λ, is equal to the product of the local extinction coefficient times the infinitesimal path length ds.

In order to describe the extinction over an *extended* path between points s_1 and s_2 ($s_2 \geq s_1$), we simply integrate:

$$\log[I_\lambda(s_2)] - \log[I_\lambda(s_1)] = -\int_{s_1}^{s_2} \beta_e(s) \, ds, \qquad (7.6)$$

or

$$I_\lambda(s_2) = I_\lambda(s_1) \exp\left[-\int_{s_1}^{s_2} \beta_e(s) \, ds\right] . \qquad (7.7)$$

This equation gives a general form of *Beer's law*. From Beer's law follow several extremely important definitions and associated facts which I urge you to memorize before you continue reading:

- The integral quantity inside the brackets is called the *optical path* between points s_1 and s_2 (also known as *optical depth* or optical *thickness* when measured vertically in the atmosphere) :

$$\tau(s_1, s_2) \equiv \int_{s_1}^{s_2} \beta_e(s) \, ds . \qquad (7.8)$$

  The optical path is dimensionless, as it must be, since it appears as the argument of the transcendental function exp(). It may take on any nonnegative value. It is zero when $s_1 = s_2$ or when $\beta_e = 0$ between s_1 and s_2; otherwise it is positive.

- By exponentiating the optical path τ, we get the *transmittance* between s_1 and s_2:

$$t(s_1, s_2) \equiv e^{-\tau(s_1, s_2)} . \qquad (7.9)$$

  The transmittance is a dimensionless quantity ranging from near zero (for $\tau \to \infty$) to one (for $\tau = 0$). From (7.7) we see that

$$I_\lambda(s_2) = t(s_1, s_2) I_\lambda(s_1) . \qquad (7.10)$$

Thus, $t \approx 1$ implies very weak attenuation of the beam between s_1 and s_2, whereas $t \approx 0$ implies near total extinction of the beam. Note that no matter how large τ, the transmittance is never identically zero, though it is often vanishingly small.

- If β_e happens to be constant between s_1 and s_2, then (7.8) simplifies to

$$\tau = \beta_e(s_2 - s_1) \, . \tag{7.11}$$

- Each (dimensionless) unit of optical path corresponds to a reduction of I_λ to $e^{-1} \approx 37\%$ of its original value.

- Consider the propagation of a ray along an extended path from s_1 to s_N. Break that path into several sub-paths; e.g., from s_1 to s_2, s_2 to s_3, s_{N-1} to s_N, etc. Then from (7.8) it can be readily shown that the total optical path can be written

$$\tau(s_1, s_N) = \tau(s_1, s_2) + \tau(s_2, s_3) + \cdots + \tau(s_{N-1}, s_N) \, ,$$

$$\tag{7.12}$$

and the corresponding transmittance can be written

$$t(s_1, s_N) = t(s_1, s_2) \cdot t(s_2, s_3) \cdots \cdot t(s_{N-1}, s_N) \, . \tag{7.13}$$

In plain English, (1) *the total optical path equals the* **sum** *of the individual optical paths;* and (2) *the total transmittance equals the* **product** *of the individual transmittances.*

- Consider the propagation of a ray over an optical path $\tau(s_1, s_2) \ll 1$. That is, the medium is relatively transparent over the distance in question. This can occur if either that geometric distance Δs is sufficiently short or the extinction coefficient β_e is sufficiently small. In this case, the transmittance is approximated by

$$t = \exp(-\tau) \approx 1 - \tau(s_1, s_2) = 1 - \beta_e(s_2 - s_1), \tag{7.14}$$

where the equality on the right holds if we take β_e to be constant.

- If a medium doesn't scatter ($\tilde{\omega} = 0$), then whatever is not transmitted along a given path must be absorbed. Thus, the path *absorptance* in this case is

$$a = 1 - t.$$ (7.15)

If the medium does scatter ($\tilde{\omega} > 0$), then the absorptance is, in general, less than that defined above, but it cannot be computed from a simple formula.

Problem 7.2: A cloud layer has a vertical profile of β_e that is quadratic in altitude z between cloud base z_{base} and cloud top z_{top}, with maximum $\beta_{e,m}$ at the midpoint of the cloud. At the base and top of the cloud, $\beta_e = 0$.
(a) Find the quadratic equation that describes $\beta_e(z)$ within the cloud layer.
(b) Find an expression for the total optical path τ measured vertically through the cloud layer.
(c) Typical values for the above parameters for solar radiation incident on a thin cloud layer might be $z_{base} = 1.0$ km, $z_{top} = 1.2$ km, and $\beta_{e,m} = 0.015$ m^{-1}. Compute the total optical path for this case.
(d) Based on your answer to (c), compute the vertical transmittance t through the cloud.

7.2.2 Mass Extinction Coefficient

We have already introduced the concept of an extinction coefficient β_e which is a measure of how strongly radiation is attenuated by absorption and/or scattering as it traverses a given geometric distance Δs. It is possible, and sometimes desirable, to describe the strength of extinction not by reference to a fixed geometric distance, but rather to a fixed mass of material or even a fixed number of particles.

For example, consider again the example of a clear glass petri dish on an overhead projector. Let's start with the glass half-full of clear water and then add 10 drops of India ink. Once the ink and the water are well-mixed, the solution will noticeably attenuate the light passing through the Petri dish. One can, in principle, measure the total transmittance t as well as the depth of the solution in the dish and, from those two pieces of information, use (7.9) and (7.11) to compute the extinction coefficient β_e of the water-ink mixture.

Problem 7.3:   Assume the measured transmission through the glass is 70% and the depth of the ink-water solution is 10 cm. Compute β_e.

Now consider what happens if you add enough water to the mixture to fill the Petri dish to the rim. If you repeat the previous measurements of transmittance and depth, you will find that the transmittance remains unchanged, even though the depth of the solution has doubled! Your new value for the extinction coefficient β_e will be half of what it was previously. Clearly, the total transmittance through the column is conserved with respect to dilution of the ink by clear water, as long as the solution remains confined to the same horizontal area (i.e., the container has vertical sides).

Furthermore, if you were to leave the water out altogether and simply spread a single drop of ink uniformly over the bottom of the Petri dish (this is admittedly difficult to do in practice), the total transmittance would again be conserved, although the thickness of the layer is now very small, implying very large β_e.

After a little thought, we conclude that the one constant in the above experiment is the total mass of ink per unit area in the dish, since dilution by water only spreads it out vertically but not horizontally. Further reflection leads us to define a new quantity called the *mass extinction coefficient* k_e which relates our previous *volume* extinction coefficient β_e to the density ρ of the relevant material:

$$\beta_e = \rho k_e .$$ (7.16)

In our experiment with the ink, the density ρ refers to that of just the diluted mass of ink in the solution. This density in turn is given by

$$\rho = \frac{M}{HA} ,$$ (7.17)

where M is the mass of concentrated ink pigment added to the dish, H is the depth of the solution, and A is the horizontal area of the dish. Adding water increases H but does not change A or M; therefore ρ decreases as the solution becomes more dilute.

The total vertical transmittance through the solution is thus given by

$$t = \exp(-\tau) = \exp(-\beta_e H)$$
$$= \exp\left[-k_e\left(\frac{M}{HA}\right)H\right] = \exp\left[-k_e\left(\frac{M}{A}\right)\right], \tag{7.18}$$

so that we discover

$$\tau = k_e\frac{M}{A}. \tag{7.19}$$

As you can see, H does not appear on the right hand side. This is consistent with the observation that we can dilute the column as much or as little as we like and still get the same total transmittance, as long as M and A are fixed.

Note that k_e has dimensions of area per unit mass. You can think of this as an *extinction cross-section per unit mass*. The extinction cross-section can in turn be thought of as the equivalent area of an opaque object blocking the same total amount of radiation (assuming equal illumination everywhere). That is to say, if India ink pigment has a mass extinction coefficient k_e of, say, 100 m^2 kg^{-1}, then one kg of pure ink pigment poured into a large body of clear water (and mixed thoroughly) has the capacity to block as much total sunlight from reaching the bottom as would a 100 m^2 sheet of opaque metal foil.[2] Obviously, the larger the area over which the ink is spread, the less intense the attenuation at any one point, but the total remains the same.

The concept of mass extinction coefficient is very handy precisely because, unlike the case for the volume extinction coefficient, it is nearly constant for most substances in the atmosphere irrespective of dilution, as long as all other variables (e.g., pressure, temperature, etc.) are held constant. This is particularly convenient when dealing with highly variable atmospheric constituents, such as water vapor.

---

[2]Strictly speaking, this equivalence holds only if the ink is spread out thinly enough (i.e., over a large enough area) so that the transmission is close to 100% at any point.

7.2.3　Extinction Cross-Section

There is one further extinction variable that frequently arises in contexts involving known concentrations (number densities) of particles. Such particles might be molecules of an absorbing gas, droplets of water in a cloud, or perhaps individual soot particles in a plume of smoke.

To return to our previous thought experiment, what if, instead of finding a proportionality between the volume extinction coefficient β_e and the mass density ρ, we instead relate the former to the *number density or concentration N* of microscopic particles of pigment in the ink? If we set up the proportionality as follows —

$$\beta_e = \sigma_e N\,, \tag{7.20}$$

we find that the constant of proportionality σ_e has dimensions of area. It is thus an extinction cross-section with the same physical interpretation as discussed earlier but now referenced to a single particle rather than a unit mass. It follows that

$$\sigma_e = k_e m\,, \tag{7.21}$$

where m is the mass per particle.[3]

One place where the idea of an extinction cross-section σ_e per particle is especially convenient and intuitive is in clouds. In the visible and infrared part of the spectrum, a single cloud droplet has an extinction cross-section that is similar, but not identical, to its geometric cross-section πr^2, where r is the droplet radius. In fact, we may define an *extinction efficiency* Q_e according to

$$Q_e \equiv \frac{\sigma_e}{A}\,, \tag{7.22}$$

where A is the geometric cross-sectional area of the particle. In the case of a spherical droplet, $A = \pi r^2$, where r is the radius.

---

[3]Equations (7.20)–(7.21) assume that all of the particles are identical. We will generalize later to distributions of dissimilar particles.

One might surmise (incorrectly, as it turns out) that Q_e could range only from zero to one. That is, a particle should not be able to extinguish more radiation than its geometric cross-section would imply — in plain English again, it shouldn't cast a shadow bigger than itself. Unfortunately, however, our physical intuition lets us down in this instance. On the contrary, for cloud droplets in the visible spectrum, $Q_e \approx 2$ on average, and for certain wavelengths, it can be even larger! The reasons for this apparent paradox will be examined more closely in Chapter 12; for now, simply ascribe it to the wave properties of radiation.

7.2.4 Generalization to Scattering and Absorption

Throughout the last section, we have talked exclusively about *extinction*, and we defined a *mass extinction coefficient* and *extinction cross-section* to go along with the previously defined *volume extinction coefficient*. Recalling that extinction is the sum of absorption and scattering, it makes sense to define completely analogous mass- and particle-normalized quantities for those two processes:

$$\beta_a = \rho k_a = N\sigma_a \qquad \beta_s = \rho k_s = N\sigma_s ,\qquad (7.23)$$

where k_a and k_s are the mass absorption coefficient and mass scattering coefficient, and σ_a and σ_s are the absorption cross-section and scattering cross-section. The latter can in turn be written in terms of absorption and scattering *efficiencies* as follows:

$$\sigma_a = Q_a A \qquad \sigma_s = Q_s A ,\qquad (7.24)$$

where A is the geometric cross-sectional area of a particle.

It follows that the single scatter albedo can be written in terms of any of these quantities as follows:

$$\tilde{\omega} = \frac{\beta_s}{\beta_e} = \frac{k_s}{k_e} = \frac{\sigma_s}{\sigma_e} .\qquad (7.25)$$

Problem 7.4: Complete the following table, using the information in each column to determine the missing values in the same column.

	(a)	(b)	(c)	(d)
k_e [m²/kg]	3.89×10^2	?	0.45	?
N [m⁻³]	?	?	80	10^9
A [m²]	2.8×10^{-19}	7.07×10^{-14}	?	3.14×10^{-10}
Q_e	?	0.2	0.6	?
$\tilde{\omega}$	0	0.1	?	0.9
m [kg]	7.3×10^{-26}	1.41×10^{-17}	?	4.19×10^{-12}
ρ [kg/m³]	4.8×10^{-4}	?	3.35×10^{-4}	?
σ_e [m²]	?	?	1.89×10^{-6}	?
β_e [m⁻¹]	?	1.41×10^{-4}	?	0.628
β_s [m⁻¹]	?	1.41×10^{-5}	6.03×10^{-5}	?

7.2.5 Generalization to Arbitrary Mixtures of Components

In the above discussion, we assumed we were dealing with a single absorbing or scattering substance; either ink or milk. In each case, we conveniently ignored the fact that we were actually dealing with a two-component mixture, where one of the components was water. We were able to get away with this because, for the purposes of this demonstration at least, pure water is completely nonabsorbing and nonscattering at visible wavelengths.

In the atmosphere, we have to deal with a mixture of a wide variety of gases, as well as clouds and aerosols, all of which have the capacity to absorb and/or scatter radiation in at least some, if not all, spectral bands. We therefore have to generalize our previous relationships to properly account for such mixtures. This is not difficult: all you have to remember is that *the total volume extinction, scattering, and absorbing coefficients for a mixture are equal to the sums of the corresponding coefficients for the individual components.* That is,

$$
\begin{aligned}
\beta_e &= \sum_i \beta_{e,i} = \sum_i \rho_i k_{e,i} = \sum_i N_i \sigma_{e,i}, \\
\beta_a &= \sum_i \beta_{a,i} = \sum_i \rho_i k_{a,i} = \sum_i N_i \sigma_{a,i}, \\
\beta_s &= \sum_i \beta_{s,i} = \sum_i \rho_i k_{s,i} = \sum_i N_i \sigma_{s,i},
\end{aligned}
\tag{7.26}
$$

where ρ_i and N_i, respectively, are the (diluted) density and particle (e.g., molecule) number concentration of the ith constituent, and the remaining subscripted variables are the corresponding radiative coefficients.

The single scatter albedo of the mixture is determined by first finding the combined β_s and β_e and then taking the ratio, as usual.

7.3   Plane Parallel Approximation

Now that we have introduced the fundamental concepts and variables relevant to radiative transfer in an arbitrary medium, let us take the first step toward adapting these specifically to the atmosphere. In Section 7.2, I introduced equations describing the transmission of radiation over a finite distance along an arbitrary path. The idea is that you can pick any direction from a given starting point, integrate the extinction coefficient β_e over that path up to some ending point, and use Beer's Law to compute the transmittance between the two points. We used the variable s to denote the geometric distance along the path, with s_1 denoting the starting point and s_2 the endpoint ($s_2 \geq s_1$). This approach is completely general, in that it makes no assumptions whatsoever about how β_e varies as a function of horizontal or vertical position in the atmosphere.

As a matter of fact, the atmosphere is usually highly *stratified*. That is to say, properties such as pressure, density, temperature, composition, etc., usually vary much more rapidly in the vertical direction z than they do in the horizontal directions x and y. For example, it is usually necessary to move vertically only 1 km in the atmosphere to experience somewhere around a $7°$C change in temperature; horizontally, it might be necessary to travel a hundred kilometers or more to experience a similar temperature change. Similarly, horizontal pressure gradients are typically less than 1 mb per 20 km, whereas vertical pressure gradients are of the order of 1 mb per 8 *meters*. Since air density is determined primarily by pressure and (absolute) temperature via the ideal gas law

$$\rho = \frac{p}{R_d T} ,$$

(7.27)

where R_d is the gas constant for air, it follows that density also varies much more dramatically in the vertical than in the horizontal directions.

One obvious exception to the above rule is clouds. Many clouds *do* exhibit strong horizontal as well as vertical structure. Nevertheless, even clouds (especially *stratiform* clouds – e.g., stratus, stratocumulus, nimbostratus, altostratus, cirrostratus, etc.) are often organized in great sheets whose horizontal dimension greatly exceeds their vertical thickness. If you have ever spent time looking out a window during a cross-country airline flight, you may have noticed that you can sometimes traverse hundreds of kilometers over a more or less continuous sheet of clouds below you, especially in the vicinity of synoptic-scale weather disturbances. Thus, although it is by no means *always* the case, it is at least *sometimes* safe (and in any case very convenient) to treat even cloud layers as varying much more rapidly in the vertical than the horizontal.

For all of the above reasons, it is quite common (perhaps too common!) to treat the atmosphere for radiative purposes as *plane parallel*. That is, at a given location, we ignore horizontal variations in the structure of the atmosphere and assume instead that all relevant radiative properties depend strictly on the vertical coordinate z. Another term you will sometimes see that refers to the same approximation is *slab geometry*.

We also ignore the curvature of the earth in the plane parallel approximation, since any ray of light that is not traveling at a very shallow angle will pass through most of the mass of the atmosphere long before the earth's curvature comes into play. A good rule of thumb for the validity of this approximation is that $H/\cos\theta \ll R$, where θ is the angle of the ray relative to vertical, H is the effective depth of the atmosphere ($H \sim 10$ km for many purposes), and $R \approx 6373$ km is the radius of the earth. Obviously, this criterion is no longer satisfied if $\cos\theta$ becomes very small, as it does when θ approaches $90°$. Usually, however, we are concerned primarily with radiation transporting energy more or less vertically through the atmosphere, in which case we can ignore this complication.

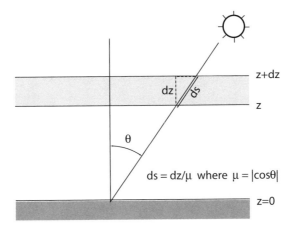

Fig. 7.4: Relationship between slant and vertical paths in a plane parallel atmosphere.

7.3.1 Definition

Mathematically, we invoke the plane parallel assumption via the following simplifications:

$$\beta_e(x, y, z) \approx \beta_e(z) , \tag{7.28}$$

$$T(x, y, z) \approx T(z) , \qquad \text{etc.} \tag{7.29}$$

Since everything now depends only on vertical distance z, the path distance s we used earlier in computing transmittance etc. along a ray (Fig. 7.4) may now be expressed as

$$s = \frac{z}{\mu} , \tag{7.30}$$

where we have introduced the following new definition for convenience:

$$\mu \equiv |\cos \theta| . \tag{7.31}$$

As before, θ is the angle of propagation of the ray relative to zenith (i.e., straight up). Note, therefore, that $0 \leq \mu \leq 1$ regardless of whether the ray is propagating upward or downward.

Combining the above definitions with our earlier expressions for transmittance, optical path, etc., we have the following expressions valid for a plane parallel atmosphere:

The *optical thickness* between levels z_1 and z_2 is

$$\tau(z_1, z_2) = \int_{z_1}^{z_2} \beta_e(z)\, dz \,, \qquad (7.32)$$

and the transmittance for a ray propagating with direction μ is

$$t(z_1, z_2) = \exp\left[-\frac{1}{\mu}\tau(z_1, z_2)\right], \qquad (7.33)$$

where $z_2 > z_1$.

Note that the optical thickness in a plane parallel atmosphere, as given above, is deliberately defined so as not to depend on the direction of propagation μ. Thus, it doesn't matter whether the sun is directly overhead ($\mu = 1$) or nearly setting on the horizon ($\mu \to 0$); the optical thickness of the atmosphere between levels z_1 and z_2 is the same. However, when computing the transmittance t of a ray of the sun as it passes between the two levels, it *is* of course necessary to account for μ, since the ray experiences a much longer optical *path* when the sun is low in the sky.

Just in case you've forgotten, let me reiterate that all of the above definitions still assume that we're talking about monochromatic radiation. That is, the parameters β_e, τ, t, etc., are all implicitly functions of wavelength.

Problem 7.5: At a certain wavelength in the visible band, the optical thickness of the cloud-free atmosphere is $\tau^* = 0.2$. Determine the transmittance of sunlight at this wavelength when the sun is $10°$ above the horizon.

Problem 7.6: A particular plane parallel cloud has liquid water density $\rho_w = 0.1$ g m^{-3} and thickness $\Delta z = 100$ m. At a certain wavelength, the mass extinction coefficient of the cloud droplets is $k_{e,w} = 150$ m^2/kg, and the single scatter albedo is $\tilde{\omega}_w = 1.0$. However, the air in which the droplets are suspended is itself absorbing at this wavelength, having volume absorption coefficient $\beta_{a,v} = 10$ km^{-1} and $\tilde{\omega}_v = 0$.
(a) Compute the combined β_e, β_a, β_s, and $\tilde{\omega}$ for the mixture.
(b) Compute the total optical thickness τ of the cloud layer.
(c) If radiation with intensity $I_{\lambda,\text{top}}$ is incident on the top of the cloud from a zenith angle $\theta = 60°$, compute the directly transmitted intensity $I_{\lambda,\text{bot}}$.

7.3.2 Optical Depth as Vertical Coordinate

In a plane parallel atmosphere, we may choose any level z in the atmosphere and evaluate the optical thickness between that level and another, higher, level z_{top}, according to (7.32). Because β_e is never negative (though it may be effectively zero at some levels), the optical thickness is always a nonnegative quantity. Moreover, it can never increase as z gets closer to z_{top}. If we choose z_{top} to be effectively at infinity — i.e., in outer space where there is no atmosphere left to contribute to additional radiative extinction, then we can define an *optical depth* that is a function of only z:

$$\tau(z) \equiv \lim_{z_{\text{top}} \to \infty} \tau(z, z_{\text{top}}) = \int_z^\infty \beta_e(z')dz' . \qquad (7.34)$$

An important property of $\tau(z)$ is that it starts at some positive value $\tau^* \equiv \tau(z = 0)$ at sea level and then decreases with height until it reaches zero at some level z that is effectively above the top of the atmosphere,[4] where $\tau \approx 0$.

Because of this property, $\tau(z)$ may be employed as a vertical coordinate for radiative transfer purposes. That is, I might tell you

---

[4]Strictly speaking, the atmosphere has no upper limit, but by the time you reach an altitude of a couple hundred kilometers, the residual gases found there are so tenuous as to make no significant contribution to radiative extinction.

that the top of a cloud is located at $\tau = 0.4$ (in dimensionless units) rather than at $z = 4$ km. Radiation in a plane-parallel atmosphere doesn't "care" about vertical altitude in geometric units, only about how much absorbing atmosphere it must traverse. Hence, changes in altitude expressed in units of τ are more convenient as a basis for describing the net effect of that change on a propagating beam of radiation.

In particular, one may adapt our earlier definitions of transmittance etc. in the following ways:

The optical thickness between levels z_1 and z_2 (where $z_2 > z_1$) is given by

$$\tau(z_1, z_2) = \tau(z_1) - \tau(z_2) , \tag{7.35}$$

where the appearance of only one altitude in the arguments of the τ on the right hand side reminds us that we're measuring it between the altitude in question and the top of the atmosphere.

Likewise, the transmittance of a ray propagating with direction μ from level z_1 to z_2 (or vice versa) is

$$t(z_1, z_2) = \exp\left[-\frac{1}{\mu}\tau(z_1, z_2)\right] = \frac{t(z_1)}{t(z_2)} , \tag{7.36}$$

where the transmittance from level z to the top of the atmosphere is of course

$$t(z) \equiv e^{-\frac{\tau(z)}{\mu}} . \tag{7.37}$$

7.4　Applications to Meteorology, Climatology, and Remote Sensing

7.4.1　The Transmission Spectrum of the Atmosphere

In the preceding sections of this chapter, we developed the machinery for relating the transmission of radiation through the atmosphere to the material properties of the atmosphere at every point along the path. To at least first order, these properties are embodied in the volume extinction coefficient β_e and the single scatter albedo $\tilde{\omega}$, both of which are generally functions of position (in three dimensions) and wavelength λ. Recall that if you know β_e and $\tilde{\omega}$, you can easily obtain β_s and β_a, and vice versa, so there is no single "correct" way to describe the radiative properties of the atmosphere. Also, there are times when it is more convenient to work with the mass-normalized or particle-normalized quantities k_e, σ_e, etc., but it is straightforward to convert between these and β_e, etc., if the amount (mass density ρ or particle concentration N) of the relevant constituents is known.

We are now ready to undertake a survey of the observed transmission characteristics of the atmosphere at various wavelengths. For now, we only want to answer the following basic questions:

- At which wavelengths is the cloud-free atmosphere reasonably transparent?

- At which wavelengths is the cloud-free atmosphere strongly absorbing, and which constituents are responsible for the absorption?

- How do the extinction and scattering properties of clouds vary with wavelength?

In later chapters, we will revisit all of the above questions in a much more detailed way.

Absorption by Atmospheric Gases

Except at short visible and UV wavelengths (where scattering by air molecules can be important), the overall transmittance of the cloud-free atmosphere is controlled primarily by absorption due to various constituent gases. Where absorption is strong, the transmittance is small; where absorption is weak or absent, the transmittance is close to 100%. Table 7.1 lists a number of radiatively important constituents and their approximate abundances. Two points are worth highlighting right away:

- Some constituents make up a large fraction of the total mass of the atmosphere. In fact, nitrogen (N_2) and oxygen (O_2) alone

Table 7.1: Key constituents of air in the troposphere and stratosphere.

Constituent	Fraction by volume in (or relative to) dry air	Significant absorption bands	Remarks
N_2	78.1%	—	
O_2	20.9%	UV-C, MW near 60 and 118 GHz, weak bands in VIS and IR	
H_2O	(0–2%)	numerous strong bands throughout IR; also in MW, especially near 183 GHz	highly variable in time and space
Ar and other inert gases	0.936%	—	monoatomic
CO_2	370 ppm	near 2.8, 4.3, and 15 μm	concentration as of 2001; increasing 1.6 ppm per year
CH_4	1.7 ppm	near 3.3 and 7.8 μm	increasing due to human activities
N_2O	0.35 ppm	4.5, 7.8, and 17 μm	
CO	0.07 ppm	4.7 μm (weak)	
O_3	$\sim 10^{-8}$	UV-B, 9.6 μm	highly variable concentration; high in stratosphere and in polluted air
$CFCl_3, CF_2Cl_2$, etc.	$\sim 10^{-10}$	IR	industrial origin

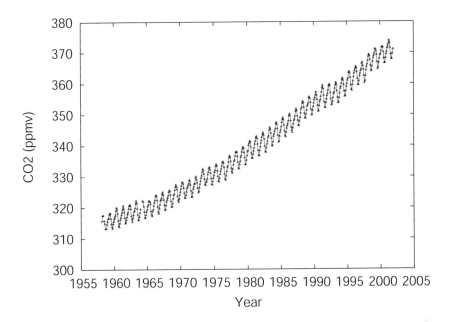

Fig. 7.5: Measurements of atmospheric carbon dioxide concentration at Mauna Loa Observatory, Hawaii. (Source: C.D. Keeling and T.P. Whorf, Scripps Institute of Oceanography, University of California.)

are responsible for approximately 99% of the total. Many others, however, such as carbon dioxide (CO_2), methane (CH_4), and ozone (O_3), are present only in trace amounts. As we shall see shortly, *many of the less abundant constituents have a disproportionally large influence on atmospheric transmission.*

- Some constituents, such as nitrogen, oxygen, argon (Ar), and other so-called permanent gases are present in the atmosphere in nearly unvarying concentrations. The concentration of others, such as water vapor (H_2O) and ozone, can vary wildly from one time and location to another. The atmospheric concentration of CO_2 does not vary much from location to location; however, it is experiencing a steady upward trend over time as a result of fossil fuel use by humans (Fig. 7.5). *Many of the variable constituents are more important for atmospheric radiation than the permanent gases, a fact that has profound implications for climate variability.*

Figure 7.6 depicts the vertical transmittance of the entire cloud- and aerosol-free atmosphere as a function of wavelength from the visible to the microwave.[5] It also depicts separately the transmittance spectrum for selected individual gases as if they were the only absorbers present. Recall that *the total atmospheric transmittance due to all constituents is the product of the transmittances due to the individual constituents.* Thus, if any one constituent is a strong absorber at a given wavelength, then the atmosphere will be effectively opaque at that wavelength, even if all other constituents are nonabsorbing at the same wavelength.[6]

Starting in the ultraviolet band, we see that the atmosphere is almost completely opaque to radiation with wavelengths shorter than 0.3 μm. This absorption is due to oxygen at the very short wavelengths of the UV-C band and to ozone in the UV-B band. In most of the UV-A band, on the other hand, the atmosphere is rather transparent.

---

[5]We are considering only the effects of absorption and not molecular scattering in this depiction.

[6]Note that this depiction gives a highly smoothed, "big picture" view. As we shall see in Chapter 9, the atmospheric absorption bands are extremely complex when viewed at fine spectral resolution.

ZENITH ATMOSPHERIC TRANSMITTANCE

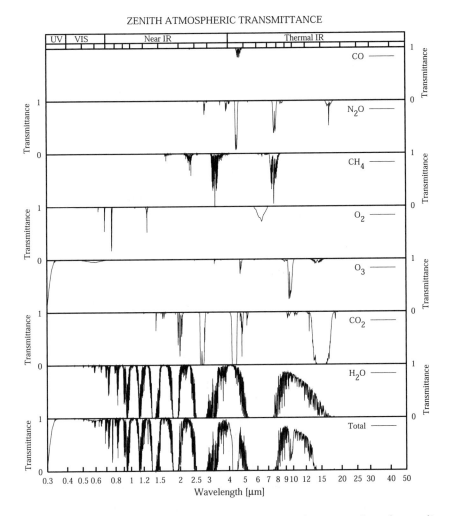

Fig. 7.6: Zenith transmittance of the cloud- and aerosol-free atmosphere for conditions typical of a midlatitude summertime atmosphere. Each upper panel depicts the absorption contribution due to a single atmospheric constituent; the bottom panel depicts the combined effect of all constituents. Molecular scattering, which becomes increasingly important for wavelengths shorter than about 0.5 μm, is not considered in these plots.

Problem 7.7: The absorption cross-section of a single O_2 molecule is approximately 7×10^{-29} m^2 at a wavelength of 0.24 μm (it increases sharply for even shorter wavelengths). Given a standard

> sea level pressure p_0 of 1.01×10^5 Pa, a molar fraction for oxygen of 21%, a mean molecular mass $\overline{m}$ for air of 29 kg/kmole, gravitational acceleration $g = 9.81$ m/s^2, and Avogadro's constant $N_A = 6.02 \times 10^{26}$ kmole^{-1}, compute (a) the mass per unit area of the atmospheric column assuming hydrostatic balance, (b) the number of oxygen molecules per unit area in the column, and (c) the optical thickness and vertical transmittance due to molecular oxygen at 0.24 μm.

Throughout most of the visible band (0.4 μm$<\lambda<$0.7 μm), the atmosphere is quite transparent, apart from a few weak and narrow absorption bands due to oxygen or ozone.

In the near IR band (0.7 μm$<\lambda<$4 μm) things start to get more interesting. Over this relatively narrow range of wavelength, the atmosphere swings several times between being almost perfectly transparent to being almost perfectly opaque. Most of the absorption is due to water vapor; however there are also important contributions from CO_2, CH_4, and N_2O.

As already mentioned, water vapor is a highly variable component of the atmosphere. The plot appearing in Fig. 7.6 was derived for the typical atmospheric conditions of a station in the middle latitudes during summertime. In a colder, drier environment, the total amount of water vapor present in the column will be drastically smaller, so that the atmosphere may be substantially more transparent in some spectral bands than indicated in this plot. In a moist tropical environment, of course, the reverse is true.

Through the thermal IR band (4 μm$<\lambda<$50 μm) there are broad bands of near-total absorption due to CO_2 (near 4 μm), water vapor (from 5–8 μm), ozone (near 9.6 μm), and again CO_2 ($\lambda>$13 μm). However, there is also a wide band within which the atmosphere is rather transparent from 8–13 μm, terminated only by the ozone band and increasing absorption by water vapor beyond 12 μm.

The far IR band (50 μm$<\lambda<$1 mm) is not terribly important in the calculation of radiative fluxes in the atmosphere, nor is it used much for remote sensing. For both reasons, it is hard to find plots of atmospheric transmission in this band. As a rule of thumb, however, it can be said that water vapor is the dominant absorber throughout most of this band.

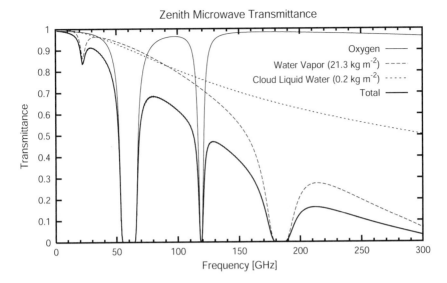

Fig. 7.7: Zenith atmospheric opacity in the microwave band under typical midlatitude conditions, including the effects of a moderately thick nonprecipitating cloud layer.

The microwave band is of interest primarily for remote sensing, mainly below 300 GHz. Fig. 7.7 depicts the principal features of the absorption spectrum in this band. There is a strong absorption band due to oxygen centered on 60 GHz; this band plays an important role in satellite retrievals of atmospheric temperature. A second, somewhat narrower oxygen band is also present at 118 GHz. There is a very strong water vapor band centered on 183.3 GHz; this band is used in microwave retrievals of atmospheric humidity profiles.

All three of the microwave absorption bands just mentioned are strong enough to render the atmosphere completely opaque at the centers of the bands. A difference between the oxygen bands and the water vapor bands, however, is that the latter is only present to the degree that water vapor is present. In an extremely dry arctic atmosphere, the 183.3 GHz band is substantially weaker than shown in Fig. 7.7.

Last but not least, there is a weak water vapor absorption line located near 22 GHz. Despite its weakness (indeed, partly *because* of its weakness), microwave observations made at this frequency have long been crucial for retrieving the total (vertically integrated) water vapor content of the atmosphere.

Apart from the major absorption bands just mentioned, Fig. 7.7 reveals a strong tendency for the atmosphere to become more opaque with increasing frequency, with the standard midlatitude atmosphere becoming nearly opaque by 300 GHz. This tendency is due to the so-called *continuum absorption* by water vapor; that is, absorption that is not concentrated in a few discrete lines or bands. It is partly because of the increasing dominance of water vapor continuum absorption that frequencies higher than 300 GHz are not terribly useful for remote sensing, except perhaps for observing cirrus clouds that lie well above the majority of water vapor in the troposphere.

Throughout every major band just discussed, there exist spectral *windows* for which the cloud-free atmosphere is relatively transparent. For example, the entire visible band is a spectral window, as is the 8–13 μm region in the thermal IR band and the 80–100 GHz and 0–40 GHz regions in the microwave band. If no clouds are present, then a satellite observing upwelling radiation within a window region has a more or less unobstructed view of the earth's surface. Also, radiation emitted by the earth's surface at wavelengths falling within one of the windows in the thermal IR band readily escapes to space, so that these window regions play an important role in surface cooling.

In many spectral windows, the atmosphere is not perfectly transparent but has a moderate component of absorption due to water vapor or some other constituent. Such regions of the spectrum are often referred to as "dirty windows," because radiation originating from the surface remains observable from space but significant corrections for atmospheric absorption and emission must be applied, especially when the atmosphere is humid.

One final important comment concerning the gaseous absorption features we have been discussing: The plots above give a somewhat simplified depiction of the actual dependence of transmittance on wavelength. If you were to "zoom in" on any one of the absorption bands discussed above, you would find that it represents a complex aggregate of many very closely spaced "lines" of absorption. There may be hundreds of such lines in a very narrow wavelength band. In the gaps between individual lines, the at-

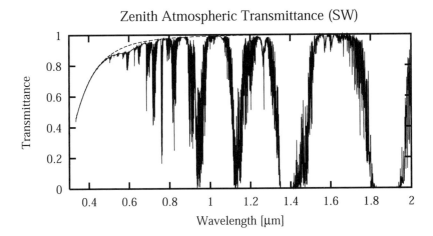

Fig. 7.8: Detail of atmospheric transmission in the shortwave portion of the spectrum, for a summer midlatitude atmosphere. This plot includes the effects of scattering by air molecules (dashed/smooth curve on left).

mosphere may be substantially more transparent than indicated by Fig. 7.6. Likewise, at the exact centers of isolated narrow lines, some of which fall within the so-called "dirty windows", the atmosphere may be more opaque than indicated. The reasons for the enormous complexity of absorption line spectra, and methods for dealing with it, are the subject of later chapters.

Scattering by Clear Air

In the previous subsection, we outlined the major absorption features of atmospheric gases. In the absence of clouds, it is largely *absorption* by gases that controls the overall opacity of the atmosphere. However, at short wavelengths (visible and shorter), molecules of air have the capacity to significantly *scatter* EM radiation. Although we will not look at the details of such scattering until Chapter 12, it is worth mentioning now that the scattering cross-section σ_s of an air molecule is approximately proportional to λ^{-4}. Thus, extinction of radiation via scattering is 9.3 times stronger at 0.4 μm (the short wavelength limit of the visible band) than it is at 0.7 μm (the long wavelength limit). In the UV band it is stronger still, while in most of the IR band it is negligible. The uppermost curve in Fig. 7.8 shows how vertical transmission through the atmosphere is reduced by molecular scattering.

Extinction and Scattering by Aerosols and Clouds

In addition to the gas molecules that make up most of the atmosphere, there are also countless small particles of dust, salt, water, and other materials suspended in the air. Some, such as the water droplets that make up a visible cloud, are comparatively large (order 10 μm radius), while many other aerosol types are typically much smaller than 1 μm.

Depending on the size and composition, these particles can either scatter or absorb radiation or, more commonly, both. Clouds in the visible band strongly scatter sunlight but absorb very little; hence they are rather opaque but appear white. A plume of smoke from a forest fire, on the other hand, may not appear as optically dense as a typical water cloud, but it usually has a gray or brown color to it even when viewed from above, suggesting that at least some absorption is taking place.

Ignoring water and ice clouds for the moment, it is difficult to generalize about the contribution of aerosols to the extinction of radiation in the atmosphere, partly because their concentration and composition are so highly variable. However, it is safe to say that the contribution of "background" aerosols to the total optical thickness τ^* is rarely more than a few tenths of a unit at visible wavelengths and tends to be even smaller still at infrared and longer wavelengths (Fig. 7.8). Aerosol optical depths only reach comparatively large values (order unity or greater) in association with fires, volcanoes, dust storms, and severe pollution episodes.

Clouds are another story: because the droplets they contain are large compared with most other aerosols and because the total mass of liquid or frozen water (integrated vertically over the atmospheric column) can also be large (order 0.1 to 1 kg/m^2), they routinely achieve optical thicknesses large enough to completely block the direct rays of the sun. In the microwave band, clouds are considerably more transparent; nevertheless, their radiative effects are never completely negligible.

Because ordinary clouds consist of nearly pure water droplets or ice particles, the degree to which clouds absorb radiation (in addition to scattering it) is a function of the imaginary part n_i of the index of refraction of water or ice, as discussed in Chapter 4. If n_i is zero at a given wavelength, then a cloud can only scatter radiation at that wavelength; if n_i is nonzero, then the cloud will also absorb to at least some degree. We will examine this problem in far greater detail in a later chapter; for now it is enough to point out that clouds quickly switch over from being almost purely scattering ($\tilde{\omega} \approx 1$) in the visible band to strongly absorbing ($\tilde{\omega}<1$) in the IR band and beyond. However, the details of this transition are different for liquid water and ice; hence there are wavelengths (e.g., near 1.7 μm; see Fig. 4.1) for which a water cloud is significantly less absorbing than an ice cloud. Satellite sensors with channels at suitable wavelengths can exploit this difference to distinguish between water and ice clouds.

7.4.2   Measuring Solar Intensity from the Ground

We have already seen that the solar flux S_0 at the top of the atmosphere is of key importance to the radiation budget of the earth and atmosphere. Furthermore, because atmospheric absorption of solar radiation is a function of wavelength, it is important to accurately know how the solar intensity varies with wavelength.

Prior to the (relatively recent) advent of satellites equipped with devices for measuring the solar spectrum, it was impossible to measure solar intensity directly. Ground-based measurements are always affected by a certain degree of attenuation of the solar beam by atmospheric absorption and scattering. If the atmospheric transmittance were known, then of course the unattenuated solar intensity could be computed from the ground measurements, but there was no direct method for inferring transmittance either without knowing the strength of the solar source. This presented a classic "Catch 22" problem to atmospheric scientists and astrophysicists. Yet reasonable estimates of the solar spectrum were obtained years before the first satellite measurements were made. How was this done?

Let us assume that the atmosphere is plane parallel and that the properties of the atmosphere are essentially constant over the period of a day. These assumptions are generally met only on a

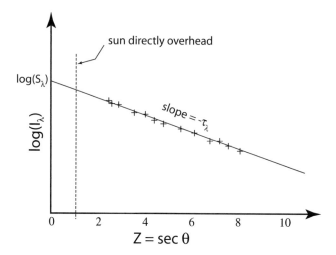

Fig. 7.9: Schematic relationship between the log-intensity of solar radiation at wavelength λ and the secant of the solar zenith angle, for an atmospheric optical depth τ_λ. The plus symbols represent individual measurements at different times of day, from which the slope and intercept of the best-fit line may be determined.

perfectly clear day with no significant change in humidity, surface pressure, etc. For any given wavelength λ, the two unknowns in this problem are the solar intensity S_λ and the atmospheric optical depth τ_λ.

At any particular time on the day in question, Beer's Law states that the intensity of solar radiation measured at sea level is

$$I_\lambda = S_\lambda e^{-\frac{\tau_\lambda}{\mu}} , \tag{7.38}$$

where $\mu = \cos\theta$ and θ is the solar zenith angle. Taking logarithms of both sides yields

$$\log(I_\lambda) = -\frac{\tau_\lambda}{\mu} + \log(S_\lambda) . \tag{7.39}$$

If we define a $Z = 1/\mu = \sec\theta$, then the above is a linear equation of the form $Y = mZ + B$, where $Y \equiv \log(I_\lambda)$, the slope $m \equiv -\tau_\lambda$, and the Y-intercept $B \equiv \log(S_\lambda)$.

All that is needed now is a series of measurements of Y for different values of Z; i.e., at different times of day as the sun rises, reaches its highest position (smallest θ) at noon, and then sets again. By plotting a series of such measurements on a graph, one may readily determine both the slope m and the intercept B, which may then be converted to τ_λ and S_λ, respectively. Fig. 7.9 illustrates the principle.

Problem 7.8: A ground-based radiometer operating at $\lambda = 0.45\,\mu m$ is used to measure the solar intensity $I_\lambda(0)$. For a solar zenith angle $\theta = 30°$, $I_\lambda(0) = 1.74 \times 10^7$ W m$^{-2}\mu$m^{-1}sr^{-1}. For $\theta = 60°$, $I_\lambda(0) = 1.14 \times 10^7$ W m$^{-2}\mu$m^{-1}sr^{-1}. From this information, determine the top-of-the-atmosphere solar intensity S_λ and the atmospheric optical thickness τ_λ.

7.4.3 Transmittance in an Exponential Atmosphere

To a fair approximation, the density ρ of the atmosphere decays exponentially with height z. That is,

$$\rho(z) \approx \rho_0 e^{-\frac{z}{H}} , \tag{7.40}$$

where ρ_0 is the density at sea level and $H \approx 8$ km is the *scale height*; i.e., the altitude change that leads to a factor e change in density. If a certain constituent of the atmosphere, such as carbon dioxide, is well-mixed, then the density of just that constituent is given by

$$\rho_1(z) \approx w_1 \rho_0 e^{-\frac{z}{H}} , \tag{7.41}$$

where w_1 is the mixing ratio (mass of constituent per unit mass of air).

Let us further assume for simplicity that the constituent in question has a mass absorption coefficient of k_a that depends on λ but is otherwise independent of temperature, pressure, w, etc. (we will see later that this is rarely the case for real absorbers; nevertheless, the dependence of k_a on environmental variables is usually much weaker than it is on λ). Finally, let's assume that the atmosphere is nonscattering at the wavelength in question, so that $k_e = k_a$.

By combining (7.41) with (7.16), we have an expression for the volume extinction coefficient as a function of altitude:

$$\beta_e(z) = k_a w_1 \rho_0 e^{-\frac{z}{H}} . \tag{7.42}$$

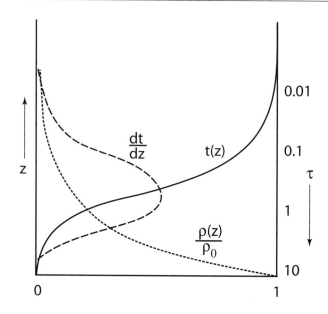

Fig. 7.10: Illustration of the relationship between transmittance t between the top of the atmosphere and altitude z and the absorption/emission weighting function $W(z) = dt/dz$ for an atmosphere with exponential density profile $\rho(z)$.

Armed with this information, we can now answer the following questions:

1. What is the relationship between altitude z and optical depth τ as a vertical coordinate, as discussed in Section 7.3.2?

2. What is the transmittance from the top of the atmosphere to any level z?

3. When radiation (e.g., sunlight) is incident on the top of the atmosphere, where does it get absorbed, and at what altitude is the rate of absorption strongest?

The answer to each of these questions depends directly on the answer to the previous one. Let's address each in turn.

Optical Depth

From (7.34) and (7.42), we have

$$\tau(z) = \int_z^\infty \beta_e(z')dz' = k_a w_1 \rho_0 \int_z^\infty e^{-\frac{z'}{H}}dz' , \qquad (7.43)$$

or

$$\tau(z) = k_a w_1 \rho_0 H e^{-\frac{z}{H}} . \qquad (7.44)$$

Recall from (7.35) that we can also use the above equation to determine the optical thickness $\tau(z_1, z_2)$ of an atmospheric layer bounded by two arbitrary levels z_1 and z_2, since $\tau(z_1, z_2) = |\tau(z_1) - \tau(z_2)|$.
    The *total* atmospheric optical depth is just

$$\tau^* \equiv \tau(0) = k_a w_1 \rho_0 H . \qquad (7.45)$$

We see that τ starts at zero at the top of the atmosphere, and increases ever more rapidly as one moves downward toward the surface, where it reaches its maximum value of τ^*. When optical depth is used as a vertical coordinate, therefore, a unit change of τ corresponds to a smaller change of z at low altitudes than it does at higher altitudes.
    Note, by the way, that (7.43) can also be written

$$\tau(z) = k_a u(z) , \qquad (7.46)$$

where

$$u(z) \equiv \int_z^\infty \rho_1(z')dz' \qquad (7.47)$$

is defined as the *mass path* of the constituent in question between altitude z and the top of the atmosphere. This quantity has dimensions of mass per unit horizontal area. The definition given by (7.47) is valid regardless of the functional form of the constituent density $\rho_1(z)$. When $z = 0$ is substituted into (7.47), we have the *total mass path* u_{tot} of the constituent.
    In the atmospheric science literature, there are many equivalent names and symbols assigned to the same quantity. For example, if the constituent in question is water vapor, then the total mass path of water vapor in the atmosphere is variously known as *total precipitable water*, *column-integrated water vapor*, the *water vapor burden*, and *the water vapor path*, depending on the author and the context.

Transmittance

From (7.37), the transmittance between altitude z and the top of the atmosphere (regardless of whether the radiation is propagating upward or downward) is determined by the optical depth $\tau(z)$ and by the cosine of the zenith (or nadir) angle $\mu = |\cos\theta|$:

$$t(z) = \exp\left[-\frac{\tau(z)}{\mu}\right] = \exp\left[-\frac{k_a w_1 \rho_0 H}{\mu}e^{-\frac{z}{H}}\right] . \tag{7.48}$$

This expression is admittedly a bit awkward-looking, in that one rarely encounters functions that are exponentials of exponentials! Apart from this minor peculiarity, it poses no computational problems.

Absorption

We already noted that, in a nonscattering atmosphere, the total absorption along a path is just equal to one minus the transmittance along that path. Thus, the total absorptance between z and the top of atmosphere is $a = 1 - t(z)$. A much more interesting and important question, however, is *where* that absorption is occurring.

Consider the absorption of solar radiation within the layer bounded by z_1 and z_2, where $z_2 > z_1$. This must be equal to the absorption between z_1 and the top of the atmosphere minus that occurring between z_2 and the top of the atmosphere:

$$a(z1, z2) = [1 - t(z_1)] - [1 - t(z_2)] = t(z_2) - t(z_1) . \tag{7.49}$$

Let us define $\Delta z = z_2 - z_1$ and look at the local *absorption per unit altitude*:

$$W(z) = \lim_{\Delta z \to 0}\left[\frac{a(z, z + \Delta z)}{\Delta z} = \frac{t(z + \Delta z) - t(z)}{\Delta z}\right] , \tag{7.50}$$

which of course reduces to

$$\boxed{W(z) = \frac{dt(z)}{dz} . \tag{7.51}}$$

The above relationship is extremely important, and you should spend some time thinking about its implications before you move on. It states that, for radiation incident at the top of the atmosphere, *the local rate of absorption within the atmosphere equals the local rate of change of transmittance from level z to the top of the atmosphere.*

Let us take things a step further: Noting that $t(z) = e^{-\tau(z)/\mu}$, we have

$$W(z) = \frac{d}{dz}e^{-\frac{\tau(z)}{\mu}} = -\frac{1}{\mu}e^{-\frac{\tau(z)}{\mu}}\frac{d\tau(z)}{dz}. \qquad (7.52)$$

Noting further that $\tau(z) = \int_z^\infty \beta_e(z')dz'$, we have

$$\frac{d\tau(z)}{dz} = -\beta_e(z), \qquad (7.53)$$

thus

$$W(z) = \frac{\beta_e(z)}{\mu}e^{-\frac{\tau(z)}{\mu}} = \frac{\beta_e(z)}{\mu}t(z). \qquad (7.54)$$

That is, $W(z)$ equals the local extinction coefficient at level z times the transmittance from z to the top of the atmosphere.

Note that the above relationships (7.51) and (7.54) do *not* depend on any assumptions about the specific profile of absorption coefficient $\beta_a(z)$; that is, we haven't yet invoked the assumption of exponentially decaying density. In fact, they can be generalized so as to apply to *any* path in *any* nonscattering, non-plane parallel atmosphere:

$$W(s) = \frac{dt(s,s')}{ds} = \beta_e(s)t(s,s'), \qquad (7.55)$$

where s is the distance along the path toward the source of the radiation at $s = s'$ and $t(s)$ is the transmittance between s and s'.

Does this relationship between local absorption and the rate of change of transmittance make physical sense? Consider a perfectly transparent atmosphere. The transmittance $t(z)$ is then constant and equal to one for all z; therefore $dt/dz = 0$, and the local absorption per unit distance is also zero, as you would expect. Now consider the rate of absorption deep within a strongly absorbing atmosphere. Except near the very top of that atmosphere, $t(z) \approx 0$ for all z, so again $dt/dz \approx 0$ and there is no local absorption of radiation incident at the top of the atmosphere. That is to say, there's essentially nothing left *to* absorb, because everything already got absorbed at a higher altitude!

To summarize, it is *by definition* the range of z over which the transmittance drops from near one to near zero (when moving downward through the atmosphere) that most of the incident radiation is absorbed, and it is of course where the change in transmittance is most rapid that the absorption is most rapid.[7]

Let us conclude this discussion by working out the math for our idealized exponential atmosphere. All that is necessary is to substitute our expressions for $\beta_a(z)$ and $t(z)$, from (7.42) and (7.48) respectively, into (7.54), yielding

$$W(z) = \frac{1}{\mu}k_a w_1 \rho_0 e^{-\frac{z}{H}} \exp\left[-\frac{k_a w_1 \rho_0 H}{\mu}e^{-\frac{z}{H}}\right] , \qquad (7.56)$$

which can be written in simpler form by substituting (7.45):

$$W(z) = \frac{\tau^*}{H\mu}e^{-\frac{z}{H}} \exp\left[-\frac{\tau^*}{\mu}e^{-\frac{z}{H}}\right] . \qquad (7.57)$$

The characteristic shape of $W(z)$ is depicted schematically by the dotted line in Fig. 7.10. As explained above, it is nearly zero at high altitudes where the atmospheric density is vanishingly small; it is also zero at low levels, below the maximum depth to which radiation can penetrate. Somewhere in between, of course, it has its maximum value, which is where $t(z)$ is changing most rapidly.

Qualitatively, we expect the *altitude of peak absorption* to depend on the strength of absorption; i.e., on the value of k_e at the wavelength in question. If k_e is small, the atmosphere is relatively transparent, and radiation penetrates to lower altitudes, or even to ground level, before the rate of absorption becomes strong. If k_e is large, then absorption is strongest at high altitudes where the density is still very small; at lower levels no radiation remains to be absorbed.

We can find the altitude of the peak of $W(z)$ using the standard approach: Take the derivative with respect to z, set the result equal to zero, and solve for z:

$$\frac{dW(z)}{dz} = \frac{d}{dz}\frac{\tau^*}{H\mu}e^{-\frac{z}{H}} \exp\left[-\frac{\tau^*}{\mu}e^{-\frac{z}{H}}\right] = 0 , \qquad (7.58)$$

---

[7]The layer of the atmosphere in which solar radiation of a particular wavelength and incidence angle is absorbed — i.e., where $W(z) > 0$ — is sometimes referred to as the *Chapman layer*, after the scientist who first studied it.

$$e^{-\frac{z}{H}} \exp\left[-\frac{\tau^*}{\mu} e^{-\frac{z}{H}}\right] \left[\frac{\tau^*}{\mu} e^{-\frac{z}{H}} - 1\right] = 0 \,. \tag{7.59}$$

The equality is satisfied when

$$\frac{\tau^*}{\mu} e^{-\frac{z}{H}} = 1 \,. \tag{7.60}$$

Using (7.44) and (7.45), we find that the above condition can be rewritten as

$$\boxed{\frac{\tau(z)}{\mu} = 1 \,.} \tag{7.61}$$

In other words, *the peak of the absorption weighting function occurs at the altitude z for which the optical path, measured in the direction of incidence from the top of the atmosphere, equals one.*

Later, we will see that the above absorption weighting function is identical to the *emission weighting function* describing the contribution of various atmospheric levels to emitted radiation observed from space. For now, I will just point out that this is a natural consequence of Kirchhoff's Law.

Problem 7.9: At three different wavelengths λ_1, λ_2, and λ_3, the profile of absorption coefficient due to a certain atmospheric constituent is given by

$$\beta_e(z) = k_n \rho_0 \exp[-z/H] \,, \tag{7.62}$$

where $\rho_0 = 4$ g/m^3 is the density of the constituent at sea level, and $H = 8$ km is the scale height. The wavelength-dependent mass extinction coefficients k_1, k_2, and k_3, respectively, are 0.05, 0.10, and 0.15 m^2 kg^{-1}. Find the altitudes z_n of the corresponding peaks of the absorption weighting functions $W(z)$ for radiation incident at the top of the atmosphere with $\theta = 60°$.

Problem 7.10: When temperature is held nearly constant, the mass absorption coefficient of water vapor in the spectral window between 8 and 13 μm is given approximately by $k_a \approx A\rho_v$, where ρ_v

is the water vapor density. The vertical profile of ρ_v can in turn be modeled as $\rho_v(z) \approx \rho_{v,0} \exp(-z/H_v)$, where $\rho v, 0$ is the vapor density at sea level and H_v is the scale height. (a) Find an expression for the volume absorption coefficient $\beta_a(z)$ due to water vapor. (b) Find an expression for the optical depth $\tau(z)$. (c) If z_{fm} is the altitude below which a fraction f of the total column water vapor mass V_{tot} is found, what is the altitude z_{ft} below which the same fraction of the total optical depth is found? (d) Find an expression for the total optical depth τ^* in terms of H_v and the total column water vapor V. (e) If $H_v = 2$ km and $V = 30$ kg m^{-2} (typical values in the middle latitudes), and if the corresponding zenith transmittance t at a particular wavelength in the spectral window is 95%, determine the value of A.

7.4.4 Optical Thickness and Transmittance of a Cloud Layer

Clouds consist of a very large number of very small water droplets and/or ice crystals suspended in air. In the case of liquid water clouds, typical droplet radii fall between 5 μm and 15 μm, though smaller or larger droplets are also possible (droplets approaching 100 μm are large enough to fall out of the cloud as drizzle and are regarded as precipitation rather than cloud droplets). Typical droplet concentrations range from 10^2 to 10^3 droplets per cubic centimeter.

Many liquid water clouds are thick enough to block virtually all direct sunlight. That is, if a cloud passes between you and the sun, you often cannot make out the sun's disk. Instead, you may see only a diffuse gray illumination contributed by solar radiation that has been scattered numerous times in various directions before emerging from the bottom of the cloud. Of course, much of the radiation that is scattered within the cloud ends up emerging from the top instead of the bottom.

When a photon of sunlight is incident on the top of a cloud layer, it will experience one of four possible fates:

1. It may pass directly through the cloud without being scattered or absorbed even once. The fraction of incident radiation that passes straight through the cloud in this way is called the *direct transmittance* t_{dir}.

2. It may be scattered one or more times and then emerge from the bottom of the cloud layer. The corresponding fraction is called the *diffuse transmittance* t_{diff}.

3. It may be scattered one or more times and then emerge from the top of the cloud layer. The corresponding fraction of the incident flux is called the *reflectance* (or albedo) r, by analogy to a reflecting surface, as discussed in the previous chapter.

4. Whatever is neither transmitted nor reflected by the cloud layer must be absorbed. This fraction is called the in-cloud *absorptance a*.

Obviously, the four terms must sum to one; thus

$$t_{dir} + t_{diff} + r + a = 1 \,. \tag{7.63}$$

Often, it is convenient to lump the diffuse and direct transmittance together, in which case we refer to the *total transmittance* as

$$t = t_{dir} + t_{diff} \,, \tag{7.64}$$

so that

$$t + r + a = 1 \,. \tag{7.65}$$

The above properties of clouds are of profound importance for the atmospheric radiation budget. In particular, the reflectivity r of a cloud layer helps determine how much of the solar radiation incident on the top of the atmosphere gets immediately reflected back to space, forever lost as far as the energy budget of the earth and atmosphere is concerned. The total transmittance t limits the amount of solar radiation available to directly heat the surface. And of course the in-cloud absorptance a defines the fraction that contributes to direct heating of the atmospheric layer in which the cloud resides.

For any given cloud, the values of the above four variables depend on its optical thickness τ^*, the single scatter albedo $\tilde{\omega}$, and details of *how* radiation is scattered by the constituent cloud droplets.

Monodisperse   Polydisperse

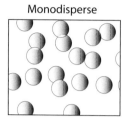 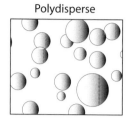

Fig. 7.11: Illustration of the definitions of monodisperse and polydisperse for cloud water droplets.

The three properties t_{diff}, r, and a all include contributions from *multiple scattering* of radiation within the cloud layer. We will not have the tools to address multiple scattering until a later chapter.

We do, however, already have the tools to evaluate the optical thickness τ^* of a cloud layer in terms of the cloud droplet radii r, concentrations N, and extinction efficiencies Q_e. The direct transmittance t_{dir} then follows from (7.33):

$$t_{\text{dir}} = e^{-\tau^*/\mu} \ . \tag{7.66}$$

Monodisperse Cloud

Let us start by considering an ideal plane parallel cloud composed entirely of cloud droplets of identical radius r in a concentration N per unit volume. Such a cloud composed of equal-sized droplets is called *monodisperse* , as contrasted with a more realistic cloud composed of *polydisperse* cloud droplets (Fig. 7.11). From (7.20) and (7.22), we have the volume extinction coefficient

$$\beta_e = N Q_e \pi r^2 \ . \tag{7.67}$$

Usually, it is difficult to directly measure either N or r but somewhat easier to measure or estimate the cloud water density ρ_w, which is the mass of condensed cloud water per unit volume of air. Typical values for ρ_w lie in the range 0.1–1 g/m^3, where the lower values are usually found in stratiform clouds experiencing weak up-lift, whereas values in excess of 1 g/m³ are most often found in the cores of vigorous convective updrafts.

For our monodisperse cloud, the cloud water density is just the number concentration of droplets times the mass of water in each droplet:

$$\rho_w = N \frac{4}{3} \pi r^3 \rho_l , \qquad (7.68)$$

where $\rho_l \approx 1000$ kg/m³ is the density of pure water. Combining with (7.16) and (7.67), we find that the volume extinction coefficient is given by

$$\beta_e = NQ_e \pi r^2 = k_e \rho_w = k_e N \frac{4}{3} \pi r^3 \rho_l , \qquad (7.69)$$

which allows us to solve for the mass extinction coefficient:

$$k_e = \frac{3Q_e}{4\rho_l r} . \qquad (7.70)$$

This result is interesting, but perhaps not surprising. It tells us that the same mass of water broken up into droplets extinguishes more radiation if the droplets are small and numerous than if they are large and relatively few.

Is (7.70) consistent with everyday experience? Consider moderate falling rain and thick fog. At visible wavelengths, $Q_e \approx 2$ for both cases. But for rain, the drop radius r is on the order of 1 mm; for fog it is a hundred times smaller, or about 10 μm. Substituting these values into (7.70) yields $k_e \approx 1.5$ m²/kg for rain and $k_e \approx 150$ m²/kg for fog. Yet both rain and fog can yield liquid water concentrations ρ_w on the order of 0.1 g per cubic meter of air. Thus, the volume extinction coefficient β_e can be on the order of 0.15 km⁻¹ and 15 km⁻¹ for rain and fog. In the first case, the transmittance along a 1 km path is 86%; in the second, it is for all practical purposes zero!

Let's return to the problem of determining the optical thickness of the cloud layer with cloud water density profile $\rho_w(z)$ between cloud base z_{bot} and cloud top z_{top}:

$$\tau^* = \int_{z_{bot}}^{z_{top}} \beta_e(z) \, dz = \int_{z_{bot}}^{z_{top}} k_e \rho_w(z) \, dz . \qquad (7.71)$$

Since we're assuming that k_e is constant in this problem, we can take it out of the integral and simply write

$$\tau^* = k_e L ,\tag{7.72}$$

where the *liquid water path* (vertically integrated mass of cloud water per unit horizontal area) is defined as

$$L \equiv \int_{z_{bot}}^{z_{top}} \rho_w(z)\, dz .\tag{7.73}$$

Combining (7.72) and (7.70) and using $Q_e \approx 2$, we get

$$\tau^* \approx \frac{3L}{2\rho_l r} .\tag{7.74}$$

To summarize, the total optical depth of our plane parallel cloud layer is proportional to the liquid water path L and inversely proportional to radius of the constituent cloud droplets.[8]

Typical values of L range from essentially zero to as much as 0.5 kg m^{-2} or so in heavy stratiform cloud layers. For $r = 10$ μm, this yields an optical thickness of up to 75 or so. In order for even as much as, say, one percent of incident sunlight to be *directly* transmitted, we have a maximum τ^* of

$$\tau^*{}_{1\%} = -\mu \ln(0.01) \approx 4 ,\tag{7.75}$$

which corresponds to a liquid water path L on the order of only 0.03 kg m^{-2}. Such a value might correspond to a cloud layer that is a mere 30 m thick and has a relatively low average cloud water density of only 0.1 g m^{-3}. We therefore conclude that all but the very thinnest clouds are nearly opaque to direct solar radiation. Nevertheless, diffuse transmittance in clouds can be quite significant even in optically thick clouds.

Cloud Condensation Nuclei and Cloud Optical Thickness

Although we have not yet shown this rigorously, common sense tells us that, all other factors being equal, an optically thick cloud

---

[8]We are neglecting any contribution by the air itself to any absorption within the cloud layer. At some wavelengths in the solar band, absorption by water vapor or other constituents cannot be neglected.

will reflect more sunlight than an optically thin cloud. We showed further that the optical thickness is proportional to liquid water path L and inversely proportional to droplet radius r.

The liquid water path L is generally controlled by the cloud-scale dynamics and thermodynamics of the air in which the cloud forms; that is, by temperature and humidity, local ascent rate, mixing, etc. For example, if a saturated parcel of air is lifted moist-adiabatically from one temperature and pressure level to a higher level in the atmosphere, the total mass of condensed water can be predicted very easily using a standard thermodynamic diagram such as a Skew-T/log-P chart.

What is *not* predictable from bulk thermodynamics alone is whether the condensed water will appear in the form of relatively few large droplets or instead as numerous smaller droplets. That characteristic of a cloud is determined by the number of *cloud condensation nuclei* (CCN) that get activated and become cloud droplets when the cloud first forms.

All other factors being equal, clean air masses containing very few CCN will produce few cloud droplets, but those droplets will be relatively large. Continental and/or polluted air masses may contain one or two orders of magnitude more CCN and therefore produce clouds containing correspondingly higher concentrations of much smaller cloud droplets. It can be shown that

$$\tau^* = Q_e \left[\frac{9\pi L^2 H}{16\rho_l^2} N \right]^{\frac{1}{3}}, \tag{7.76}$$

where H is the geometric thickness of the cloud layer. This relationship tells us that, for a cloud layer of fixed depth and total liquid water path, the optical thickness $\tau^* \propto N^{1/3}$.

The above relationship is of more than just academic interest. Climate scientists have come to realize that industrial pollution contributes vast quantities of aerosols to the atmosphere, many of which are capable of serving as CCN. It is now apparent that this pollution may be increasing the average reflectivity of clouds and therefore reducing the fraction of solar radiation which is absorbed by the earth and atmosphere. The expected effect of aerosol pollution is thus a *decrease* in average global temperature over time, in contrast to the increased "greenhouse warming" expected from increased CO_2 concentrations. Some climate change specialists now suspect that the indirect cooling effect of aerosols may have helped mask the expected warming due to CO_2 increases, preventing the observed warming to date from being as large as that predicted by many climate models. Indeed, there are those who believe that the aerosol effect may be beneficial because of its moderating influence on greenhouse warming. That optimistic view may be premature, however, since it glosses over important regional, seasonal, and altitude-dependent differences in the radiative impact of aerosols versus CO_2. A partial cancellation of the *globally averaged* radiative impacts of each pollutant does not necessarily ensure that *regional* climate responses to anthropogenic pollution will be negligible.

Problem 7.11:   Derive (7.76).

Problem 7.12:   A certain cloud layer has geometric thickness $H = 0.1$ km and liquid water path $L = 0.01$ kg m^{-2}. Taking $Q_e \approx 2$ and the solar zenith angle $\theta = 60°$, compute the direct transmittance t_{dir} for (a) $N = 100$ cm^{-3} (characteristic of clean maritime environments), and (b) $N = 1000$ cm^{-3} (characteristic of continental environments).

Polydisperse Cloud[†]

In our above analysis of the effect of droplet concentration and radius on cloud optical thickness, we assumed that all cloud droplets had the same size. This is a reasonable approach when the purpose is just to gain qualitative insight into how the radiative properties of clouds depend on drop size and number. It is insufficient, however, for anything that requires accurate calculations of those properties.

In reality, of course, the droplets found in any given cloud are distributed over a range of sizes. We may describe the *drop size dis-*

tribution in any given case via a function $n(r)$, such that

$$n(r)\, dr = \begin{Bmatrix} \text{number of droplets (per unit volume of} \\ \text{air) whose radii fall in the range } [r, r+dr] \end{Bmatrix} . \quad (7.77)$$

It follows that $n(r)$ has dimensions of "per unit volume per unit interval of r", or $length^{-4}$. Often, the units will be written as $[\mathrm{m}^{-3}\, \mu\mathrm{m}^{-1}]$.

With the above definition of $n(r)$, one may immediately derive several related quantities. For example, the *total* number of droplets of all sizes (per unit volume), is just

$$N = \int_0^\infty n(r)\, dr . \quad (7.78)$$

The total number of droplets whose radius is smaller than some radius r' is

$$N(r < r') = \int_0^{r'} n(r)\, dr . \quad (7.79)$$

The total surface area (per unit volume of air) contributed by droplets of all sizes is obtained by first multiplying $n(r)$ by the expression for the surface area of a single droplet of radius r and then integrating over all sizes:

$$A_{\mathrm{sfc}} = \int_0^\infty n(r)\left[4\pi r^2\right] dr . \quad (7.80)$$

An analogous approach can be used to obtain those radiative and cloud physical quantities that we already worked with in the case of a monodisperse cloud. For example, the local cloud water density is given by

$$\rho_w = \int_0^\infty n(r)\left[\rho_l \frac{4\pi}{3} r^3\right] dr . \quad (7.81)$$

Finally, the local volume extinction coefficient is obtained as

$$\beta_e = \int_0^\infty n(r)\left[Q_e(r)\pi r^2\right] dr , \quad (7.82)$$

where the expression in brackets represents the extinction cross-section of a single droplet of radius r. The mass extinction coefficient can then be written as

$$k_e \equiv \frac{\beta_e}{\rho_w} = \frac{\int_0^\infty n(r)\left[Q_e(r)\pi r^2\right] dr}{\int_0^\infty n(r)\left[\rho_l \frac{4\pi}{3} r^3\right] dr} . \quad (7.83)$$

If we again take $Q_e \approx 2$ for all r (valid when the droplets are large compared with the wavelength of the radiation), we find that the above simplifies to

$$k_e \approx \frac{3}{2\rho_l r_{\text{eff}}} , \tag{7.84}$$

where the *effective drop size* r_{eff} is *defined* as

$$r_{\text{eff}} \equiv \frac{\int_0^\infty n(r)r^3 \, dr}{\int_0^\infty n(r)r^2 \, dr} . \tag{7.85}$$

The total optical depth of the cloud layer is then approximately

$$\tau^* \approx \frac{3L}{2\rho_l r_{\text{eff}}} , \tag{7.86}$$

where L is the vertically integrated liquid water path defined by (7.73) and (7.81). We see that this expression is identical to our earlier expression (7.74) derived for a monodisperse cloud, except that we have replaced the single radius r with the effective radius r_{eff} defined by (7.85). The latter can therefore be thought of as the cloud droplet radius a monodisperse cloud would have to have in order to have the same optical thickness τ^* as a given polydisperse cloud.

Let me emphasize that the utility of the above definition of effective radius r_{eff} is compromised slightly by the assumption that Q_e is not a strong function of r. This will not always be the case, especially when the the droplets contributing most of the total cloud water mass are not much larger than the wavelength (that is, when it is not true that $x \gg 1$). Also, the optical thickness τ^* is only one of several radiative parameters that ultimately determine the overall reflectivity and transmittance of a cloud layer. Thus, it is not always safe to assume radiative equivalence between a polydisperse cloud with effective radius r_{eff} and a monodisperse cloud with $r = r_{\text{eff}}$.

Nevertheless, it is common to use satellite observations of cloud-top reflectivity at two or more wavelengths to try to infer r_{eff} for the cloud in question, and considerable recent research has been devoted to demonstrating a link between r_{eff} and anthropogenic pollution, for the reasons discussed in the previous subsection.

Problem 7.13: The gamma distribution is often used to describe the size distribution of cloud droplets. The distribution is defined by

$$n(r) = ar^\alpha \exp(-br) \quad .$$

It is called a gamma distribution because

$$\int_0^\infty r^k \exp(-br)\, dr = \frac{\Gamma(k+1)}{b^{k+1}} \quad ,$$

where $\Gamma(x)$ is the Euler gamma function. $\Gamma(x)$ is essentially a generalization of the well-known factorial $n!$ to a continuous function, since $\Gamma(x+1) = x!$ for positive integer values of x. It follows that $\Gamma(x+1)/\Gamma(x) = x$, which will prove useful in a couple of the parts below.

Express the following quantities in terms of the parameters a, b, and α:

a) the total number of droplets per unit volume N,

b) the mean droplet radius $\bar{r}$,

c) the droplet surface area per unit volume A_{sfc},

d) the cloud water density ρ_w,

e) the extinction coefficient β_e in the solar band, assuming that $Q_e \approx 2$,

f) the effective radius r_{eff}.

g) Determine the parameters a and b that yield the the following properties of the cloud droplet distribution: $N = 100$ cm^{-3}, $r_{\text{eff}} = 10$ μm, $\alpha = 3$. Be careful about unit consistency! (Numerical values of a and b are more convenient to work with if expressed in units of cm$^{-3}\mu$m^{-4} and μm^{-1}, respectively. This is equivalent to choosing cm^{-3} as the preferred unit for a volume of air and μm as the preferred unit of radius.)

h) Graph $n(r)$, using units of μm for the r and cm$^{-3}\mu$m^{-1} for $n(r)$.

i) Using the values you derived for a and b, compute the values of each of the properties you found in parts (b)–(e). In each case, convert to reasonably standard, or at least convenient, units.

CHAPTER 8

In the previous chapter, we began our examination of how monochromatic radiation interacts with the atmosphere, focusing initially on the *extinction* (or, conversely, *transmission*) of radiation by atmospheric gases and clouds. If the depletion by the atmosphere of radiation from an external source, such as the sun, were the only process we had to worry about, life would be simple indeed. But we already know from our previous discussion of simple radiative balance models that the atmosphere both absorbs and emits radiation. And we already hinted that Kirchhoff's Law implies a correspondence between absorption and emission that is just as valid for the atmosphere as it is for a solid surface.

We are now ready to expand our understanding of radiative transfer to include both extinction and thermal emission. Eventually, we will also have to come to grips with the problem of scattering as another potential source of radiation along a particular line of sight. But that is a subject for a later chapter. In this chapter, we will restrict our attention to problems in which scattering can be safely ignored. This is not an unreasonable approach for the majority of real-world problems involving the thermal IR, far IR, or microwave bands.

8.1 Schwarzschild's Equation

Consider the passage of radiation of wavelength λ through a layer of air with infinitesimal thickness ds, measured along the direction of propagation. If the radiant intensity is initially I, then the reduction in I due to absorption is

$$dI_{\text{abs}} = -\beta_a I \, ds \, , \tag{8.1}$$

where we are using (7.4) applied to the case that the single scatter albedo $\tilde{\omega} = 0$ and therefore $\beta_e = \beta_a$.

The quantity $\beta_a ds$ can be thought of as the absorptivity a of the thin slice of the medium, since it describes the fraction of the incident radiation that is lost to absorption. But Kirchhoff's Law tells us that the absorptivity of any quantity of matter in local thermodynamic equilibrium (LTE) is equal to the emissivity of the same matter. Therefore, we can expect the thin layer of air to *emit* radiation in the amount

$$dI_{\text{emit}} = \beta_a B \, ds \, , \tag{8.2}$$

where we are using the symbol B here as a convenient short-hand[1] for the Planck function $B_\lambda(T)$. The *net* change in radiant intensity is therefore

$$dI = dI_{\text{abs}} + dI_{\text{emit}} = \beta_a (B - I) \, ds \, , \tag{8.3}$$

or

$$\boxed{\frac{dI}{ds} = \beta_a (B - I) \, .} \tag{8.4}$$

This equation is known as *Schwarzschild's Equation* and is the most fundamental description of radiative transfer in a nonscattering medium. Schwarzschild's Equation tells us that the radiance along a particular line of sight either increases or decreases with distance traveled, depending on whether $I(s)$ is less than or greater than $B[T(s)]$, where $T(s)$ is the temperature at point s.

Let us now consider the intensity of radiation arriving at a particular sensor looking backward along the direction of propagation.

---

[1]Note that we have also dropped the subscript λ from I and other quantities, as all relationships discussed in this chapter should be understood as applying to radiative transfer at a single wavelength.

Much as we did previously for a plane parallel atmosphere, we can introduce

$$\tau(s) = \int_s^S \beta_a(s') \, ds' \tag{8.5}$$

as the *optical path* between an arbitrary point s and the sensor positioned at S. By this definition, $\tau(S) = 0$. Differentiating yields

$$d\tau = -\beta_a \, ds \, , \tag{8.6}$$

which, when substituted into Schwarzschild's Equation, gives

$$\frac{dI}{d\tau} = I - B \, . \tag{8.7}$$

We can integrate this equation by multiplying both sides by the integrating factor $e^{-\tau}$ and noting that

$$\frac{d}{d\tau}[Ie^{-\tau}] = e^{-\tau}\frac{dI}{d\tau} - Ie^{-\tau} \, , \tag{8.8}$$

so that

$$e^{-\tau}\frac{dI}{d\tau} - Ie^{-\tau} = -Be^{-\tau} \tag{8.9}$$

becomes

$$\frac{d}{d\tau}[Ie^{-\tau}] = -Be^{-\tau} \, . \tag{8.10}$$

We then integrate with respect to τ between the sensor at $\tau = 0$ and some arbitrary point τ':

$$\int_0^{\tau'} \frac{d}{d\tau}[Ie^{-\tau}] \, d\tau = -\int_0^{\tau'} Be^{-\tau} \, d\tau \, , \tag{8.11}$$

which simplifies to

$$[I(\tau')e^{-\tau'}] - I(0) = -\int_0^{\tau'} Be^{-\tau} \, d\tau \tag{8.12}$$

or

$$I(0) = I(\tau')e^{-\tau'} + \int_0^{\tau'} Be^{-\tau} \, d\tau \, . \tag{8.13}$$

Let's stop a moment and carefully study this equation, because it is remarkably far-reaching in its implications for radiative transfer. On the left hand side is $I(0)$ which is the radiant intensity observed by the sensor stationed at $\tau = 0$. On the right hand side are two terms:

1. The intensity I at position $\tau = \tau'$, multiplied by the transmittance $t(\tau') = e^{-\tau'}$ between the sensor and τ'. This term therefore represents the attenuated contribution of any radiation source on the far side of the path. For example, for a downward-viewing satellite sensor, $I(\tau')$ could represent emission from the earth's surface, in which case $e^{-\tau'}$ is the total atmospheric transmittance along the line-of-sight.

2. The integrated thermal emission contributions $B d\tau$ from each point τ along the line of sight between the sensor and τ'. Again, these contributions are attenuated by the respective path transmittances between the sensor and τ', hence the appearance of $t(\tau) = e^{-\tau}$ inside the integral.

Although we went through some minor mathematical gymnastics to get to this point, our analysis of the resulting equation is in fact consistent with a common-sense understanding of how radiation "ought" to work. Among other things, (8.13) tells us that $I(0)$ is not influenced by emission from points for which the intervening atmosphere is opaque ($t \approx 0$). It also tells us that, in order to have emission from a particular point along the path, β_a must be nonzero at that point, since otherwise $d\tau$, and therefore $B d\tau$, is zero.

Key Point: *Almost all common radiative transfer problems involving emission and absorption in the atmosphere (without scattering) can be understood in terms of (8.13)!*[2]

Let us try to gain more insight into (8.13) by rewriting it in a couple of different forms. Let's start by using the fact that $t = e^{-\tau}$, so that

$$dt = -e^{-\tau}\, d\tau . \tag{8.14}$$

---

[2]The only exceptions are those in which local thermodynamic equilibrium (LTE) doesn't apply, as discussed in Section 6.2.3.

With these substitutions, we now have

$$I(0) = I(\tau')t(\tau') + \int_{t(\tau')}^{1} B \, dt \, . \qquad (8.15)$$

With this form, we can see that equal increments of changing transmittance along the line of sight carry equal weight in determining the total radiance seen at $\tau = 0$.

Finally, let's consider the relative contribution of emission as a function of geometric distance s along the path. Noting that

$$dt = \frac{dt}{ds} ds \, , \qquad (8.16)$$

we have

$$I(S) = I(s_0)t(s_0) + \int_{s_0}^{S} B(s)\frac{dt(s)}{ds} ds \, , \qquad (8.17)$$

where s_0 is the geometric point that coincides with our chosen optical limit of integration τ'. Comparing this form with (7.55), it suddenly dawns on us that the integral on the right hand side can be written

$$\int_{s_0}^{S} B(s)\frac{dt(s)}{ds} ds = \int_{s_0}^{S} B(s)W(s) ds \, , \qquad (8.18)$$

where the *weighting function* $W(s)$ for thermal emission is *exactly the same as the weighting function for absorption of radiation traveling in the opposite direction!*

A Digression on the Emission Weighting Function[†]

Let us take a minute to show how general the above result really is. Although our focus in this chapter is on the atmosphere, the validity of $W(s) = dt(s)/ds$ as a measure of where emitted radiation is coming from is not restricted to the atmosphere. Consider, for example, the surface of an opaque, perfectly absorbing medium positioned at s', such that the transmittance between an external point and arbitrary s is a step function; i.e.,

$$t(s) = \begin{cases} 1 & s > s' \\ 0 & s < s' \end{cases} \qquad (8.19)$$

For this case $dt(s)/ds \equiv W(s) = 0$ for any $s \neq s'$ and infinite for $s = s'$. In fact, we can write

$$W(s) = \delta(s - s') , \qquad (8.20)$$

where $\delta(x)$ is the Dirac δ-function. If you have not heard of this function before, then let me quickly summarize its key properties:

$$\delta(x) = \begin{cases} \infty & x = 0 \\ 0 & x \neq 0 \end{cases} \qquad (8.21)$$

In other words, $\delta(x)$ is a function that is zero everywhere except at $x = 0$, where it is an infinitely tall, infinitely narrow spike. Despite these unusual properties, the area under the curve is defined to be finite and equal to one. That is,

$$\int_{-\infty}^{x} \delta(x - x') \, dx' = \begin{cases} 0 & x < x' \\ 1 & x > x' \end{cases} \qquad (8.22)$$

This is of course consistent with (8.19) and (8.20).

Now if you think about it a bit, you will realize that the product of $\delta(x - x')$ with $f(x')$ is just the same δ-function, but multiplied by the value of $f(x = x')$. Thus, (8.22) implies

$$\int_{x_1}^{x_2} \delta(x - x')f(x') \, dx' = \begin{cases} f(x) & x_1 < x < x_2 \\ 0 & \text{otherwise} \end{cases} \qquad (8.23)$$

Let us now look at what this implies for (8.18), given (8.20):

$$I(S) = I(s_0)t(s_0) + \int_{s_0}^{S} B(s)\delta(s - s')ds , \qquad (8.24)$$

where we will take s_0 to be an arbitrary point below our surface at s', so that $s_0 < s' < S$. Since the medium in question is opaque by assumption, the transmittance $t(s_0) = 0$, and we're left with

$$I(S) = \int_{s_0}^{S} B(s)\delta(s - s')ds , \qquad (8.25)$$

or, invoking (8.23),

$$I(S) = B(s') . \qquad (8.26)$$

We have just confirmed, in an admittedly roundabout way, what we already knew: The emitted intensity from a opaque blackbody is just the Planck function B evaluated at the surface of the black-body. Why did we go to all this trouble? My purpose was simply to demonstrate that (8.17) is quite general (for a nonscattering and nonreflecting medium) and is valid even when the transmittance t is a discontinuous function of distance along a path.

8.2   Radiative Transfer in a Plane Parallel Atmosphere

Let us now adapt (8.17) to a plane-parallel atmosphere. We will start by considering the case that a sensor is located at the surface $(z = 0)$, viewing downward emitted radiation from the atmosphere. The appropriate form of the radiative transfer equation is then

$$I^{\downarrow}(0) = I^{\downarrow}(\infty)t^* + \int_0^{\infty} B(z)W^{\downarrow}(z)dz \,, \tag{8.27}$$

where $z = \infty$ represents an arbitrary point beyond the top of the atmosphere, and $t^* \equiv \exp(-\tau^*/\mu)$ is the transmittance from the surface to the top of the atmosphere. Recall that we are using $B(z)$ here as a shorthand for $B_{\lambda}[T(z)]$, where $T(z)$ is the atmospheric temperature profile. Because the transmittance $t(0,z)$ between the surface and altitude z decreases with increasing z, our weighting function $W^{\downarrow}(z)$ in this case is given by

$$W^{\downarrow}(z) = -\frac{dt(0,z)}{dz} = \frac{\beta_a(z)}{\mu}t(0,z) \,. \tag{8.28}$$

Unless the sensor is pointing at an extraterrestrial source of radiation, such as the sun, $I^{\downarrow}(\infty) = 0$. In this case, the first term on the right vanishes, and the observed downward intensity is strictly a function of the atmospheric temperature and absorption profiles.

Now let's consider a sensor above the top of the atmosphere looking down toward the surface. We then have

$$I^\uparrow(\infty) = I^\uparrow(0)t^* + \int_0^\infty B(z)W^\uparrow(z)dz \,, \tag{8.29}$$

where

$$W^\uparrow(z) = \frac{dt(z,\infty)}{dz} = \frac{\beta_a(z)}{\mu}t(z,\infty) \,. \tag{8.30}$$

Note the strong similarity between (8.27) and (8.29). Both state that the radiant intensity emerging from the bottom or top of the atmosphere is the sum of two contributions: 1) the transmitted radiation entering the atmosphere from the opposite side, and 2) a weighted sum of the contributions of emission from each level z within the atmosphere.

8.2.1 The Emissivity of the Atmosphere

Consider the case that $T(z) = T_a$, where T_a is the temperature of an isothermal atmosphere. Then $B[T(z)] = B(T_a) = constant$, so that (8.27), together with (8.28), can be written

$$I^\downarrow(0) = I^\downarrow(\infty)t^* + B(T_a) \int_0^\infty -\frac{dt(0,z)}{dz} \, dz \,. \tag{8.31}$$

The integral reduces to $t(0,0) - t^* = 1 - t^*$, yielding

$$I^\downarrow(0) = I^\downarrow(\infty)t^* + B(T_a)[1 - t^*] \,. \tag{8.32}$$

By the same token, (8.29)and (8.30) can be manipulated to yield

$$I^\uparrow(\infty) = I^\uparrow(0)t^* + B(T_a)[1 - t^*] \,. \tag{8.33}$$

Recall that the absorptivity of a nonscattering layer is just one minus the transmittance, and that Kirchhoff's Law states that absorptivity equals emissivity. The interpretation of the above two equations is thus remarkably simple: *The total radiant intensity is just the sum of (a)the transmitted intensity of any source on the far side plus (b) Planck's function times the emissivity of the entire atmosphere.*

In reality, of course, the atmosphere is never isothermal. Nevertheless, it is sometimes convenient to use equations similar in form to (8.32) and (8.33) to describe the atmospheric contribution to the observed radiant intensity:

$$I^{\downarrow}(0) = I^{\downarrow}(\infty)t^* + \overline{B}^{\downarrow}[1 - t^*] , \qquad (8.34)$$

$$I^{\uparrow}(\infty) = I^{\uparrow}(0)t^* + \overline{B}^{\uparrow}[1 - t^*] , \qquad (8.35)$$

where

$$\overline{B}^{\downarrow} = \frac{1}{1 - t^*} \int_0^\infty B(z)W^{\downarrow}(z) \, dz , \qquad (8.36)$$

$$\overline{B}^{\uparrow} = \frac{1}{1 - t^*} \int_0^\infty B(z)W^{\uparrow}(z) \, dz , \qquad (8.37)$$

give the *weighted average* Planck function values for the entire atmosphere.

Problem 8.1: Show that when $1 - t^* \ll 1$, $W^{\downarrow}(z) \approx W^{\uparrow}(z) \approx \beta_a(z)/\mu$, so that $\overline{B}^{\downarrow} \approx \overline{B}^{\uparrow}$.

8.2.2 Monochromatic Flux [†]

Sometimes it is not the intensity but rather the flux that we care about. For example, if we ignore extraterrestrial sources (appropriate for the LW band), we can compute the downwelling monochromatic flux $F^{\downarrow}$ at the surface simply by integrating $I^{\downarrow} \cos \theta$ over one hemisphere of solid angle, according to (2.59):

$$F^{\downarrow} = -\int_0^{2\pi}\int_{\pi/2}^{\pi} I^{\downarrow}(\theta, \phi) \cos \theta \sin \theta \, d\theta d\phi.$$

There are two simplifications we can make before we even take the obvious step of substituting (8.27). First, in our plane parallel atmosphere, nothing depends on ϕ; therefore we can immediately deal with the integration over azimuth, leaving

$$F^\downarrow = -2\pi \int_{\pi/2}^{\pi} I^\downarrow(\theta) \cos\theta \sin\theta \, d\theta .$$ (8.38)

Second, we can substitute $\mu = |\cos\theta|$ as our variable for describing zenith angle. For downwelling radiation, $\cos\theta < 0$, so in this instance $\mu = -\cos\theta$ and $d\mu = \sin\theta d\theta$; using (8.27), we are now able to write

$$F^\downarrow(0) = 2\pi \int_0^1 \left[\int_0^\infty B(z) W^\downarrow(z,\mu) \, dz \right] \mu d\mu .$$ (8.39)

Only $W^\downarrow$ depends on μ. Therefore, if we wish, we can reverse the order of integration and write

$$F^\downarrow(0) = \int_0^\infty \pi B(z) W_F^\downarrow(z) \, dz ,$$ (8.40)

where

$$W_F^\downarrow(z) \equiv 2 \int_0^1 W^\downarrow(z,\mu) \mu \, d\mu = -2 \int_0^1 \frac{\partial t(0,z;\mu)}{\partial z} \mu \, d\mu$$ (8.41)

may be thought of as a *flux weighting function*. You should recognize the term $\pi B(z)$ appearing in (8.40) as the monochromatic flux you would expect from an opaque blackbody having the temperature found at altitude z. With a little more rearrangement, we can write

$$W_F^\downarrow(z) = -\frac{\partial}{\partial z}\left[2 \int_0^1 t(0,z;\mu)\mu \, d\mu \right] = -\frac{\partial t_F(0,z)}{\partial z} ,$$ (8.42)

where the monochromatic *flux transmittance* t_F between levels z_1 and z_2 is defined as

$$t_F(z_1,z_2) \equiv 2 \int_0^1 t(z_1,z_2;\mu)\mu \, d\mu = 2 \int_0^1 e^{-\frac{\tau(z_1,z_2)}{\mu}} \mu \, d\mu .$$ (8.43)

Problem 8.2: Find expressions analogous to (8.40)–(8.42) for both the downwelling and upwelling flux at an arbitrary altitude z in the atmosphere.

Unfortunately, there is no simple closed-form solution to the integral in (8.43), though it is easily solved numerically. However, it turns out that the above expression for t_F behaves very much like the simple "beam" transmittance $t = \exp(-\tau/\mu)$ — that is, it decreases quasi-exponentially from one to zero as τ goes from zero to infinity. Therefore, in order to deal with the integral, it is common to use the approximation

$$ t_F = 2 \int_0^1 e^{-\frac{\tau}{\mu}} \mu \, d\mu \quad \approx \quad e^{-\tau/\bar{\mu}}, \qquad (8.44) $$

where $\bar{\mu}$ describes an *effective* zenith angle such that the corresponding beam transmittance is approximately equal to the flux transmittance between two levels.

Problem 8.3:
  (a) Show that, for any specified value of τ in (8.44), there is always a value of $\bar{\mu}$ between zero and one that makes the relationship exact.
  (b) Find an expression for $\bar{\mu}$ that is valid for the case that $\tau \ll 1$.

Although the "perfect" value of $\bar{\mu}$ is a function of τ, numerical experiments reveal that you can often get away with choosing a single constant value that yields a reasonable *overall* fit between the approximate expression

$$ W_F^\downarrow(z) \approx -\frac{\partial t(0, z; \bar{\mu})}{\partial z}, \qquad (8.45) $$

and the exact expression (8.42). The most commonly used value is $\bar{\mu} = 1/r$, where $r = 5/3$ is the so-called *diffusivity factor* that arises in certain theoretical analyses of the flux transmittance.

Problem 8.4:   If you have access to software that can numerically evaluate integrals, then graph $t_F(\tau)$ for $0 < \tau < 2$. Compare your accurate results with those obtained using the above value for $\bar{\mu}$.

8.2.3   Surface Contributions to Upward Intensity

Equation (8.29) described the intensity of monochromatic radiation as seen looking downward from the top of the atmosphere. One of the terms appearing in this equation is the upward radiant intensity at the surface $I^\uparrow(0)$. This is the only term whose value cannot be directly computed from knowledge of $\beta_a(z)$ and $T(z)$ alone (for given wavelength λ and viewing direction μ). Therefore, in order to have a complete, self-contained expression for $I^\uparrow(\infty)$, it is necessary to find an explicit expression for $I^\uparrow(0)$.

The expression we supply for $I^\uparrow(0)$ depends on what we assume about the nature of the surface. But regardless of those assumptions, there are two contributions that must be considered: 1) emission by the surface itself, and 2) upward reflection of atmospheric radiation incident on the surface.

Specular Lower Boundary

Let us first consider the simplest possible case: that of a specular surface with emissivity ε. In this case, the reflectivity $r = 1 - \varepsilon$, and we have

$$I^\uparrow(0) = \varepsilon B(T_s) + (1 - \varepsilon)I^\downarrow(0) , \tag{8.46}$$

where T_s is the temperature of the surface (not necessarily the same as the surface *air* temperature!), and $I^\downarrow$ is evaluated for the same μ as $I^\uparrow$. Now recall that we have already derived an expression for $I^\downarrow(0)$, namely (8.27). Combining the latter with (8.29) and (8.46) yields:

$$I^\uparrow(\infty) = \left[\varepsilon B(T_s) + (1 - \varepsilon)\int_0^\infty B(z)W^\downarrow(z)\,dz\right]t^* \tag{8.47}$$
$$+ \int_0^\infty B(z)W^\uparrow(z)\,dz ,$$

where we have assumed that there is no extraterrestrial source of downward radiation in the direction of interest (i.e., we're not looking at the sun's reflection). Given the appropriate weighting functions $W^\uparrow$ and $W^\downarrow$, we have a self-contained expression for the radiant intensity that would be observed by a downward-viewing satellite sensor.

If we wish, we can use the notation developed in the previous subsection to hide the integrals:

$$I^\uparrow(\infty) = \left[\varepsilon B(T_s) + (1 - \varepsilon)\overline{B}^\downarrow[1 - t^*]\right] t^* + \overline{B}^\uparrow[1 - t^*] . \tag{8.48}$$

There are three limiting cases of the above that help persuade us that our analysis makes sense. The first is that of a perfectly transparent atmosphere ($t^* = 1$), in which case our equation reduces to the expected dependence on surface emission alone:

$$I^\uparrow(\infty) = \varepsilon B(T_s) . \tag{8.49}$$

The second is that of a perfectly opaque atmosphere ($t^* = 0$), in which case surface emission and reflection are both irrelevant, and we have

$$I^\uparrow(\infty) = \overline{B}^\uparrow = \int_0^\infty B(z)W^\uparrow(z) \, dz . \tag{8.50}$$

The third occurs when the surface is nonreflecting; i.e., $\varepsilon = 1$, in which case we have

$$I^\uparrow(\infty) = B(T_s)t^* + \overline{B}^\uparrow[1 - t^*] . \tag{8.51}$$

It would be tempting to interpret the last of these as showing a linear relationship between $I^\uparrow$ and atmospheric transmittance t^*, but remember that $\overline{B}^\uparrow$ also depends on the atmospheric opacity. In general, *as the atmosphere becomes more opaque,* $\overline{B}^\uparrow$ *represents emission from higher (and therefore usually colder) levels of the atmosphere.*

Lambertian Lower Boundary [|]

As discussed in Chapter 5, the "opposite" of specular reflection is a Lambertian reflection, for which radiation incident on the surface from any direction is reflected equally in all directions. When the surface is Lambertian, the upward directed radiance at the surface $I^\uparrow(0)$ includes contributions due to the reflection of downwelling radiation from all possible directions. Combining (8.29) with (5.12), (5.8), and (8.40), we get

$$I^\uparrow(\infty, \mu) = \left[\varepsilon B(T_s) + (1 - \varepsilon) \int_0^\infty B(z) W_F^\downarrow(z) \, dz \right] t^*$$

$$+ \int_0^\infty B(z) W^\uparrow(z, \mu) \, dz \, , \tag{8.52}$$

where we have made the dependence of $W^\uparrow$ and $W^\downarrow$ on μ explicit.

Problem 8.5:   Derive (8.52).

Problem 8.6:   Equation (8.52) assumes there is no extraterrestrial source of radiation. Generalize it to include a columnated source (e.g., the sun) of monochromatic flux S (measured normal to the beam). The cosine of the zenith angle of the source is μ_0.

Problem 8.7:   Equations (8.27)–(8.30) were derived for radiant intensities observed at the bottom and top of the atmosphere, respectively. Generalize these to describe the downward and upward intensities $I^\downarrow(z)$ and $I^\uparrow(z)$ at *any* arbitrary level z in the atmosphere. Include explicit expressions for the new weighting functions $W^\downarrow(z)$ and $W^\uparrow(z)$ in terms of $\beta_a(z)$, etc.

8.3   Applications to Meteorology, Climatology, and Remote Sensing

This chapter introduced the relationships that describe the transfer of monochromatic radiation in an atmosphere that doesn't *scatter* appreciably but does *absorb* and *emit* radiation. When do these conditions apply?

As a general rule of thumb (see Chapter 12 for details), the longer the wavelength, the larger a particle has to be before it is capable of scattering appreciably. You can definitely neglect scattering by air molecules for wavelengths falling anywhere in the infrared or microwave bands. Cloud droplets and cloud ice particles continue to scatter appreciably throughout most of the near IR band, but in the thermal and far IR bands, water clouds (and to a lesser extent ice clouds) tend to look a lot like blackbodies. By the time you get to the microwave band, about the only particles for which scattering can't be neglected are precipitation particles — i.e., raindrops, snowflakes, hailstones, etc.

In short, you're *usually* safe using the relationships derived in this chapter throughout the thermal IR and microwave bands (excepting precipitation), while you're almost *never* safe using them in the solar (shortwave) part of the spectrum.

As you already know, the thermal IR band plays an extremely important role in the exchange of energy within the atmosphere, and between the atmosphere, the surface, and outer space. In principle, one might take the relationships we derived for monochromatic intensities and simply integrate them over both wavelength and solid angle in order to obtain broadband radiative fluxes at any level in the atmosphere. This is easier said than done, however, owing to the extreme complexity of the dependence of $\beta_a(z)$ on wavelength, as we shall see in Chapter 9. It is necessary to develop special methods for efficiently computing longwave (broadband) flux, and flux divergence, in the atmosphere. Some of these methods will be outlined in Chapter 10.

The relationships developed earlier in this chapter are therefore most directly useful in the context of infrared and microwave remote sensing. Most satellite sensors operating in these bands observe intensities rather than fluxes of radiation, and most do so for very narrow ranges of wavelength, so that in many cases the observed intensities can be thought of as quasi-monochromatic.

In the following, we will take a look at real-world atmospheric emission spectra and also outline the principles behind temperature and humidity profile retrieval. Since all of these topics are closely

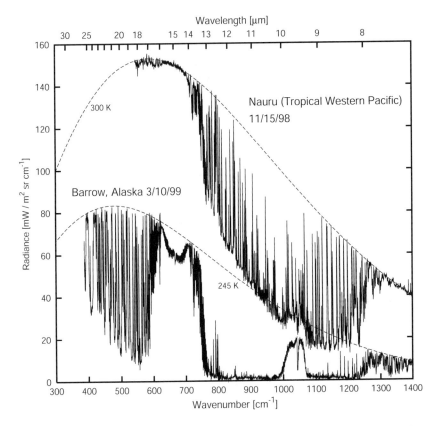

Fig. 8.1: Two examples of measured atmospheric emission spectra as seen from ground level looking up. Planck function curves corresponding to the approximate surface temperature in each case are superimposed (dashed lines). *(Data courtesy of Robert Knuteson, Space Science and Engineering Center, University of Wisconsin-Madison.)*

tied to the absorption spectra of various atmospheric constituents, you might find it helpful to go back and review the major absorption bands depicted in Fig. 7.6.

8.3.1   The Spectrum of Atmospheric Emission

A *spectrometer* is a device that measures radiant intensity as a function of wavelength. Infrared spectrometers have been deployed on satellites, which view the atmosphere looking down from above, and at fixed and mobile research stations on the ground, where they can measure the atmospheric emission spectrum reaching the surface. In addition, spectrometers are occasionally flown on research aircraft. The latter may view downward, upward, or both.

For an upward-viewing instrument at ground level, the relevant form of the radiative transfer equation is given most generally by (8.27), but here we will assume that there are no extraterrestrial sources of radiation:

$$I^{\downarrow}(0) = \int_0^{\infty} B(z)W^{\downarrow}(z)dz .$$ (8.53)

For a satellite sensor viewing downward, we have

$$I^{\uparrow}(\infty) = B(T_S)t^* + \int_0^{\infty} B(z)W^{\uparrow}(z)dz ,$$ (8.54)

where we are assuming that the surface is nonreflective and has temperature T_S, so that $I^{\uparrow}(0) = B(T_S)$.

For the sake of the discussion to follow, we needn't worry about the detailed shape of the weighting functions $W^{\uparrow}(z)$ and $W^{\downarrow}(z)$. The important thing to remember is that when the atmosphere is very opaque, the measured radiation will be due principally to emission from the nearest levels of the atmosphere; when it is less opaque, the relevant weighting function will include emission from more remote levels. Finally, when the atmosphere is *very* transparent, the instrument will "see through" the atmosphere, measuring primarily the radiance contribution (if any) from the far side — e.g., the surface for a downward-looking instrument or "cold space" for an upward-looking one.

Of course, no matter what the source of the measured radiance, we can always interpret that radiance as a brightness temperature T_B, according to (6.13). If the atmosphere happens to be opaque at a particular wavelength, then the brightness temperature in turn gives you a reasonable estimate of the physical temperature at the level where the weighting function peaks.

Figure 8.1 shows a pair of relatively high-resolution IR spectra measured at ground level under two different sets of conditions. One was taken at a location in the tropical western Pacific, where atmospheric temperatures are warm and humidity is high. The other was taken at an arctic location in late winter, where temperatures are very cold and the atmosphere contains only small amounts of water vapor. Both were taken under cloud-free skies.

As complicated as these spectra appear to the untrained eye, the interpretation is really rather simple. Let's take it one step at a time.

- The two dashed curves depict the Planck function at temperatures representative of the *warmest* atmospheric emission seen by the instrument at each location. At the tropical site, this is 300 K; at the arctic site, it's 245 K. Note that these curves serve as an approximate *upper bound* to the radiance measured in any wavelength band.

- In the tropical case, there are two spectral regions for which the measured radiance is very close to the reference curve at 300 K. One is associated with $\lambda > 14 \ \mu$m ($\tilde{\nu} < 730 \ \text{cm}^{-1}$); the other with $\lambda < 8 \ \mu$m ($\tilde{\nu} > 1270 \ \text{cm}^{-1}$). In both of these bands, we can infer that the atmosphere must be quite opaque, because virtually all of the observed radiation is evidently being emitted at the warmest, and therefore lowest, levels of the atmosphere. Referring to Fig. 7.6 in section 7.4.1, we find that these features are consistent with (a) strong absorption by CO_2 in the vicinity of 15 μm, (b) strong absorption by water vapor at wavelengths longer than 15 μm, and (c) strong absorption by water vapor between 5 and 8 μm.

- The two water vapor absorption bands mentioned above are also evident in the arctic emission spectrum (for which the measurements extend to a somewhat longer maximum wavelength of 25 μm). However, because the atmosphere is so dry in this case, these bands are not as uniformly opaque and therefore the measured radiance is quite variable. In fact, between 17 and 25 μm, the general impression is of a large number of strong water vapor lines separated by what might be termed "microwindows." The most transparent of the latter is found near 18 μm (560 cm^{-1}).

- Between 8 and 13 μm in the tropical spectrum, observed brightness temperatures are considerably colder than the surface, and in some cases as cold as 240 K. This broad region may be regarded as a "dirty window" — the atmosphere overall is fairly transparent, but there are a large number of individual absorption lines due to water vapor.

- In the arctic spectrum, the above window "opens up" substantially, because there is far less water vapor in the atmospheric column to absorb and emit radiation. Therefore, observed radiances between 8 and 13 μm are generally quite low indeed — the instrument effectively has an unobstructed view of cold space.

- A clear exception to the above statement is found between 9 and 10 μm. Referring again to Fig. 7.6, we infer that the culprit this time is the ozone absorption band centered at 9.6 μm. This band, while not totally opaque, emits sufficiently strongly to raise the brightness temperature to around 230 K, much warmer than the surrounding window region. The "cold" spike at the center of the ozone band corresponds to an isolated region of relative transparency.

- Carefully examining the tropical emission spectrum, we discover that the 9.6 μm ozone band is apparent there as well. But because the surrounding window is much less transparent in this case, the ozone band does not stand out nearly as strongly.

- Now let's take a closer look at the CO_2 band in the arctic spectrum. At 15 μm, the measured brightness temperature of approximately 235 K is significantly *colder* than it is on the edges of the band near 14 and 16 μm, where the brightness temperature is close to the maximum value of 245 K. Yet we know that at the center of the band, where absorption is the strongest, the emitted radiation should be originating at the levels closest to the intrument, namely in the lowest few meters of the atmosphere. How do we explain this apparent paradox? In fact, there is no paradox; we are simply witnessing the effects of a strong *inversion* in the surface temperature profile — i.e., a sharp *increase* in temperature with height in the lowest few hundred meters of the atmosphere.[3] At the center of the CO_2

---

[3]Deep surface inversions, relatively uncommon elsewhere, are the rule in wintertime polar regions.

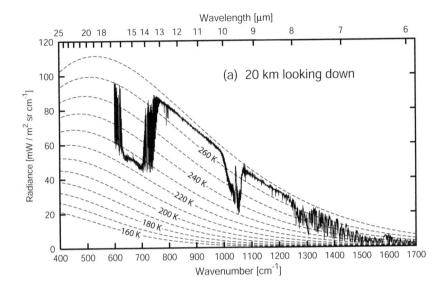

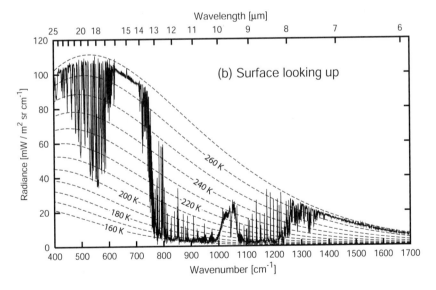

Fig. 8.2: Coincident measurements of the infrared emission spectrum of the cloud-free atmosphere at (a) 20 km looking downward over the polar ice sheet and (b) at the surface looking upward. *(Data courtesy of David Tobin, Space Science and Engineering Center, University of Wisconsin-Madison.)*

band, the spectrometer records emission from the coldest air right at the surface. At the edges of the band, where the air is less opaque, it sees emission from the warmer layer of air at the top of the inversion. This example hints at the possibility of using remote measurements of atmospheric emission to infer atmospheric temperature structure. We will return to that topic shortly.

Let's now take a look at how the atmospheric emission spectrum changes depending on whether you are looking down from above or looking up from the surface. Fig. 8.2 gives us a rare opportunity to compare the two perspectives for the same atmospheric conditions: an aircraft flying at 20 km altitude measured the upwelling emission spectrum at exactly the same time and location as a surface instrument looking up measured the downwelling spectrum. The measurements in this case were taken over the arctic ice pack and are therefore comparable in some respects to the arctic spectrum already discussed. The following exercise asks you to provide the physical interpretation:

> **Problem 8.8:**   Based on the measured spectra depicted in Fig. 8.2, answer the following questions: (a) What is the approximate temperature of the surface of the ice sheet, and how do you know? (b) What is the approximate temperature of the near-surface *air*, and how do you know? (c) What is the approximate temperature of the air at the aircraft's flight altitude of 20 km, and how do you know? (d) Identify the feature seen between 9 and 10 μm in both spectra. (e) In Fig. 8.1, we saw evidence of a strong inversion in the near-surface atmospheric temperature profile. Can similar evidence be seen in Fig. 8.2? Explain.

We'll conclude our discussion of atmospheric emission spectra by looking at examples of satellite observations made under diverse conditions around the globe (Fig. 8.3). Once again, I'll leave most of the physical interpretation as an exercise. Only one new point requires a brief explanation, because it didn't arise in our previous discussion of surface- and aircraft-measured spectra. That concerns the prominent narrow spike observed at the center of the 15 μm CO_2 band in all four panels. This spike occurs where absorption is by far

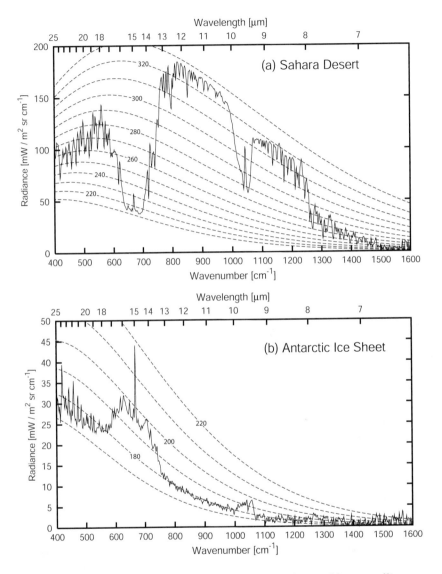

Fig. 8.3: Examples of moderate resolution IR spectra observed by a satellite spectrometer. Except for the curve labeled "thunderstorm anvil" in panel (c), all spectra were obtained under cloud-free conditions. *(Nimbus-4 IRIS data courtesy of the Goddard EOS Distributed Active Archive Center (DAAC) and instrument team leader Dr. Rudolf A. Hanel.)*

226

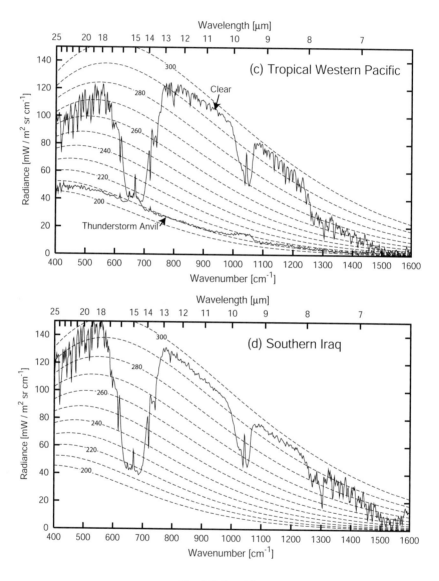

Fig. 8.3: (cont.)

the most intense of any point in the thermal IR band. From the vantage point of a satellite sensor viewing downward, emission at this wavelength therefore originates almost entirely in the stratosphere, whereas most of the remaining emission spectrum is associated primarily with the surface and troposphere.[4]

To summarize, as you move from the edge of the CO_2 band toward the center, the general tendency for satellite-observed spectra is *usually*: (i) decreasing brightness temperature as the emission weighting function $W^\uparrow$ peaks at higher (and colder) levels in the troposphere, followed by (ii) a sharp reversal of this trend at the strongly absorbing center of the band, where the weighting function peaks at an altitude solidly within the relatively warm stratosphere.

> **Problem 8.9:** Contrast the above explanation for the narrow warm spike at the center of the 15 μm CO_2 band with the explanation for the similar-appearing warm spike at the center of the 9.6 μm ozone band, as seen in several panels of Fig. 8.3.

> **Problem 8.10:** Referring to Fig. 8.3, answer each of following questions.
>
> (a) For each of the four scenes, provide an estimate of the surface temperature.
>
> (b) For which scene does the surface appear to be significantly colder than any other level in the atmosphere?
>
> (c) Compare the apparent humidity of the atmosphere over Southern Iraq with that over the Sahara Desert, and explain your reasoning.

---

[4]The *troposphere* is the layer of the atmosphere closest to the surface and is usually characterized by decreasing temperature with height. The troposphere is typically anywhere from a few km to 15 km deep, depending on latitude and season. The *stratosphere* is the deep layer above the troposphere in which temperature generally increases with height. The boundary between the troposphere and the stratosphere, called the *tropopause*, is often (though not always) the coldest point in the atmospheric temperature profile below 40 km. The layer of highest ozone concentration is found in the stratosphere between 15 and 30 km. If these facts are new to you, then I recommend that you spend an evening with Chapter 1 of WH77 and/or Section 3.1 of L02.

(d) Estimate the temperature of the thunderstorm cloud top in the Tropical Western Pacific. Why is this emission spectrum so much smoother than that for the neighboring clear atmosphere? Explain the small variations in brightness temperature that *do* show up.

(e) Explain why the ozone band at 9.6 μm shows up as a relatively warm feature in the Antarctic spectrum, but a relatively cold feature for all other scenes.

8.3.2 Satellite Retrieval of Temperature Profiles

As we have seen in Sections 7.4.1 and 8.3.1, certain atmospheric constituents — most notably CO_2, water vapor, ozone, and oxygen — are associated with strong absorption lines and bands that render the atmosphere opaque over certain ranges of wavelengths. Some of these constituents, such as CO_2 and O_2 are "well mixed" throughout the troposphere and stratosphere. That is, they are present at a constant, accurately known mass ratio w to all other constituents of the atmosphere. If you knew the density profile $\rho(z)$ of the atmosphere, then the density of the absorbing constituent would just be $\rho'(z) = w\rho(z)$. If you also knew the mass absorption coefficient $k_a(z)$ of the constituent, then you could calculate the optical depth $\tau(z)$ and thus the emission weighting function $W^\uparrow(z)$ that appears in the integral in (8.29).

The relative strength of absorption at the wavelength in question determines whether $W^\uparrow(z)$ will peak at a high or low altitude in the atmosphere. If you build a satellite sensor that is able to measure the radiant intensities I_λ for a series of closely spaced wavelengths λ_i located on the edge of a strong absorption line or band for the constituent (e.g., near 15 μm for CO_2), each channel will measure thermal emission from a different layer of the atmosphere. The closer the wavelength is to the line center, the higher in the atmosphere the weighting function will peak. The intensity of the emission is of course determined by the atmospheric temperature within that layer.

In principle, you can find a temperature profile $T(z)$ that is simultaneously consistent with each of the observed radiances I_λ for the scene in question. Typically, you would start with a "first guess"

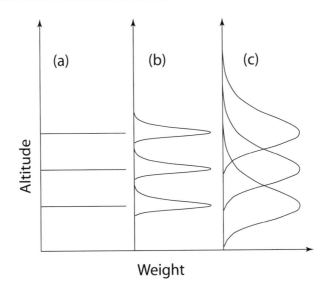

Fig. 8.4: Idealized satellite sensor weighting functions for atmospheric temperature profile retrievals. (a) Channel weighting functions resemble δ-functions; i.e., all emission observed by each channel originates at a single altitude. (b) Observed emission represents layer averages, but channel weighting functions do not overlap. (c) Realistic case, in which weighting functions not only represent layer averages but also overlap.

profile and compute the associated intensities for each channel using (8.29). You would then compare the computed intensities with the observed intensities and adjust the profile in such a way as to reduce the discrepancies. This process could be repeated until the differences for all channels fell to within some tolerance, based on the assumed precision of the instrument measurements themselves and of the model calculations of I_λ.

The above procedure (with certain important caveats; see below) is in fact not too far from that actually used in routine satellite-based temperature profile retrievals. It is not my purpose here to embark on a rigorous discussion of remote sensing theory, which is best left for a separate course and/or textbook. It is enough for now that you recognize the close connection between the radiative transfer principles discussed earlier in this chapter and an application of immense practical importance to modern meteorology.

Figure 8.4 depicts the physical basis for profile retrieval at three levels of idealization, starting with the simplest — and least realistic — on the left: If weighting functions happened to be perfectly sharp — that is, if all emission observed at each wavelength λ_i originated at a single altitude (Fig. 8.4a), then "inverting" the observations would be simple: in this case, the observed brightness temperatures $T_{B,i}$ would exactly correspond to the physical temperatures at the corresponding altitudes h_i. Your job is then essentially finished without even lifting a calculator. Of course, you wouldn't know how the temperature was varying *between* those levels, but you could either interpolate between the known levels and hope for the best or, if your budget was big enough, you could add an arbitrary number of new channels to your sensor to fill in the vertical gaps.

Slightly more realistically, panel (b) depicts the weighting functions as having finite width, so that the observed brightness temperatures correspond to an *average* of $B_\lambda[T(z)]$ over a substantial depth of the atmosphere rather than a unique temperature T_i at altitude h_i. There is now ambiguity in the retrieval, because there is no single atmospheric level that is responsible for all of the emission measured by any given channel. At best, you can estimate the *average layer temperature* associated with each channel. Nevertheless, the profile retrieval problem itself remains straightforward, because each channel contains completely independent information: there is no overlap between the weighting functions.

Unfortunately, real weighting functions are constrained to obey the laws of physics, as embodied in (8.30). This means that unless you have an unusually sharp change with altitude in the atmospheric absorption coefficient β_a, your weighting functions will be quite broad. In the worst case, the mass extinction coefficient k_a of your chosen constituent will be nearly constant with height, so that the weighting functions will be essentially those predicted for an exponential absorption profile as discussed in Section 7.4.3. The situation is somewhat better for sensor channels positioned on the edge of an absorption line (or between two lines), because *pressure broadening* (see Chapter 9) then increases k_a toward the surface, which sharpens the weighting function. Nevertheless, the improvement is not spectacular.

Therefore, given any reasonable number of channels, there is always considerable overlap between adjacent weighting functions,

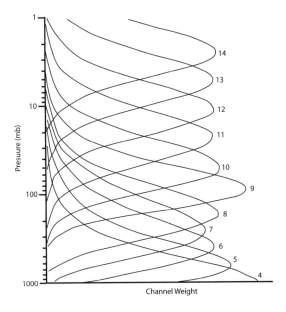

Fig. 8.5: Weighting functions for channels 4–14 of the Advanced Microwave Sounding Unit (AMSU).

as depicted schematically in Fig. 8.4c. In fact, Fig. 8.5 shows actual weighting functions for the Advanced Microwave Sounding Unit (AMSU), which has 11 channels on the edge of the strong O_2 absorption band near 60 GHz (c.f. Fig. 7.7). Although each satellite sounding device has its own set of channels and therefore its own unique set of weighting functions, those for the AMSU are fairly typical for most current-generation temperature sounders in the infrared and microwave bands.

To summarize: It is clear on the one hand that there is information about vertical temperature structure in the radiant intensities observed by a sounding instrument like the AMSU. On the other hand, one shouldn't underestimate the technical challenge of retrieving temperature profiles of *consistently useful quality* from satellite observations. In outline form, here are the main issues:

- In general, it takes far more variables to accurately describe an arbitrary temperature profile $T(z)$ than there are channels on a typical satellite sounding unit. This means that you have fewer measurements than unknowns, and the retrieval problem is *underdetermined* (or *ill-posed*). The problem is therefore not just that of finding any temperature profile that is consistent with the measurements; the real problem is of choosing the *most plausible* one out of an infinity of physically admissible candidates.

- Because of the high degree of vertical overlap between adjacent weighting functions, the temperature information contained in each channel is not completely independent from that provided by the other channels. That is to say, if you have N channels, you don't really have N independent pieces of information about your profile; you have something *less* than N, which makes the problem highlighted in the previous paragraph even worse that it appears at first glance.

- Because any measurement is inherently subject to some degree of random error, or *noise*, it is important to undertake the retrieval in such a way that these errors don't have an excessive impact on the final retrieved profile.

- Because of the large vertical width of the individual weighting functions, a satellite's view of the atmosphere's temperature structure is necessarily very "blurred" — that is, it is impossible to resolve fine-scale vertical structure in the temperature profile. As a consequence, a great many of the candidate profile solutions that would be *physically consistent* with the observed radiances $I_{\lambda,i}$ exhibit wild oscillations that are completely inconsistent with any reasonable temperature structure of the atmosphere. Effectively weeding out these bad solutions while retaining the (potentially) good ones requires one to impose requirements on the "smoothness" of the retrieved profile or limits on the allowable magnitude of the departure from the "first guess" profile.

Of course, well-established methods exist for dealing with the above challenges, and satellite temperature profile retrievals are successfully obtained at thousands of locations around the globe every day. These retrievals provide indispensable information about the current state of the atmosphere to numerical weather prediction models. Without the availability of satellite-derived temperature structure data, accurate medium- and long-range forecasts (three days and beyond) would be impossible almost everywhere, and even shorter-range forecasts would be of questionable value over oceans and other data sparse regions.

8.3.3 Water Vapor Imagery

In the previous subsection, we looked at the case that satellite-observed emission was associated with a constituent that was "well-mixed" in the atmosphere. Under that assumption, the vertical distribution of the absorber is essentially known, and variations in brightness temperature can be attributed to variations in temperature in the atmospheric layer associated with each channel.

One can also imagine the opposite situation, in which the temperature profile is reasonably well known (perhaps from satellite measurements, as described above), but the concentration of the absorbing/emitting constituent is unknown and highly variable in both time and space. Such is the case for infrared images acquired at wavelengths between about 5 and 8 μm, where atmospheric emission and absorption is very strong in connection with the water vapor band centered at 6.3 μm.

The wavelength in this band most commonly utilized for satellite imaging is 6.7 μm, where water vapor absorption is strong enough to block surface emission from reaching the satellite under most conditions, but weak enough that the imager can usually "probe" well into the troposphere without being blocked by the small amounts of water vapor found in the stratosphere and upper troposphere.

Unlike the case for CO_2 and O_2, water vapor is far from well mixed and varies wildly in concentration, both horizontally and vertically. Therefore, the emission weighting function $W^{\uparrow}$ at 6.7 μm is highly variable, peaking at low altitudes (or even the surface) in a very dry atmosphere and in the upper troposphere in a humid tropical atmosphere or when high altitude clouds are present.

As usual, the observed brightness temperature T_B is a function of the temperature of the atmosphere in the vicinity of the weighting function peak, but variations in brightness temperature are a much stronger function of height of the weighting function peak than of

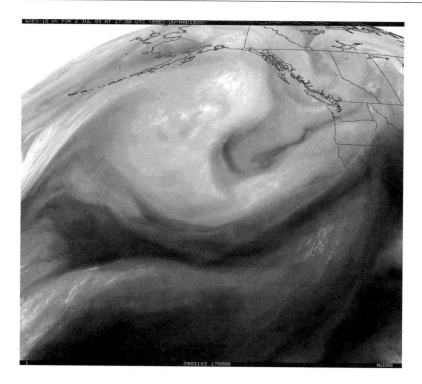

Fig. 8.6: An image of the Eastern Pacific and west coast of North America taken by the GOES-West geostationary weather satellite at a wavelength of 6.7 μm. This wavelength falls within the strong water vapor absorption band centered on 6.3 μm.

the temperature at any specific altitude.

Consequently *dry*, cloud-free air masses typically produce relatively *warm* brightness temperatures, because the observed emission originates at the warm lower levels of the atmosphere. *Humid* air masses, on the other hand, produce *cold* brightness temperatures, because emission then originates principally in the cold upper troposphere. In fact, globally speaking, there is often a roughly inverse correlation between brightness temperature at 6.7 μm and air mass temperature, because warm tropical air masses are capable of supporting higher water vapor content, and may also be associated with colder tropopause temperatures, on average, than cold extratropical air masses.

An example of a 6.7 μm image is shown in Fig. 8.6. In this instance, the most dramatic features are the very dark (warm) bands snaking across the subtropical Pacific. These bands are presumably associated with regions of strong subsidence (sinking motion) in connection with the subtropical high pressure belt. The effect of subsidence is to bring extremely dry air from the upper troposphere down to relatively low levels, allowing the imager to "see" warm emission from the lowest kilometer or two. Elsewhere, deep humidity and some high-level clouds connected with a weakening extratropical cyclone produce bands of relatively cold brightness temperatures. Overall, one has an impression of a three-dimensional "surface" representing the upper boundary of the most humid layer of the atmosphere. This humidity structure is of course invisible in the conventional visible and IR images shown previously for the same time (Figs. 5.6 and 6.9).

Because the observed brightness temperature depends both on the amount and detailed vertical distribution of water vapor present and on the temperature structure of the atmosphere, it is generally not possible to retrieve quantitative humidity information using this channel alone. However, if you have several channels with varying sensitivity to water vapor absorption, they can be used in combination with temperature sounding channels to obtain vertical profiles of humidity. Of course, the same practical difficulties that were outlined for the temperature profile retrieval problem are encountered here as well. If anything, they are worse, because there are few useful criteria for distinguishing a "realistic" from an "unrealistic" humidity profile, except for the need to avoid supersaturation. Also, because the temperature profile cannot be retrieved with perfect precision, errors in this profile "feed through" to the humidity profile retrieval and constitute an additional source of error.

CHAPTER 9

Absorption by Atmospheric Gases[†]

In the previous chapter, we developed the mathematical tools for describing monochromatic radiative transfer, including both absorption and thermal emission, in a nonscattering atmosphere. Specifically, given the absorption profile $\beta_a(z)$ and temperature profile $T(z)$ in a plane parallel atmosphere, we can use (8.27) through (8.30) to compute the atmospheric contribution to the radiant intensity, as seen from the surface looking up or from a satellite looking down. With only slight modifications, they may be used to compute monochromatic intensities at *any* level z between the surface and the top of the atmosphere.

In these equations, it is the absorption coefficient β_a that directly links absorption and emission at any specific wavelength to the material composition of the atmosphere. In Section 7.4.1, we saw that a relatively small number of constituents, such as water vapor, carbon dioxide, and a few other trace gases, are responsible for almost all of the important features in the observed absorption/emission spectrum of the atmosphere. However, we have not yet examined *why* certain gases strongly absorb radiation at certain wavelengths nor *how* their absorption properties are influenced by temperature and pressure.

Is it really necessary, you ask, for the nonspecialist to know the whys and hows of atmospheric absorption? Even without that insight, does anything prevent you from computing broadband fluxes (for example), simply by integrating monochromatic intensities over both solid angle and wavelength? No, of course not. All you need is a reasonably accurate specification of $\beta_a(\lambda, p, T, \ldots)$ for each relevant constituent. Such models are already available "off the shelf."

But while it is technically possible to learn to fly and land an airplane by rote without ever actually mastering the physical principles of flight, most of us would prefer to entrust our lives to a pilot with a deeper understanding of his/her job. When it comes to atmospheric radiation, the consequences of ignorance are less grave, but the argument is basically the same: the more you know, the less likely you are to do something embarrassing, even when working with someone else's well-tested models.

Note, by the way, that even though I conceded the possibility of blindly applying the equations cited above to the problem of computing broadband fluxes (as required for general circulation models, weather forecast models and the like), this "brute force" approach is rarely attractive for routine calculations. Quite often, we need to obtain fluxes of modest accuracy *with the least possible expenditure of computational effort*. That requires us to take advantage of highly simplified *parameterizations* of radiative absorption and emission. If you're going to stake your reputation on the results of such methods (as many atmospheric scientists do without even realizing it!), it's certainly in your interest to know where they come from and how far they can be trusted.

Atmospheric remote sensing methods typically rely on calculations of quasi-monochromatic radiant intensity. This is admittedly a far simpler computational problem than that of broadband fluxes. Nevertheless, it is the detailed absorption behavior of various atmospheric molecules that largely determine optimal channel wavelengths, spectral widths, and other instrument characteristics. Those who work with remote sensing data and/or instrumentation, as many of us can expect to do at some point in our careers, should have at least a basic understanding of these issues.

9.1   Basis for Molecular Absorption/Emission

In Chapter 2, I pointed out that EM radiation has both wavelike and particle-like properties. Recall that there are times when radiation must be viewed as waves, times when it must be viewed as a shower of quantized particles having energy $E = h\nu$, and, finally, times when it doesn't matter which view you take.

The absorption of radiation by gases turns out to be one of those cases in which the quantized (particle) nature of radiation comes to the forefront. Simply stated, interactions between radiation and individual gas molecules — whether absorption or emission — are possible only for photons having energies satisfying certain criteria. Those criteria are largely determined by the arcane, and sometimes counterintuitive, laws of quantum mechanics. But don't despair: the *consequences* of those laws aren't difficult to grasp at the level targeted by this book.

When a photon is absorbed by a system, the energy originally carried by that photon must contribute to a corresponding increase in the internal energy of the system. Likewise, when a photon is emitted, the system must give up an equivalent amount of its internal energy. There are many different ways in which internal energy may increase or decrease. Examples include:

- Changes in the translational kinetic energy of molecules (i.e., temperature).

- Changes in the rotational kinetic energy of polyatomic molecules.

- Changes in the vibrational energy of polyatomic molecules.

- Changes in the distribution of electric charge within a molecule, possibly including the complete separation (or reunification) of two components previously bound by electrostatic forces.

Collisions between molecules tend to equalize the distribution of the total internal energy in a gas among the various "storage" mechanisms listed above. Imagine, for example, that you were able to put a diatomic gas like oxygen into a unusual state in which all of its molecules had translational kinetic energy but no rotational or vibrational kinetic energy. Subsequent collisions between the molecules would quickly set many of them to spinning and vibrating again. Before long, the total internal energy would be distributed between all available storage modes, reestablishing a condition known as *local thermodynamic equilibrium* (LTE; see also Section 6.2.3).

LTE can be taken as a given for most problems in the lower and middle atmosphere, where atmospheric density is comparatively high and collisions are therefore quite frequent. This assures us that knowledge of the physical temperature of the medium is sufficient to accurately predict the distribution of the total internal energy among *all* possible modes. It also ensures that any radiative energy absorbed or emitted by a medium will quickly give rise to a commensurate change in the physical temperature of that medium.

Note, however, that the *immediate* consequence of the absorption or emission of any particular photon is usually a change in the internal energy of a single molecule. For example, the emission by a gas of a single photon might entail a reduction in the rotational energy of one molecule of the gas. For another photon, the immediate consequence of an absorption event might be a simultaneous increase in both the vibrational and rotational energy of the molecule. For yet another, the response might be an increase in the electrostatic potential energy of one of the electrons in the molecule. Yet all of these energy changes eventually get redistributed, via collisions, between all of the molecules in the vicinity, so that there is always a predictable distribution of the total internal energy in a gas among all available storage modes.

Now here is the kicker: most modes of energy storage at the molecular level and smaller are *quantized*. That is to say, a given molecule cannot have just *any* vibrational energy, but rather *only one of a discrete set of energy levels* $E_0, E_1, \ldots, E_\infty$ permitted by the laws of quantum mechanics applied to that particular molecule. The same principle applies to other modes of energy storage, such as that associated with molecular rotation and electron excitation. Only the translational kinetic energy of molecules and other unbound particles is unquantized.

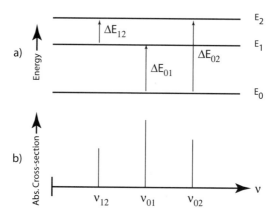

Fig. 9.1: Relationship between energy level transitions and the absorption/emission line spectrum for a hypothetical molecule with only three allowed energy levels. Panel (a) depicts the allowed transitions; panel (b) shows the corresponding positions of the lines in the spectrum, where $\nu_{ij} = \Delta E_{ij}/h$. Note that the line strengths in (b) are arbitrary.

9.2   Absorption/Emission Lines

The consequences of the quantization of energy states are far-reaching. Basically, it implies that a photon can be absorbed or emitted by a molecule *only if the interaction leads to a transition from the molecule's original state to one of its other allowed states.* Thus, if a molecule is in energy state E_0, then it can absorb a photon whose energy $\Delta E = E_n - E_0$ but not one whose energy is some other value. Furthermore, a molecule in energy state E_1 can only emit a photon with energy $\Delta E = E_1 - E_0$, since there is no other allowed transition that results in a decrease in the molecule's energy. A molecule in its base state E_0 cannot emit anything. However, the condition of LTE ensures that, for any given temperature above absolute zero, a predictable percentage of the molecules in a gas may be found in any given energy state. This ensures that a predictable set of allowed transitions (for both absorption and emission) is always available within any macroscopic sample of the gas in question.

Consider a hypothetical molecule with only three allowed energy states E_0, E_1, and E_2 (Fig. 9.1a). There are then three transitions available for the absorption of an incoming photon: $E_0 \rightarrow E_1$, $E_0 \rightarrow E_2$, and $E_1 \rightarrow E_2$. Each of these transitions corresponds to a specific photon energy ΔE and therefore, according to (2.45), to a specific wavelength $\lambda = c/v = hc/\Delta E$ at which absorption may occur. For all other wavelengths, the molecule is nonabsorbing.

If we plot the absorption cross-section as a function of wavelength for our hypothetical molecule, we get an absorption *line spectrum* similar to Fig. 9.1b. The *positions* of the lines are determined by energy changes associated with the allowed transitions. The *relative strengths* of the lines are determined by a) the fraction of molecules that are in the particular initial state required for the transition and b) the intrinsic likelihood that a photon having the right energy and encountering a molecule in the required energy state will actually produce the relevant transition.[1]

It is possible for more than one transition to contribute to a single absorption line, if they correspond to the same change of energy. For example, if the energy levels for the above hypothetical molecule were equally spaced, then both the $E_0 \rightarrow E_1$ and $E_1 \rightarrow E_2$ transitions would correspond to the same photon wavelength. The absorption spectrum would then consist of only two lines rather than three, with one occurring at half the wavelength of the other one. The latter, in this example, would be called *degenerate*, in that it is really two lines collapsed into one. Multiple degeneracies occur in some real gases; the associated absorption lines are often quite strong in comparison to their nondegenerate neighbors.

Problem 9.1: Consider a hypothetical molecule with N allowed energy levels E_i.

(a) Determine the total number of possible transitions that could lead to the absorption of a photon.

(b) If the energy levels happen to be equally spaced, then how many *distinct* absorption lines result from the above transitions?

---

[1] Although the existence of absorption lines is justified here by invoking the quantized nature of radiation and of energy transitions in molecules, it turns out that there is a close analogy as well to the absorption of energy by a classical damped harmonic oscillator. If the frequency of the external wave coincides with the resonant frequency of the oscillator, absorption occurs, otherwise it does not. Some features of line absorption can be explained in classical terms using this analogy (see for example TS99, Section 3.3). For this reason, you will sometimes hear the term *resonant absorption* used to describe line spectra of the type discussed above, as contrasted with *nonresonant* (or continuum) absorption spectra that do not exhibit line structure.

The energies carried by the photons of interest to atmospheric scientists cover a wide range — five orders of magnitude from $\sim 10^{-23}$ J for microwaves to $\sim 10^{-18}$ J for the far UV band. Because the quantization of energy states in atoms and molecules is quite different for the different modes of energy storage, different wavelength bands tend to be associated with different types of transitions.

For example, the allowed rotational energy states of most molecules are rather closely spaced; hence transitions between rotational states tend to involve low-energy photons, such as those in the far IR and microwave bands. On the other extreme, the tightly bound electrons in the inner shell of an atom require large amounts of energy in order to be "kicked up" to a higher level of excitation; consequently, this kind of transition is important primarily for the absorption and emission of X-rays. Intermediate energies are associated with transitions in the outer electronic shells, and with vibrational transitions. The following table gives the dominant transition type within the wavelength bands of interest to us:

Wavelengths	Band	Dominant transition
$>20\ \mu$m	Far IR, microwave	Rotation
$1\ \mu$m– $20\ \mu$m	Near IR, thermal IR	Vibration
$<1\ \mu$m	Visible, UV	Electronic

As we'll see later, low-energy transitions, such as those associated with rotation, often occur simultaneously with higher energy transitions due to vibration and/or electronic excitation. The total energy change is the sum of the individual changes. The effect of such combinations is to add fine-scale structure to the absorption line spectrum that would result from "pure" vibrational or electronic transitions alone.

This book assumes that the reader has had little if any prior instruction in quantum physics. The following discussion of quantized energy transitions is therefore intentionally simplistic and largely descriptive, though mathematical relationships are derived for a few simple cases.[2] My purpose here is to give you a qualitative understanding of why atmospheric absorption spectra look the way they do, and why certain trace constituents, like CO_2, are far more important for radiation than are other far more prevalent species, like nitrogen. We will begin by examining the physical basis for the absorption line spectra associated with rotational, vibrational, and electronic transitions separately and in combination. This will be followed by a discussion of absorption line shape and width and, finally, by a survey of principal atmospheric absorbers.

9.2.1 Rotational Transitions

Moments of Inertia of Molecules

Let's first begin with a quick review of some familiar relationships from freshman physics. All physical objects, including molecules, have mass. According to Newton's law the mass m is a measure of the object's resistance to linear acceleration, i.e.,

$$F = ma \tag{9.1}$$

where F is the applied force and a is the resulting acceleration. Also, the mass figures prominently in the object's translational kinetic energy product, which is given by

$$E_{kt} = \frac{1}{2}mv^2 , \tag{9.2}$$

where v is the speed. In the case of molecules in a gas, their average translational kinetic energy is proportional to the absolute temperature of the gas. Also, the linear *momentum* is given by

$$p = mv . \tag{9.3}$$

The above relationships all apply to linear motion by a mass; completely analogous relationships also exist for rotational motion. In particular, all physical objects that are not point masses have *moments of inertia*. Analogous to the role of mass in linear acceleration,

---

[2]More detailed treatments may be found in S94 (Section 3.2), TS02 (Section 4.5), and GY95 (Chapter 3).

the moment of inertia I is a measure of the object's resistance to *rotational* acceleration when subjected to a torque T:

$$T = I\frac{d\omega}{dt} .$$ (9.4)

Similarly, the *rotational kinetic energy* is given by

$$E_{kr} = \frac{1}{2}I\omega^2 .$$ (9.5)

Finally, the *angular momentum* is given by

$$L = I\omega .$$ (9.6)

The moment of inertia I depends not only on the mass m but also on how that mass is distributed in space about the object's center of gravity. Specifically, it is the sum of the products of the masses δm_i of each volume element in the object with the squares of their respective distance r_i from the axis of rotation:

$$I = \sum_i r_i^2 \delta m_i .$$ (9.7)

Thus, for two objects of equal mass, the more compact object will have the smaller moment of inertia. A hula hoop has about the same mass as a softball, but a hula hoop spinning about its axis at the rate of one revolution per second stores much more energy and angular momentum then does a softball spinning at the same rate.

In one sense, the analogy between rotational and translational measures of energy and momentum is very close — indeed, the respective equations for linear and rotational acceleration, kinetic energy, and momentum all have similar algebraic forms. In two respects, however, the picture is slightly more complicated for rotational motion than it is for translational motion.

First of all, translational motion is not quantized — a molecule is allowed to have any speed (how could this *not* be the case, since there is no absolute frame of reference for translational motion?). Rotational motion at the molecular level, on the other hand, *is* quantized according to the laws of quantum mechanics, and this discretization of energy/angular momentum states is responsible for the existence absorption/emission lines in connection with rotational transitions.

Secondly, any object has only one mass m, but it has *three* principal moments of inertia I_1, I_2, I_3. Each of these corresponds to one of three perpendicular axes of rotation whose overall orientation is determined by the particular mass distribution (i.e., shape) of the object. Although the actual axis of rotation of an object is not constrained to coincide with one of the principal axes, the overall angular momentum and/or rotational kinetic energy can nevertheless be analyzed in terms of the projection of the angular velocity vector on each of the three principal axes.

For objects having simple symmetry, it is often easy to guess the alignment of the principal axes and to judge the relative size of the corresponding moments of inertia. A rectangular brick, for example, has principal axes passing at right angles through each face and through the center of mass. The corresponding moments of inertia will be different for each axis: smallest for rotation about the longest axis of the brick (because the mass is most compactly distributed about that axis) and largest for rotation about the axis passing through the shortest dimension of the brick (because more of the mass is found at a greater distance from that axis).

For many common shapes, one or more of the moments of inertia have the same value. For example, a pencil has one very small moment of inertia corresponding to rotation about its lengthwise axis and two much larger, identical moments of inertia corresponding to rotation about any pair of axes at right angles to the first. A flat circular disk has one large moment of inertia about its radial axis and two smaller and equal moments of inertia about any pair of perpendicular axes that pass edgewise through the disk. A uniform sphere or a cube has three identical moments of inertia; moreover, it is irrelevant in these cases how you define the principal axes, because rotation about *any* axis is equivalent.

We are now ready to see how the above concepts apply to molecules. Let us start by considering an isolated atom. Virtually the entire mass of any atom is confined to its nucleus which, on a molecular scale, has a vanishingly small radius. For all practical purposes relevant to atmospheric radiation, a single atom has effectively zero moment of inertia for any axis of rotation; i.e.,

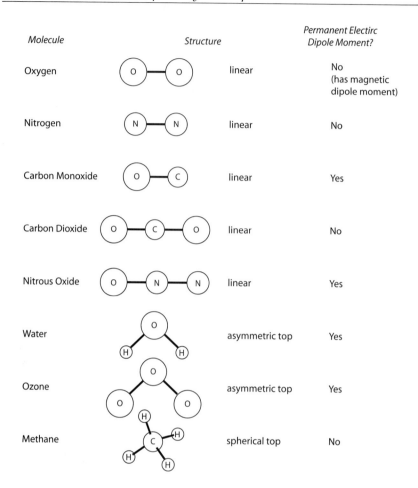

Molecule	Structure	Permanent Electirc Dipole Moment?
Oxygen	linear	No (has magnetic dipole moment)
Nitrogen	linear	No
Carbon Monoxide	linear	Yes
Carbon Dioxide	linear	No
Nitrous Oxide	linear	Yes
Water	asymmetric top	Yes
Ozone	asymmetric top	Yes
Methane	spherical top	No

Fig. 9.2: Molecular structure of several key atmospheric constituents. Also indicated is whether the molecule has a permanent electric dipole moment (note that oxygen has a permanent magnetic dipole moment).

$I_1 = I_2 = I_3 \approx 0$. It follows that *isolated atoms exhibit no rotational transitions of interest to us.*

A diatomic molecule, on the other hand, consists of two bound atoms, each with finite mass, separated by a finite distance. Moreover, the distance separating the two atoms is quite large compared with the radius of the individual nuclei. One of the axes of rotation can be taken to pass through the two nuclei. For this axis, the moment of inertia $I_1 = 0$. The remaining two axes are perpendicular to each other and to the first; for them the moments of inertia are nonzero and $I_2 = I_3$. These properties also apply more generally to a *linear* polyatomic molecule — i.e., any molecule with all of its constituent atoms lying in a straight line.

Finally, we come to nonlinear polyatomic molecules, which have three nonzero moments of inertia. Depending on the symmetry of the molecule, there are three possible cases: 1) all moments of inertia equal, corresponding to a *spherical top* molecule, 2) two equal and one different in the case of a *symmetric top* molecule, and 3) all three different — the so-called *asymmetric top*.

The significance of the above distinctions lies in the number of mechanically dissimilar modes of rotation available to a given molecule. There can be no rotational energy, and therefore no absorption or emission of radiation, in connection with a principal axis for which $I = 0$. Furthermore, axes of rotation for which the moments of inertia are equal are energetically indistinguishable and therefore give rise to identical absorption spectra. Thus, linear and spherical top molecules have the fewest distinct modes of rotation, and therefore the simplest absorption spectra due to rotational transitions, while asymmetric top molecules have the richest set of possible transitions, and therefore the most complex rotation spectra.

The following table summarizes the different types of rotational symmetry, in order of increasing complexity, and lists the most important atmospheric molecules in each category (see also Fig. 9.2).

Description	Moments of Inertia	Examples
Monoatomic	$I_1 = I_2 = I_3 = 0$	Ar
Linear	$I_1 = 0; I_2 = I_3 > 0$	N_2, O_2, CO_2, N_2O
Spherical top	$I_1 = I_2 = I_3 > 0$	CH_4
Symmetric top	$I_1 \neq 0; I_2 = I_3 > 0$	NH_3, CH_3Cl, CF_3Cl
Asymmetric top	$I_1 \neq I_2 \neq I_3$	H_2O, O_3

Quantization of Angular Momentum

A diatomic molecule may be regarded as a two-body rigid rotator consisting of two masses m_1 and m_2 separated by distance $r = r_1 + r_2$, where r_i is the distance of each mass m_i from the axis of rotation. For any freely rotating body, the axis of rotation concides with the *center of mass* which, in this example, satisfies $m_1 r_1 = m_2 r_2$. It can be shown from (9.7) that the moment of inertia $I_2 = I_3 = I$ (recall that $I_1 = 0$ for a linear molecule) is given by

$$I = m'r^2 \, , \tag{9.8}$$

where we introduce the so-called *reduced mass*

$$m' \equiv \frac{m_1 m_2}{m_1 + m_2} \, . \tag{9.9}$$

.

If the molecule is rotating with angular velocity ω, then its kinetic energy of rotation is

$$E = \frac{1}{2} I \omega^2 = \frac{L^2}{2I} \, , \tag{9.10}$$

where

$$L = I \omega \tag{9.11}$$

is the angular momentum. Quantum mechanics tells us (via Schrödinger's equation), that the angular momentum of our rigid molecule is restricted to discrete values given by

$$L = \frac{h}{2\pi} \sqrt{J(J+1)} \, , \tag{9.12}$$

where $J = 0, 1, 2, \ldots$ is the *rotational quantum number*. Combining the above with (9.10) yields a set of discrete energy levels

$$E_J = \frac{1}{2} I \omega^2 = \frac{J(J+1)h^2}{8\pi^2 I} \, . \tag{9.13}$$

Problem 9.2: Equations (9.11) and (9.12) imply that the angular velocity ω of an object can only take on discrete (quantized) values. Explain why this quantization is not observable for macroscopic objects like frisbees and hula hoops.

Rotational Absorption Spectrum

If we now consider transitions between adjacent rotational states J and $J+1$ (it turns out that none other are allowed by quantum mechanics), we find that the associated energy change is

$$\Delta E = E_{J+1} - E_J = \frac{h^2}{8\pi^2 I}\left[(J+1)(J+2) - J(J+1)\right], \qquad (9.14)$$

or

$$\Delta E = \frac{h^2}{4\pi^2 I}(J+1). \qquad (9.15)$$

The corresponding photon frequency ν is then

$$\nu = \Delta E/h = \frac{h}{4\pi^2 I}(J+1), \qquad (9.16)$$

or

$$\nu = 2B(J+1), \qquad (9.17)$$

where B is the *rotational constant* defined as

$$B = \frac{h}{8\pi^2 I}. \qquad (9.18)$$

From (9.17), we see that the rotational absorption line spectrum of our simple diatomic molecule consists of a series of equally spaced lines separated by $\Delta\nu = 2B$.

Problem 9.3: Oxygen (O_2; molecular mass 32.0 kg/kmole) is a diatomic molecule whose lowest-frequency rotational absorption band is found at a frequency of 60 GHz.

(a) From the relationships given in this section, find the distance r separating the two oxygen atoms in the molecule.

(b) How many revolutions per second does an O_2 molecule make in the $J = 1$ state?

We have just discussed the quantization of rotational energy, and the associated line spectrum, for the simplest case: that of a diatomic molecule with only one nonzero moment of inertia I and rotational quantum number J. Analogous relationships exist for nonlinear molecules possessing up to three different moments of inertia

I_n and associated rotational quantum numbers J_n. Each quantum number J_n has its own distinct set of energy levels, the spacing of which is determined by the value of I_n. In this case, however, the absorption or emission of a photon often entails a *simultaneous* change in two or more of the rotational quantum numbers. Because of the likelihood of simultaneous transitions, the rotation line spectrum of a nonlinear molecule is considerably more complex and irregular than that of a linear molecule.

There are additional complications that I will mention but not dwell on. For example, both vibrational and rotational motions can perturb the moments of inertia I_n from their static values — e.g., by slightly stretching the mean interatomic distance r. These interactions can give rise to slight shifts in the positions of lines relative to the "pure" case. Since the perturbing influence is itself quantized, the usual result is the splitting of what would otherwise be a single line into family of closely spaced lines.

Dipole Moments

The above discussion hopefully gives you some insight into the basic nature of rotational line spectra, but there is one final issue that we have not yet considered. In order for a molecule to interact with an electromagnetic wave via rotational transitions, it must possess either a magnetic or electric *dipole moment*. That is to say, an externally applied magnetic or electric field, respectively, must have the capacity to exert a torque on the molecule.

For example, the needle in a compass has a magnetic dipole moment. The earth's magnetic field exerts a torque on the needle that causes it to rotate until it is aligned with the field. Likewise, a molecule with no *net* electric charge but with an asymmetric internal distribution of positive and negative charge can have an electric dipole moment that allows it respond to an external electric field by changing its orientation.

A diatomic molecule that is also *homonuclear* — i.e., consisting of two identical atoms (e.g, N_2 or O_2) — has no permanent electric dipole moment because of the symmetry of the distribution of positive and negative charge within the molecule. The same applies to a symmetric linear triatomic molecule at rest, such as CO_2. A *het-*

eronuclear diatomic molecule, such as carbon monoxide (CO), will generally have a permanent electric dipole. Also, with the exception of CO_2 and CH_4, all triatomic (and larger) molecules of interest to us for atmospheric radiation, such as H_2O, N_2O, and O_3, have permanent electric dipole moments due to various asymmetries in their structure.

Here is the "bottom line" for rotational absorption by atmospheric constituents:

- As noted previously, monoatomic constituents such as argon (Ar) and other noble gases have effectively zero moment of inertia I and therefore no rotational transitions.

- Molecular nitrogen (N_2), the most abundant atmospheric constituent, has neither electric nor magnetic dipole moment and therefore has no rotational absorption spectrum.

- Oxygen (O_2) also has no electric dipole moment but, unlike most other diatomic gases, it does have a permanent magnetic dipole moment. This property is what permits it to have rotational absorption bands at 60 and 118 GHz.

- Carbon dioxide (CO_2) and methane (CH_4) have no permanent electric or magnetic dipole moment and are therefore radiatively inactive with respect to pure rotational transitions. However, bending vibrational motions can break the linear symmetry of the molecule and introduce an oscillating dipole moment whose presence permits combined vibration-rotation transitions at shorter wavelengths (see Section 9.2.2).

- All other major molecules found in the atmosphere exhibit permanent electric dipole moments and therefore also major rotational absorption bands.

9.2.2 Vibrational Transitions

The covalent bonds between two atoms in a molecule arise from a balance of attractive and repulsive electrostatic forces. The former dominates when the two atoms are relatively widely separated;

the latter, due to mutual repulsion of the positively charged nuclei, takes over when the atoms get pushed too close together. The arrangement of atoms in a molecule at rest corresponds to the positions for which all attractive and repulsive forces exactly cancel.

Diatomic Molecules

The molecular bond is thus not rigid but behaves like a spring. In particular, for sufficiently small displacements, the force between two atoms in a diatomic molecule is given by

$$F = -k(r' - r) , \tag{9.19}$$

where k is analogous to a spring constant, and F is thus the restoring force when the separation r is smaller or greater than the equilibrium separation r'. Because the atoms have mass, the molecule would, in the classical limit, behave like a simple harmonic oscillator with resonant frequency

$$\nu' = \frac{1}{2\pi}\sqrt{\frac{k}{m'}} , \tag{9.20}$$

where m' is the reduced mass defined by (9.9).

In the quantum mechanical limit, however, the actual vibrational frequency ν of the the oscillator is quantized according to

$$\nu = \left(v + \frac{1}{2}\right)\nu' , \tag{9.21}$$

where v (letter 'V', not Greek 'nu') is the *vibrational quantum number* and, like the rotational quantum number J, can only take on non-negative integer values.

The energy associated with each frequency ν is the same as it is for a photon with the same frequency:

$$E_v = h\nu = \left(v + \frac{1}{2}\right)h\nu' . \tag{9.22}$$

A vibrational transition $\Delta v = \pm N$ therefore entails a change of energy

$$|\Delta E_v| = Nh\nu' , \tag{9.23}$$

and we see, somewhat to our amazement, that the photon frequency associated with the transition is just an integer multiple of the classical resonant frequency of the harmonic oscillator.

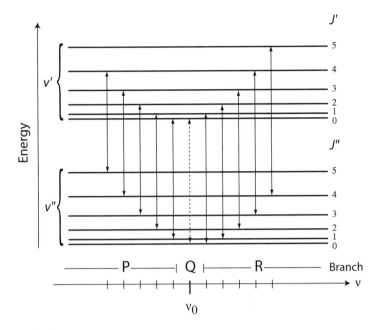

Fig. 9.3: Vibrational-rotational transitions for $\Delta v = \pm 1, \Delta J = [-1, 0, +1]$, showing the relative positions of the transitions in the spectrum. The P-branch corresponds to transitions involving $\Delta J = -1$, while the R-branch corresponds to $\Delta J = +1$. The Q-branch, when present, represents a superposition of all possible transitions involving $\Delta J = 0$ and occurs close to frequency $v_0 = \Delta E / h$, where ΔE is the energy associated with pure vibrational transitions.

Vibration/Rotation Spectra

There are two important points to note:

- Vibrational transitions tend to be associated with considerably larger energies than rotational transitions. Therefore vibrational transitions give rise to absorption/emission lines at much shorter wavelengths — e.g., in the thermal and near IR bands — than those due to pure rotational transitions, which are generally associated with the far IR and microwave bands.

- Vibrational and rotational transitions may, and often do, occur simultaneously. It follows from the previous point that the energy (and photon wavelength) of combined vibration/rotation transition is slightly greater or less than that of a pure vibrational transition, depending on whether the rotational quantum number J increased or decreased during the transition. The effect of rotational transitions is therefore to split up vibrational absorption lines into a series of rather closely spaced separate lines.

The second of the above points is illustrated by Fig. 9.3, which depicts the positions of lines associated with various combinations of $\Delta v = \pm 1$ and $\Delta J = [-1, 0, 1]$. The nominal frequency of a pure vibrational transition ($\Delta J = 0$) is indicated in this figure as v_0 and is approximately the same regardless of the value of J in force when the transition occurs. The associated absorption/emission lines, when present (see below), belong to what spectroscopists refer to as the Q *branch* of the vibration/rotation spectrum.[3]

For transitions involving $\Delta J = -1$ and $\Delta J = +1$, respectively, the absorption lines associated with $\Delta v = 1$ are spread out slightly below or above v_0. These lines do not overlap because of the uneven spacing of the rotational energy levels. The lines associated with $\Delta J = -1$ belong to the so-called P *branch*; the $\Delta J = +1$ transitions are known as the R *branch*.

Note that for certain molecular configurations, quantum mechanics *requires* a vibrational transition of $\Delta v = \pm 1$ to be accompanied by a nonzero rotational transition (typically $\Delta J = \pm 1$). In such cases, the central Q branch is absent and the absorption spectrum consists of the P and R branches alone.

Polyatomic Molecules

When a molecule consists of more than two atoms, the variety of possible vibrational motions increases substantially and, in general, consist of combinations of bending and stretching of interatomic bonds. It turns out that, for a given molecular structure, any physically admissible vibrational motion can be expressed as the superposition of a finite set of *normal modes*, each of which can be considered independently of the others, and each of which is associated

---

[3]In actuality, the rate of rotation of the molecule has a weak influence on vibrational energy levels, so that the Q branch is very finely split into a number of nearly overlapping lines (not pictured in Fig. 9.3).

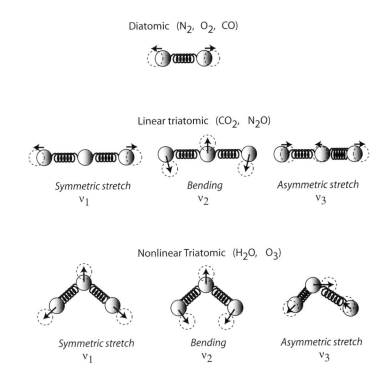

Fig. 9.4: Illustration of normal modes of vibration for simple molecules.

with its own set of vibrational energy levels. The situation is analogous to the existence of three distinct rotational quantum numbers for aspherical top molecules, but the number of possible vibrational modes is a function of the structure of the molecule.

For the diatomic molecule considered earlier, the sole possible vibrational mode consisted of stretching and compressing motions along the axis of the molecule. Its vibrational energy levels can therefore be expressed in terms of only one vibrational quantum number v.

For triatomic molecules, there are three energetically distinct modes: (1) symmetric stretching, (2) asymmetric stretching, and (3) bending.[4] The nature of these vibrational motions is illustrated in

---

[4]For a linear molecule such as CO_2, there are actually two normal modes associated with bending - one lying in each of two orthogonal planes. However, these two modes are energetically equivalent and therefore needn't be considered

Fig. 9.4. For this case, three vibrational quantum numbers v_1, v_2, v_3 are required to describe all possible vibrational energy levels. During the absorption or emission of a photon, transitions may occur in one, two, or three of these quantum numbers simultaneously. It follows that the vibrational absorption spectra of triatomic molecules is considerably more complex than those of diatomic molecules.

For molecules consisting of four or more atoms — e.g., methane (CH_4), chlorofluorocarbons, etc., the number of normal modes multiplies very rapidly, and the associated absorption spectrum becomes very rich indeed. In general, a molecule consisting of $n > 1$ atoms has $N = 3n - 6$ normal modes if it is nonlinear, or $N = 3n - 5$ if it is linear.

> **Problem 9.4:** Chlorofluorocarbons (CFCs) are synthetic compounds that have strong absorption bands in the IR band. One of the simplest CFCs has the formula $CFCl_3$. Given that it is a nonlinear molecule, how many vibrational normal modes does it have?

> **Problem 9.5:** Assume that a molecule has N distinct vibrational quantum numbers v_i. If we only consider transitions of the form $\Delta v_i = \{-1, 0, 1\}$ for each v_i individually, how many energy transitions are possible for which one or more of these change simultaneously?

9.2.3   Electronic Transitions

Having discussed rotational and vibrational transitions, we now briefly consider a third transition type, which involves the energy levels of the electrons orbiting an atomic nucleus. Just as energy has to be added to a satellite in order to raise it to a higher orbit above the earth's surface, the energy associated with an electron increases with its mean distance from the nucleus. As before, the allowed energy levels of electronic orbits are quantized. Also, the more tightly

---

separately.

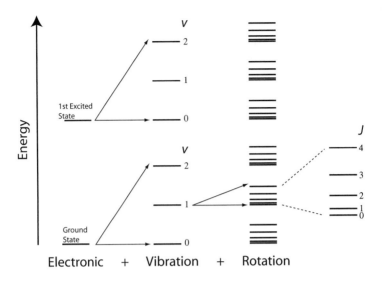

Fig. 9.5: Schematic depiction of the superposition of electronic, vibrational and rotational energy levels. The absorption spectrum of a molecule is determined by all nonforbidden transitions between pairs of levels in the righthand column.

bound an electron is to a nucleus, the larger the magnitude of the energy steps ΔE between levels.

In general, a photon can be absorbed when its energy corresponds to the excitation of an electron to a more energetic state; a photon of an appropriate wavelength can be emitted when an excited electron drops back to a lower state.

For the purposes of this book, it is principally the outermost electrons that are of interest, since transitions between their ground state and the first excited state are associated with photon wavelengths in the near IR, visible and ultraviolet bands. Inner electrons, which are more strongly bound by attractive forces to the nucleus, tend to have energy transitions corresponding to very short wavelengths.

At ordinary atmospheric temperatures, collisions between molecules are very rarely energetic enough to kick electrons into excited states. Those few that do briefly find themselves in an excited state, for whatever reason, usually give up their energy again in the course of subsequent collisions without emitting a photon. There are therefore extremely few electrons found *naturally* in excited states and even fewer opportunities for the spontaneous emission of photons due to electronic transitions back to the ground state. This fact is of course consistent with the sharp fall-off in thermal emission at the short wavelength end of the Planck function.

When electron orbits in atmospheric molecules *are* found in an excited state, it is usually because of the absorption of an incoming photon with the right energy, usually one of solar origin. As for rotational and vibrational transitions, we therefore expect to find discrete absorption lines associated with each allowed transition to higher electronic orbital states.

9.2.4   Combined Energy Transitions and Associated Spectra

As noted in the previous subsections, each atmospheric molecule has associated with it a number of discrete energy levels associated with electronic, vibrational, and rotational quantum states. Electronic energy states are the most widely separated and therefore correspond to photon absorption/emission at the shortest wavelengths; vibrational and rotational transitions, respectively, are associated with intermediate- and low-energy transitions.

The combination of all three modes of excitations leads to a set of discrete energy levels that are depicted schematically in Fig. 9.5. The total absorption line spectrum of the molecule is determined by all *allowed* transitions between pairs of energy levels (recall that not all transitions are allowed by quantum mechanics) and by whether the molecule exhibits a sufficiently strong electric or magnetic dipole moment (either permanent or otherwise) to be able to interact with the radiation field.

9.3   Line Shapes

The above introduction of absorption line spectra might have understandably left you with the impression that absorption by molecules can occur only at the precise wavelengths determined by the permitted energy transitions. If this were indeed the case, line

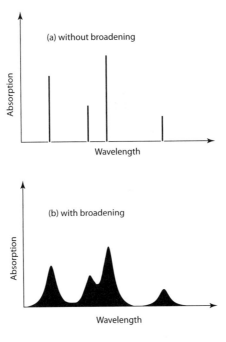

Fig. 9.6: Schematic depiction of the effect of broadening on a hypothetical line spectrum.

absorption would be completely unimportant. Why? Recall that, for natural radiation, the energy (or flux) associated with exactly one wavelength is zero. In order to account for a finite percentage of the total radiation field, it is necessary to consider a finite interval of wavelength. That being the case, if absorption lines had zero width, then no matter how strong they were and no matter how many of them were scattered through the spectrum, their practical impact on atmospheric radiative transfer would be zilch. The observed *broadening* of absorption lines is therefore of tremendous practical importance for radiative transfer, as it permits a given atmospheric constituent to absorb radiation not only at the nominal wavelength associated with a transition but also at nearby wavelengths as well (Fig. 9.6). Where absorption lines are closely spaced, as they are in much of the thermal IR band, line broadening can completely close the gaps between neighboring lines so that the atmosphere becomes effectively opaque over a continuous range of wavelength.

There are three distinct processes responsible for line broadening. Their relative importance depends on local environmental conditions.

Natural broadening: The Heisenberg uncertainty principle, which is one of the most fundamental and far-reaching early findings of quantum physics, ensures that an absorption line must have finite (though very small) width, even in the absence of other factors. Throughout most of the atmosphere, natural broadening is entirely negligible compared with the other two broadening mechanisms. We will not consider it further in this book.

Doppler broadening: Because of the random translational motions of individual molecules in any gas, absorption and emission occurs at wavelengths that are Doppler-shifted relative to the natural line position. This is the primary broadening mechanism in the mesosphere and above.

Pressure broadening: Collisions between molecules randomly disrupt natural transitions between energy states, so that emission and absorption occurs at wavelengths that deviate from the natural line position. This is the primary broadening mechanism in the troposphere and lower stratosphere.

9.3.1   Generic Description of Lines

Before going into the details of the line shapes associated with the above broadening mechanisms, it is convenient to introduce a generic framework for describing *any* individual absorption line. Specifically, there are three pieces of information that one needs to know about a line under a given set of environmental conditions:

Line position: Where does the line fall in the EM spectrum?

Line strength: How much total absorption is associated with the line?

Line shape: How is the above absorption distributed about the center of the line?

All of the above characteristics are captured succinctly in the following formulation:

$$\sigma_v = Sf(v - v_0) ,\qquad (9.24)$$

where σ_v is the absorption cross-section per molecule (or some other equivalent description, such as cross-section per unit mass) at frequency v. v_0 is the *center frequency* of the absorption line, S is the *line strength*, and $f(v - v_0)$ is the *line shape* function. In order that the strength and the shape be completely decoupled in the above description, the shape function is normalized to unit area:

$$\int_0^\infty f(v - v_0)\, dv = 1 ,\qquad (9.25)$$

so that the line strength is given by

$$\int_0^\infty \sigma_v\, dv = \int_0^\infty Sf(v - v_0)\, dv = S .\qquad (9.26)$$

Although the shape of $f(v - v_0)$ depends on the broadening mechanism, one feature common to all shape functions is that the maximum occurs at the line center $v = v_0$, and the function falls sharply and monotonically with increasing $|v - v_0|$. Moreover, the line shape is usually symmetric about v_0 (except in the microwave band); therefore it is common to succinctly characterize the overall width of the line via a parameter $\alpha_{1/2}$ known as the *half width at half-maximum*. That is to say, $\alpha_{1/2}$ represents the value of $|v - v_0|$ for which the absorption cross-section falls to half of its maximum value at the line center; i.e. $f(\alpha_{1/2}) = f(0)/2$.

Let us now consider the two major line broadening mechanisms and their implications for the shape function $f(v - v_0)$.

9.3.2 Doppler Broadening

In any gas, individual molecules are in constant motion, following random ballistic trajectories interrupted only by collisions with other molecules. The average kinetic energy of all of the molecules is proportional to the temperature. From the perspective of a stationary observer, each molecule has a random velocity component v_s toward or away from the observer. The statistical probability

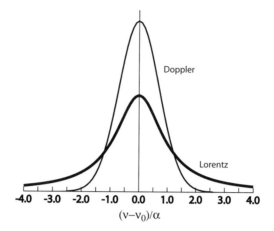

Fig. 9.7: Comparison of the Doppler and Lorentz line shapes for equal widths and strengths.

of any particular velocity component v_s along the line-of-sight s is given by the Maxwell-Boltzmann distribution

$$p(v_s) = \frac{1}{v_0\sqrt{\pi}}e^{-(v_s/v_0)^2} , \qquad (9.27)$$

where $v_0 = \sqrt{2k_BT/m}$ represents the standard deviation (or root-mean-squared value) of v_s, m is the mass per molecule ($= M/N_0$, where M is the molar mass and $N_0 = 6.02 \times 10^{23}$), T is the temperature, and k_B is the Boltzmann constant.

The motion of each molecule along a particular line-of-sight introduces a Doppler shift into the frequency of the photons it emits and absorbs, as measured from the perspective of a stationary observer. In Problem 2.2, you were asked to show that, in the case of an EM wave traveling at the speed of light c, the Doppler-shifted frequency is given by

$$\nu' = \nu(1 - v/c) , \qquad (9.28)$$

where ν is the frequency as measured by an observer who is stationary relative to the source, and ν' is the frequency measured by an observer moving with a velocity component v *away* from the source.

Because of the Doppler effect, EM frequencies that would appear not to coincide with the nominal position ν_0 of an absorption line can be absorbed, nevertheless, by any molecule having the right relative velocity. Conversely, radiation whose frequency *is* equal to v_0 can only be absorbed by those relatively few molecules whose relative velocity is close to zero. The net effect, therefore, is a decrease in the likelihood of absorption by a molecule at v_0 and an increase at nearby frequencies.

Combining (9.27) with (9.28) yields the line shape for Doppler broadening:

$$f_D(v - v_0) = \frac{1}{\alpha_D \sqrt{\pi}} \exp\left[-\frac{(v - v_0)^2}{\alpha_D^2}\right], \qquad (9.29)$$

where

$$\alpha_D = v_0 \sqrt{\frac{2k_B T}{mc^2}}. \qquad (9.30)$$

We can find the line halfwidth at half max $\alpha_{1/2}$ by setting

$$\frac{f_D(\alpha_{1/2})}{f_D(0)} = \frac{1}{2} \qquad (9.31)$$

and solving for $\alpha_{1/2}$. We find that

$$\alpha_{1/2} = \alpha_D \sqrt{\ln 2}. \qquad (9.32)$$

The interpretation of (9.29) is straightforward. This Maxwell-Boltzmann distribution of line-of-sight velocities (9.27) is Gaussian; therefore the Doppler-broadened shape of an initially narrow line is also Gaussian. The mean speed of the molecules, and therefore the line width, increases with temperature and decreases with molecular mass. The shape of the Doppler profile is depicted in Fig. 9.7.

9.3.3 Pressure Broadening

In Section 9.2, the occurrence and position of absorption lines was justified under the implicit assumption that molecules were free to make transitions between their various energy states without external interference. For gases in the tenuous upper atmosphere, this is a reasonable assumption. In the denser portions of the atmosphere (i.e., in the stratosphere and troposphere), collisions occur between molecules with very high frequency. The effect of a collision is to "shock" the molecule at a time when it might just be in the process of emitting or absorbing a photon. Not surprisingly, this adds a significant new level of complexity to the problem of predicting which wavelengths might be most readily absorbed or emitted during a particular transition. In fact, no exact theory has yet been developed to describe the so-called *pressure broadening* of absorption/emission lines that results.

It is beyond the scope of this book to go through the heuristic arguments that have been used to derive an approximate expression for the shape of pressure broadened lines. Suffice it to say that one common model invokes collision-induced random phase shifts imposed on an otherwise "pure" sinusoidal oscillation to explain the resulting "smearing" of emitted (and absorbed) frequencies about the nominal frequency v_0. The interested student is referred to Section 3.3.1 of S94 and Section 3.3 of GY95 for details.

The bottom line, for our purposes, is that pressure broadening is usually described adequately, though by no means perfectly, by the *Lorentz* line shape

$$f(v - v_0) = \frac{\alpha_L / \pi}{(v - v_0)^2 + \alpha_L^2} , \tag{9.33}$$

where α_L is the Lorentz halfwidth at half max and is roughly proportional to the number of collisions per unit time. Thus, to first order

$$\alpha_L \propto p T^{-1/2} , \tag{9.34}$$

where p is the pressure and T is the temperature. As a practical matter, α_L for any particular line is usually modeled as

$$\alpha_L = \alpha_0 \left(\frac{p}{p_0} \right) \left(\frac{T_0}{T} \right)^n , \tag{9.35}$$

where α_0 is the laboratory-measured line width at reference pressure p_0 and temperature T_0, and n is an empirically determined exponent. When measured in units of wavenumber, typical values of α_0 lie in the range 0.01–0.1 cm^{-1}, for $T_0 = 273$ K and $p_0 = 1000$ mb. The corresponding range in units of frequency is 3×10^8 to 3×10^9 Hz.

The Lorentz line shape has two notable deficiencies. One is that the *far wings* of actual absorption lines have been found to be poorly

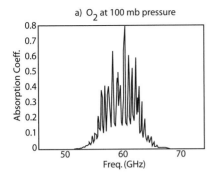 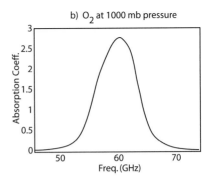

Fig. 9.8: Absorption coefficient of oxygen in the microwave band near 60 GHz, (a) at 100 mb pressure, revealing the individual lines making up the absorption band; (b) at 1000 mb, for which pressure broadening obliterates the line structure.

represented by this line shape. It might strike you as unimportant whether a line shape model does well in the far wings, where absorption due to a single line is very small anyway. However, recall that the absorption coefficient at any particular frequency ν is due to the combined contributions of *all* lines, near and far. And there are of course many more distant lines than nearby lines! In particular, at any frequency located in a spectral window where there *are* no nearby lines, *all* of the absorption is due to the accumulated far wings of countless thousands of distant lines. In general, it has been found that the Lorentz model underestimates this contribution.

Another limitation of the Lorentz model is that it is only valid when $\alpha_L \ll \nu_0$; that is, when the line width is very small compared to the center frequency. When this condition doesn't hold, then the Lorentz model is invalid, because it fails to account for the fact that line wings cannot extend down to zero frequency. This is primarily a problem in the microwave band, where ν_0 is quite small. In this case, the preferred line shape model is the *van Vleck-Weisskopf* function

$$f_{VW}(\nu - \nu_0) = \frac{1}{\pi}\left(\frac{\nu}{\nu_0}\right)^2\left[\frac{\alpha_L}{(\nu - \nu_0)^2 + \alpha_L^2} + \frac{\alpha_L}{(\nu + \nu_0)^2 + \alpha_L^2}\right].$$
(9.36)

Note that the van Vleck-Weisskopf line shape is asymmetric about ν_0 and, more importantly, is constrained to go obediently to zero as $\nu \to 0$.

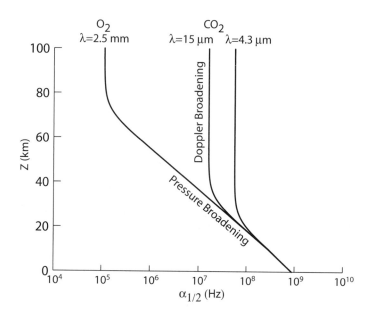

Fig. 9.9: Approximate linewidth as a function of altitude for three prominent absorption bands.

An example of the how pressure broadening affects absorption line spectra is shown in Fig. 9.8. At high altitudes, individual lines are narrow enough to be clearly separated. At lower altitudes, pressure broadening often completely obliterates the individual lines, leading to the appearance of one single broad absorption feature. Note that the careful positioning of a satellite sounding channel between lines can lead to a sharpening of the absorption/emission weighting function $W(z)$, because the mass extinction coefficient at that wavelength then sharply increases toward the surface, rather than being constant, as we assumed in the previous chapter.

9.3.4 Comparing Doppler and Pressure Broadening

The shape of the Lorentz profile is compared with the Doppler profile in Fig. 9.7 for equal values of the width parameters α_L and α_D. The most important difference is that the Lorentz shape puts much more absorption out in the far wings of the line.

Both Doppler and pressure broadening occur at all levels of the atmosphere. However, if the degree of broadening by one mechanism is substantially greater than that due to the other, then the latter may be neglected. The relative importance of each may therefore be assessed by way of the ratio of α_D to α_L, using (9.30) and (9.35):

$$\frac{\alpha_D}{\alpha_L} \approx \left[\frac{p_0}{\alpha_0 c} \sqrt{\frac{2k_B}{T_0}} \right] \frac{T\nu_0}{p\sqrt{m}} \sim [5 \times 10^{-13} \text{mb Hz}^{-1}] \left(\frac{\nu_0}{p} \right) , \quad (9.37)$$

where we have assumed that $n \approx 1/2$ and, in the far righthand terms, used "typical" values for m, T, α_0. Because pressure varies by several orders of magnitude through the atmosphere, whereas all other variables (except ν_0) typically vary by less than a factor of two, we conclude that p is the principal factor determining whether Doppler broadening or pressure broadening prevails in any given case. If we choose $\nu_0 = 2 \times 10^{13}$ *Hz* , corresponding to a wavelength of 15 μm, we find that $\alpha_D \approx \alpha_L$ at $p \sim 10$ mb. At this altitude, the two broadening processes are of roughly equal importance. For lines in the microwave band, we have $\nu_0 \sim 10^{11}$ Hz, so that the pressure level at which parity occurs is in the vicinity of 0.1 mb or less. Fig. 9.9 depicts the transition from predominantly pressure broadening at low altitudes to primarily Doppler broadening at higher altitudes for the two cases discussed above.

When α_D is of the same order of magnitude as α_L, both Doppler and pressure broadening must be considered simultaneously. In this case, it is necessary to use the hybrid *Voigt* line shape, which accounts for both mechanisms. Near the center of the line, it behaves like a Doppler profile; in the wings, it has the characteristics of the Lorentz profile. The interested student should consult p. 112 of GY95 for further details.

9.4 Continuum Absorption

The most important absorption features in the IR and microwave bands are due to bands of discrete absorption lines, as discussed above. However, outside the major resonant absorption bands, one generally finds some level of atmospheric absorption that does not exhibit line-like structure. This is known as *continuum* (or *nonresonant*) absorption, because it tends to vary smoothly with frequency.

There are at least three causes of continuum absorption, two of which, *photoionization* and *photodissociation*, are well-understood and affect primarily the very short wavelength end of the solar spectrum. The third, affecting spectral windows throughout the infrared and microwave bands, is significant both for remote sensing and for thermal radiative transfer in the atmosphere but is not as well understood.

9.4.1   Photoionization

Photoionization occurs when a photon has enough energy not only to excite an electron in an atom to a higher level but to actually strip it completely from the atom, creating a positively charged ion and a free electron. We saw earlier that ordinary electron excitation was constrained to discrete energy levels, leading to absorption/emission lines in the visible and UV bands. A fixed amount of energy is also required to ionize an atom. However, any photon *exceeding* that ionization energy can be absorbed in the course of an ionization event; the excess energy appears in the form of kinetic energy of the ion and/or the free electron. Recall that translational kinetic energy is not quantized; hence there is no constraint on the exact energy level of the photon.

The ionization of atoms requires very energetic photons. It is observed primarily in connection with X-ray and gamma radiation from extraterrestrial sources. It is therefore a phenomenon that is of relatively little interest from an atmospheric radiation point of view. However, it is responsible for the existence of the *ionosphere*, a highly conductive region of the atmosphere that has important implications for the propagation of radio waves.

9.4.2   Photodissociation

A second cause of continuum absorption is photodissociation. Just as photoionization is electronic excitation carried to the extreme that the electron completely separates from the atom, photodissociation is molecular vibration carried to the extreme that the molecule breaks into two pieces. Thus, any photon whose energy E exceeds the chemical binding energy E_{bond} between two components of a molecule can induce photodissociation, with the excess energy

$\Delta E = E - E_{bond}$ appearing as unquantized kinetic (thermal) energy.[5] At the molecular level, of course, a gain in kinetic energy is synonymous with an increase in temperature.

The binding energies in the diatomic molecules of gases like O_2, N_2, etc., tend to be large. Therefore, only very short wavelengths can dissociate them (see Section 3.4.1).

9.4.3 Continuum Absorption by Water Vapor

In addition to the above well-understood modes of continuum absorption, which are primarily active at UV wavelengths, there is also significant continuum absorption by water vapor between the major absorption bands in the infrared and microwave bands. The physical mechanism behind the water vapor continuum remains a matter of some controversy. There are basically two competing theories:

Far wings of lines - As noted earlier in this chapter, the Lorentz line shape doesn't do a good job of describing the intensity of absorption in the far wings of collision-broadened absorption lines. Therefore, one possible explanation of continuum absorption is that it is simply that portion of the accumulated contribution of the far wings of countless distant lines that is not accounted for by the Lorentz model.

H_2O clusters - Water molecules exert a significant attractive force on one another (it is for this reason that water condenses readily at relatively low temperature and pressure combinations). Therefore, molecules that encounter one another at low relative speeds tend to stick to each other, forming temporary clusters of two or more molecules that are subsequently broken up again by other collisions. Such *dimers* (two molecules), *trimers* (three) and *polymers* (many molecules) would naturally be expected to exhibit far more complex vibrational and rotational transitions than an isolated molecule. Furthermore, the range of structural configurations that these loose clusters

---

[5]Again, to return to the refrigerator magnet analogy: imagine that only 0.01 J of energy is necessary to separate a 20 g magnet from the door, but that, by whatever means, you supply 1 J of mechanical energy to the magnet (e.g., by snapping a wet dish towel at it). The magnet will acquire 0.99 J of kinetic energy, corresponding to a speed of almost 10 m/sec.

might exhibit at various points in their formation and disintegration is almost infinitely variable. There is therefore no reason to expect absorption to be limited to a finite set of discrete photon energies. Instead, we expect absorption to be smoothly distributed over a broad range of wavelengths, as is in fact observed with the water vapor continuum.

It is possible that the ultimate explanation of water vapor continuum will be found to combine elements of both theories. Regardless of the explanation, there are two points that are worth noting: (1) the strength of the continuum tends to increase steadily with frequency through the microwave and far IR bands but is weak again in the thermal and near IR bands, and (2) the volume extinction coefficient β_a is not proportional to the water vapor density ρ_v (as would be expected if the mass absorption coefficient k_a were approximately constant) but rather something closer to the *square* of that density. Therefore, continuum absorption is generally significant mainly in the lower troposphere, where water vapor density is the highest.

9.5 Applications to Meteorology, Climatology, and Remote Sensing

The main focus in this chapter has been on the following questions: (1) *how* does absorption by gases in the atmosphere occur, (2) what physical properties of molecules determine *where* in the EM spectrum absorption lines or bands will occur, and (3) by what processes are absorption lines broadened about their nominal wavelengths, and what is the shape of the resulting broadened line? I will now put some of the above ideas into a practical context with a survey of those constituents responsible for most absorption and emission in the cloud-free atmosphere.

9.5.1 Atmospheric Absorbers in the IR Band

From the perspective of most mainstream atmospheric scientists, absorption by gases in the atmosphere is mainly a feature (or defect, depending on your point of view) of the IR bands. While not discounting the importance of absorption in other bands to a handful

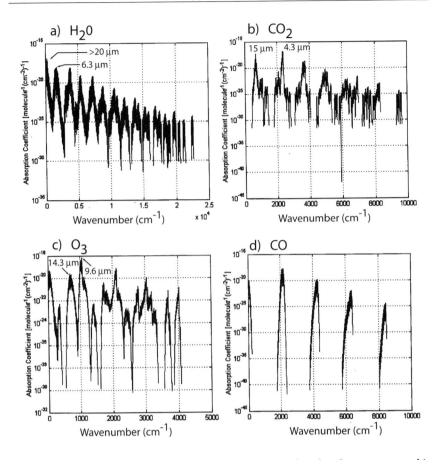

Fig. 9.10: Spectra of absorption cross-sections for several molecules encountered in the atmosphere. Absorption bands of particular significance for thermal radiative transfer in the atmosphere are labeled with the center wavelength. (a) Water vapor. (b) Carbon dioxide. (c) Ozone. (d) Carbon monoxide.

of overachievers (e.g., atmospheric chemists, stratospheric dynamicists, and microwave remote sensing specialists), it is safe to say that those individuals are not relying on this book alone for their education in atmospheric radiation.

Within the IR band (including near-, thermal-, and far-IR), the most important absorbers are carbon dioxide (CO_2), water vapor (H_2O), ozone (O_3), methane (CH_4), and nitrous oxide (N_2O). The major absorption features associated with each of these constituents was depicted in Fig. 7.6, which you may wish to refer back to occasionally while reading this section. It is perhaps no surprise that all of the above absorbers are (at least) triatomic, owing to the wealth of both rotational and vibrational transitions available in such molecules.

A broad-spectrum view of absorption by several representative molecules is depicted in Fig. 9.10. Included in this figure is a molecule of lesser importance, carbon monoxide (CO), which (fortunately for our health) is not usually present in the atmosphere in concentrations high enough to contribute much to atmospheric opacity. The reason for including CO here is to illustrate how much simpler the absorption spectrum is for a diatomic molecule, which (as discussed earlier) has just one vibration quantum number v and one rotational quantum number J.

The most obvious feature of Fig. 9.10d is the evenly spaced series of major absorption bands of CO. Although it is less apparent in this figure, each band is actually a cluster of numerous closely spaced lines, most of which overlap strongly due to pressure broadening.

The first band on the far left (near zero wavenumber) is a pure rotation band with $\Delta v = 0$, each line corresponding to a transition from a particular initial J to the next higher value. Subsequent bands, moving from left to right, are associated with vibrational transitions $\Delta v = 1, 2, \ldots$; their central positions are predicted by (9.23). The occurrence of simultaneous J transitions (both positive and negative) again splits each band into a cluster of closely spaced lines. In fact, it is not too much of a stretch to consider each major vibration-rotation band a near-clone of the one before it, since the fine-scale structure imposed by rotational transitions is similar in each case.

Turning our attention to the three triatomic molecules in Fig. 9.10(a–c), we see that the possibility of simultaneous transitions between multiple rotational and vibrational quantum numbers (up to three each) adds a fair amount of complexity to the absorption spectra. In particular, the "windows" between adjacent vibration bands are not nearly as broad and clear as they were for CO.

Note that CO_2 is the only molecule in Fig. 9.10 exhibiting no pure rotation band on the far left edge of the plot. As pointed out earlier, this is because CO_2 lacks a permanent electric dipole moment and can interact with radiation only via combined rotation-

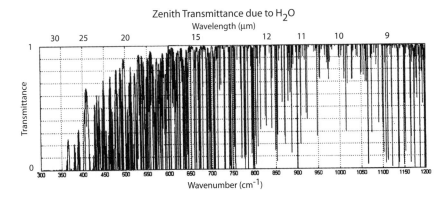

Fig. 9.11: Zenith transmittance of the atmosphere in a portion of the thermal IR band due to water vapor in a U.S. Standard atmosphere.

vibration transitions.

Let's now take a closer look at absorption by selected atmospheric molecules.

Water Vapor

Globally speaking, water vapor (H_2O) is the single most important atmospheric absorber in the IR band. Fig. 9.11 gives a moderate-resolution depiction of the zenith transmittance due to water vapor alone under the conditions of temperature and humidity found in the U.S. Standard Atmosphere. The enormous complexity, and apparent randomness, of the line structure is readily apparent. This randomness is characteristic of a nonlinear molecule, owing to the wide range of rotational transitions that are available to it.

The most transparent region of the H_2O spectrum in the thermal IR band lies between about 8 and 12 μm. At longer wavelengths (smaller wavenumbers), the spectrum is increasingly dominated by the numerous lines due to pure rotational transitions. In fact, beyond about 25 μm, the atmosphere is effectively opaque and doesn't begin to open up again until well into the microwave band (not shown).

Not shown in Fig. 9.11 but visible in Fig. 9.10 are vibration-rotation bands centered around 6.3 μm and 2.7 μm, the latter falling solidly in the near-IR band. The 6.3 μm band is due to the v_2 (bending mode) fundamental ($\Delta v = 1$), while both the v_1 (symmetric stretch) and v_3 (asymmetric stretch) fundamental modes contribute to absorption in the vicinity of 2.7 μm. Higher-order vibrational transitions ($\Delta v > 1$) contribute weak absorption bands at shorter wavelengths throughout the solar part of the spectrum. Also, as discussed earlier, not all of H_2O absorption is due to lines; there is also a significant continuum contribution throughout the IR band, though its overall intensity varies somewhat with wavelength.

An additional factor contributing to the complexity of the H_2O absorption band is the existence in the atmosphere of multiple isotopes of the constituent elements. In addition to the common hydrogen isotope ^1H, a small fraction (about 0.03%) of water molecules include at least one ^2H, or deuterium (D) atom. Also, oxygen exists both as the ^{16}O isotope and also the less common ^{18}O isotope, found in about 0.2% of water vapor molecules. Naturally, changing the nuclear masses of one or more of the constituent atoms in a molecule alters both the rotational and vibrational spectra of the molecule, adding numerous new lines to those already contributed by the most common form. However, because isotopic variations of the water molecule comprise such a small fraction of the total, most of these added lines are relatively weak.

An important property of water vapor that is not shared with other radiatively important atmospheric gases is of course its enormous variability in both time and space. There are significant ranges of the IR spectrum for which the atmosphere may be virtually opaque under conditions of high humidity but relatively transparent (or at least translucent) in a dry arctic atmosphere.

Carbon Dioxide

No other atmospheric constituent is better known to the general public as a "greenhouse gas" than carbon dioxide (CO_2). In actuality, water vapor has a larger overall impact on the radiative energy budget of the atmosphere. But CO_2 is of particular concern from a public policy point of view owing to its steadily increasing abundance in the atmosphere due to fossil fuel use (see Fig. 7.5).

CO_2 possesses two very strong rotation-vibration bands in the IR band, one centered on 4.3 μm (v_3 fundamental), the other at

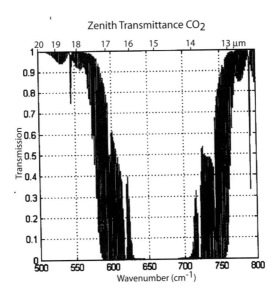

Fig. 9.12: Zenith transmittance of the atmosphere due to CO_2 in the vicinity of 15 μm.

15 μm (v_2 fundamental). The 4.3 μm band is actually the stronger of the two, but because it's located out on the edge of both the solar and longwave bands, it isn't terribly important for broadband radiative fluxes in either band.

The 15 μm band is very important for longwave radiative transfer in the atmosphere, because it is positioned near the peak of the Planck emission function for terrestrial temperatures and renders the atmosphere completely opaque between 14 and 16 μm (Fig. 9.12). Moreover, the atmosphere is at least partly absorbing for several micrometers more to either side of the above wavelengths.

Problem 9.6: The effect of the CO_2 15 μm band on atmospheric transmission to space of surface emission can be crudely approximated by assuming total opacity between 13.5 and 17 μm, and total transparency outside these limits. Use Fig. 6.4 to estimate the fraction of surface longwave emission that is reabsorbed by the CO_2 in the atmosphere (ignoring other absorbers). Assume a surface temperature of 288 K.

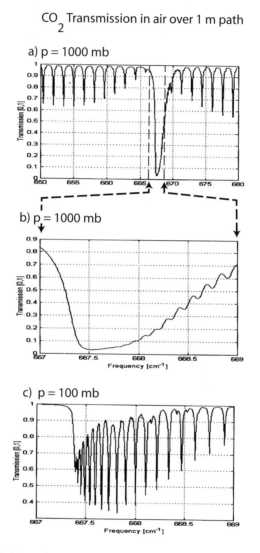

Fig. 9.13: (a) High resolution depiction of the transmission spectrum of a one-meter path through air with typical CO_2 concentration, at 1000 mb pressure. (b) Same as (a), but "zoomed in" on the central Q-branch. (c) Same as (b), but at reduced atmospheric pressure of 100 mb, revealing that what previously appeared as a single absorption line is actually a cluster of closely spaced but distinct lines.

Examining the center of the 15 μm band closely (Fig. 9.13), we find that it looks much like the idealized vibration-rotation band associated with a diatomic molecule — that is, it exhibits a strong central Q branch associated with pure vibration transitions ($\Delta v = 1$; $\Delta J = 0$), as well as the usual P branch ($\Delta v = 1$; $\Delta J = -1$) and R branch ($\Delta v = 1$; $\Delta J = +1$). Unlike the random-appearing H_2O rotation spectrum, the P and R branches for CO_2 consist of very regularly spaced lines, again as predicted for a diatomic molecule (Fig. 9.3).

Why does CO_2, which is triatomic, yield a spectrum so unlike that of another triatomic molecule, H_2O? The reason is that CO_2 is a linear molecule with effectively only one rotation mode (similar to a diatomic molecule), as compared with three for H_2O, which is an asymmetric top. This seemingly minor difference eliminates the whole universe of lines that would arise from transitions involving J_2 or J_3.

As noted also for water vapor, isotopic variations of the constituent atoms multiply the total number of lines found in the CO_2 absorption spectrum. Here we have not only the two most common oxygen isotopes ^{16}O and ^{18}O, but also two major carbon isotopes ^{12}C and ^{13}C, the latter comprising about 1% of total carbon in the atmosphere.

We conclude our discussion of CO_2 by noting that the central lines of the 15 μm band are really quite strong. Despite the diluteness of CO_2 in air (about 370 parts per million by volume), the strongest part of the central Q branch (Fig. 9.13b) absorbs all but 5% of radiation over just a 1-meter path in air at 1000 mb pressure! Also, we see that, at reduced pressure (Fig. 9.13c), the Q branch resolves into a series of very closely spaced but separate lines. Each of these is associated with a ($\Delta v = 1$; $\Delta J = 0$) transition, but depending on the rate of rotation of the molecule (i.e., value of J), there are slight differences in the energy associated with a pure $\Delta v = 1$ transition.

Ozone

Ozone (O_3), which (except in urban pollution) is confined primarily to the stratosphere, is another nonlinear triatomic molecule, like water vapor. Therefore, it possesses many of the same general absorption features as water vapor, such as a relatively strong rotation spectrum consisting of numerous quasi-randomly spaced lines, as well as three fundamental vibrational bands v_1, v_2, and v_3. These bands, respectively, are found at 9.066, 14.27, and 9.597 μm. In the atmosphere, the 14.3 μm band is essentially masked by CO_2's 15 μm band — that is, the presence or absence of ozone doesn't change much in this band, because absorption by CO_2 is already overwhelmingly strong.

The moderately strong v_1 and very strong v_3 bands are close enough to each other that they are commonly viewed as a single entity known as the 9.6 μm band of ozone. Note that this band sits squarely in the middle of the 8–12 μm "window" of H_2O as well as falling not far from the peak of the Planck function for terrestrial emission. For both reasons, ozone is an important player in the atmospheric radiation budget, especially in the stratosphere.

Ozone also has a strong band at 4.7 μm, but this is at the edge of the Planck functions for both solar and terrestrial emission (as was also the case for the CO_2 4.3 μm band) and therefore is of very limited relevance for broadband radiative fluxes. Additional vibration-rotation absorption bands can be found in the near-IR regions of the spectrum down to about 2.5 μm (see Fig. 9.10c), but these are weak and therefore of only minor importance.

Also, as is well-known to the many specialists and laypeople alike concerned about recent observed declines in stratospheric ozone concentrations, ozone exhibits very strong absorption in the UV band below 0.28 μm due to electronic rather than vibrational excitations. As was discussed in Section 3.4.1, this absorption is exceedingly important for life on earth, because of the biologically damaging effects of UV-B radiation. A near-steady-state balance between absorption of solar UV-B and re-emission of longwave IR in the 9.6 μm band is largely responsible for the temperature structure of the stratosphere and lower mesosphere.

Methane

Methane (CH_4) is a spherical top molecule with five atoms and therefore $3(5) - 6 = 9$ fundamental modes of vibration. However, because of the symmetry of the molecule (four hydrogen atoms all bound to one central carbon atom), five of the modes are equivalent, leaving only four distinct modes v_1, v_2, v_3, and v_4. The most important of these are the v_3 and v_4 fundamentals at approximately 3.3 μm and 7.6 μm, respectively. In addition, there are a few weak overtone ($\Delta v_i > 1$) and combination bands scattered through the near-IR.

Although methane is present in the atmosphere in relatively low concentrations, its 7.6 μm absorption band is strong enough, and is placed in an otherwise relatively transparent part of the atmospheric spectrum (especially in a dry atmosphere) to have a measurable impact on longwave fluxes. In addition, it is now known that methane concentrations are increasing as a direct or indirect consequence of human activities.[6]

Nitrous Oxide

Nitrous oxide (N_2O) is another minor atmospheric constituent that nevertheless has a measurable radiative impact, primarily owing to its absorption band at 7.8 μm, which acts to broaden and strengthen the absorption band already present at 7.6 μm due to methane. In addition, there is a strong 4.5 μm band which, however, is less significant for the same reasons as given for the CO_2 4.3 μm band and the ozone 4.7 μm band.

---

[6]To give just one example, widespread clearing of tropical forests has led to a marked increase in the number of methane-producing termite colonies, which thrive in the resulting open spaces!

CHAPTER 10

Broadband Fluxes and Heating Rates in the Cloud-Free Atmosphere[†]

In Chapter 9, we examined the physical basis for absorption and emission of radiation by atmospheric gases, focusing on the factors that determine line positions, shapes, and widths. There now exist extensive (though by no means perfect[1]) tabulations of line positions, strengths, and broadening parameters for all significant atmospheric absorbers. The most complete and widely used of these tabulations is the HITRAN spectroscopic data base maintained by Phillips Laboratory (formerly the Air Force Geophysics Laboratory). The 1992 edition listed 709,308 lines covering the range 0 to 2.3×10^4 cm^{-1} (i.e., wavelengths longer than 0.43 μm); new additions and corrections to existing line parameters continue to be made based on new laboratory measurements.

In short, any unfortunate soul tasked with calculating broadband fluxes and/or heating rates in the cloud-free atmosphere has to contend with the enormous complexity of the absorption spectra of atmospheric constituents. This chapter is intended to give you just a cursory survey of the tricks and simplifications used by the experts, and why they are necessary. Although some of these tech-

---

[1]The line intensities in the current data base are believed correct to within 5–10% for strong lines; weak lines are harder to measure accurately in the laboratory.

niques are also applicable to atmospheric absorption of solar radiation (especially in the near IR band), we will keep things simple by limiting our attention initially to the emission and absorption of radiation in the thermal IR band.

10.1 Line-by-line Calculations

For monochromatic radiation, we can easily generalize (8.27)–(8.30) to describe the upward and downward intensity at any level z in a plane-parallel, nonscattering atmosphere with a black lower boundary at temperature T_s and no extraterrestrial sources:

$$I_{\tilde{\nu}}^{\downarrow}(z) = \int_z^{\infty} B_{\tilde{\nu}}[T(z')] W_{\tilde{\nu}}(z',z) \, dz' \,, \tag{10.1}$$

$$I_{\tilde{\nu}}^{\uparrow}(z) = B_{\tilde{\nu}}(T_s) t_{\tilde{\nu}}(0,z) + \int_0^z B_{\tilde{\nu}}[T(z')] W_{\tilde{\nu}}(z',z) \, dz' \,, \tag{10.2}$$

where

$$t_{\tilde{\nu}}(z_1, z_2) = \exp\left[-\frac{\tau_{\tilde{\nu}}(z_1, z_2)}{\mu}\right] \,, \tag{10.3}$$

$$\tau_{\tilde{\nu}}(z_1, z_2) = \left| \int_{z_1}^{z_2} \beta_{a\tilde{\nu}}(z) \, dz \right| \,, \tag{10.4}$$

and

$$W_{\tilde{\nu}}(z',z) = \left| \frac{\partial t_{\tilde{\nu}}(z',z)}{\partial z'} \right| \,. \tag{10.5}$$

Note that we have introduced the subscript $\tilde{\nu}$ to make explicit the dependence on wavenumber,[2] and we have introduced absolute value operators to permit a more compact set of expressions valid for both upwelling and downwelling radiation.

In view of what we learned from the previous chapter about absorption spectra, it is evident that the absorption coefficient $\beta_{a\tilde{\nu}}(z)$

---

[2]Traditionally, spectroscopists working in the thermal IR band are accustomed to using wavenumber rather than wavelength to describe where they are in the spectrum.

can be expanded as

$$
\begin{aligned}
\beta_{a\tilde{v}}(z) &= \sum_{i=1}^{N} \rho_i(z) k_{a,i}(z) \\
&= \sum_{i=1}^{N} \rho_i(z) \left[k_{\text{cont},i}(\tilde{v};z) + \sum_{j=1}^{M_i} S_{ij}(z) f_{ij}(\tilde{v} - \tilde{v}_{ij};z) \right] ,
\end{aligned}
\tag{10.6}
$$

where ρ_i is the local density of each of N atmospheric constituents, M_i is the number of significant absorption lines associated with the ith constituent, S_{ij}, f_{ij} and $\tilde{v}_{ij}$ are the respective line strengths, shapes and positions, and $k_{\text{cont},i}$ represents the continuum component of absorption for that constituent, if applicable. The z-dependence in many of the above parameters arises from the influence of local temperature, pressure and constituent partial pressure on line strength and width.

In other words, in order to compute the monochromatic intensity at altitude z and zenith angle $\mu = |\cos\theta|$, you have to evaluate the sum of the contributions of all relevant absorption lines to the absorption coefficient β_a at your chosen wavenumber $\tilde{v}$, and you have to repeat this for all z'. Then you can numerically evaluate (10.1) and/or (10.2) to get the corresponding radiant intensity at your chosen level z. The above procedure is the essence of so-called *line-by-line* (LBL) calculations of radiative transfer — that is, there is an explicit summation of the individual contributions of all lines in the vicinity to the emission and absorption at each wavenumber of interest. Note that "in the vicinity" means all lines whose wings contribute nonnegligible absorption at the wavenumber in question.[3]

A couple of comments are in order. If the intended application for your radiance calculation is remote sensing, then a full LBL treatment is reasonably manageable, since you're often dealing with only an extremely narrow range of wavenumber for each sensor channel and therefore don't have to repeat the calculation many times. In fact, if the wavenumber of the calculation is far enough

---

[3]Actual LBL computer codes in wide use include FASCODE, GENLN2, and LBLRTM. All of these use various strategies to maximize computational efficiency without sacrificing precision, but the essence of the calculation remains as outlined above.

from any absorption lines, then you can probably get away with using just a single wavenumber to represent the response of your sensor channel to the atmospheric profile of temperature, humidity, etc. If, on the other hand, your channel is positioned very close to a strong absorption band (as is the case for satellite sounders), then the monochromatic intensity $I_{\tilde{\nu}}$ will probably vary strongly even over the narrow bandwidth of the sensor channel, and a numerical integration over wavenumber is required. Nevertheless, this is still not an excessive computational burden in most instances.

Far more problematic is the computation of longwave *fluxes* and *heating rates*. Recall that, in contrast to remote sensing applications, which commonly require *quasi-monochromatic radiances at only one or two levels* (e.g., the top and/or bottom of the atmosphere), the calculation of radiative heating profiles within the atmosphere requires *broadband fluxes at every level within the atmosphere*.

Getting from a monochromatic *intensity* to a monochromatic *flux* is straightforward — in fact, we already solved that problem for a plane-parallel nonscattering atmosphere in Section 8.2.2. To refresh your memory, the key result from that section is that the flux can be computed in a manner analogous to the intensity simply by substituting the *flux transmittance* $t_F(z_1, z_2)$ for the beam transmittance $t(z_1, z_2)$ and $\pi B_{\tilde{\nu}}$ for $B_{\tilde{\nu}}$, everywhere where these terms appear in equations (10.1)–(10.5). Furthermore, I pointed out that, to a pretty good approximation,

$$t_F(z_1, z_2) \approx e^{-\tau(z_1,z_2)/\bar{\mu}} , \tag{10.7}$$

where the effective zenith angle $\bar{\mu}$ is usually taken to be constant and equal to 0.6.

With the above adaptations, we have

$$F_{\tilde{\nu}}^{\downarrow}(z) = \int_z^{\infty} \pi B_{\tilde{\nu}}[T(z')] W_{F,\tilde{\nu}}(z',z)\, dz' , \tag{10.8}$$

$$F_{\tilde{\nu}}^{\uparrow}(z) = \pi B_{\tilde{\nu}}(T_s) t_{F,\tilde{\nu}}(0,z) + \int_0^z \pi B_{\tilde{\nu}}[T(z')] W_{F,\tilde{\nu}}(z',z)\, dz' , \tag{10.9}$$

where

$$W_{F,\tilde{\nu}}(z',z) = \left| \frac{\partial t_{F,\tilde{\nu}}(z',z)}{\partial z'} \right| \approx \left| \frac{\partial t_{\tilde{\nu}}(z',z;\bar{\mu})}{\partial z'} \right| . \tag{10.10}$$

So much for the easy part. Getting radiative heating profiles (for example) requires us to compute the *broadband* net flux at each level z in the atmosphere. If we use the above LBL approach, we effectively have to repeat our monochromatic calculations for **[a very large number of discrete wavenumbers]**×**[a moderate number of discrete altitudes]**. The wavenumber spacing of our calculations must be fine enough to accurately resolve the shapes of individual lines, a hurdle which is especially imposing at high altitudes, where lines are extremely narrow. In short, *the radiative heating profile problem is potentially many millions of times more expensive than the monochromatic radiance problem.*

If we only need to do this once or twice, a LBL flux calculation might still be a manageable proposition – simply let the program run on an unused computer in a back room somewhere and forget about it until word arrives that the program has completed. Unfortunately, some of the most important applications of radiative transfer calculations are found in the general circulation models (GCMs) used in climate studies and in numerical weather prediction (NWP) models. In GCMs, for example, radiative fluxes and heating profiles must be computed *at every point on the entire globe* and updated on regular time intervals as the model atmosphere evolves. It's safe to assume that, using the LBL approach and current computer technology, it would take a GCM far longer than a decade in computer time to simulate a decade of real time! Clearly this is unacceptable for graduate students trying to finish their dissertations on global warming.

Hopefully I have persuaded you that we need some way to obtain reasonably accurate broadband fluxes with greatly reduced computational effort. The goal is to find techniques for greatly streamlining the otherwise painstaking integration over complex line spectra. In this book, I will give you a fairly cursory overview of two basic strategies:

- band models, and

- the k-distribution method.

Band models have been in use in various forms for many decades and remain of both practical and historical interest. They come in two basic flavors: *wide-band emission* models and *narrow-band transmission* models. The former represent the most radical simplification of the radiative transfer equation and are widely used in applications (e.g., climate models) in which computational efficiency is of paramount importance. Narrow-band transmission models, which we will discuss in this book, are not as efficient but are capable of yielding more accurate results while still being substantially faster to execute than LBL codes.

The *k*-distribution method is a relatively recent innovation and is rapidly gaining favor in view of its ability to achieve fairly accurate results with two or three orders of magnitude less computer time than LBL methods.

For both narrow-band transmission models and the *k*-distribution method, the longwave spectrum is subdivided into N intervals $\Delta \tilde{\nu}_i$ that are each

1. large enough to encompass a significant number of absorption lines associated with a particular atmospheric constituent, and yet

2. small enough so that the Planck function $B_{\tilde{\nu}}(T)$ can be considered approximately constant and equal to $\overline{B}_i$ over the range.

Thus, the downwelling broadband longwave flux at level z can be written

$$F^{\downarrow}(z) = \int_0^{\infty} F_{\tilde{\nu}}^{\downarrow}(z) \, d\tilde{\nu} = \sum_{i=1}^{N} \int_{\Delta \tilde{\nu}_i} F_{\tilde{\nu}}^{\downarrow}(z) \, d\tilde{\nu} = \sum_{i=1}^{N} F_i^{\downarrow}(z) \, , \qquad (10.11)$$

where the flux contribution from each spectral interval can be expanded as

$$F_i^{\downarrow}(z) = \int_{\Delta \tilde{\nu}_i} F_{\tilde{\nu}}^{\downarrow}(z) \, d\tilde{\nu} = \int_{\Delta \tilde{\nu}_i} \int_z^{\infty} \pi B_{\tilde{\nu}}[T(z')] \frac{\partial t_{\tilde{\nu}}(z', z; \overline{\mu})}{\partial z'} \, dz' \, d\tilde{\nu} \, . \tag{10.12}$$

Making use of condition 2 above, and reordering the differentiation and integration operators, we can write

$$F_i^{\downarrow}(z) = \pi \Delta \tilde{\nu}_i \int_z^{\infty} \overline{B}_i[T(z')] \frac{\partial \mathcal{T}_i(z', z; \overline{\mu})}{\partial z'} \, dz' \, , \tag{10.13}$$

where the *band-averaged transmittance* is

$$\mathcal{T}_i(z', z; \overline{\mu}) = \frac{1}{\Delta\tilde{\nu}_i} \int_{\Delta\tilde{\nu}_i} t_{\tilde{\nu}}(z', z; \overline{\mu}) \, d\tilde{\nu} = \frac{1}{\Delta\tilde{\nu}_i} \int_{\Delta\tilde{\nu}_i} e^{-\tau_{\tilde{\nu}}(z',z)/\overline{\mu}} \, d\tilde{\nu} \, .$$

(10.14)

Analogous equations can of course be found for the upwelling flux $F_i^{\uparrow}(z)$.

The efficient computation of broadband fluxes evidently boils down to the problem of finding good approximations to $\mathcal{T}_i$ between two levels for the particular spectral interval $\Delta\tilde{\nu}_i$. In practice, this problem is solved in two steps:

1. Develop a method for efficiently estimating $\mathcal{T}_i$ over an arbitrary *homogeneous* path — that is, one over which line shapes and strengths can be considered constant, and

2. generalize the above method to inhomogeneous (e.g. vertical) paths, over which linewidths can be expected to vary substantially owing to pressure broadening, etc.

Band transmission models and the *k*-distribution method offer two rather different frameworks for tackling both steps. We will consider each in turn.

10.2   Band Transmission Models

Previously, when we examined the extinction of radiation (Chapter 7), we were always concerned with the fate of *monochromatic* radiation along a finite path between points s_1 and s_2. The transmittance $t(s_1, s_2)$ in this case is very nicely described by Beer's Law (7.7), which is both easy to remember and easy to apply. In particular, you'll remember that one consequence of Beer's Law is that the transmittance over an extended path is equal to the product of the transmittances over a series of shorter paths.

You can forget about Beer's law in the case of spectrally averaged transmission, except in the rare case that the medium happens to be gray over the relevant interval $\Delta\tilde{\nu}$ – that is, when $\tau_{\tilde{\nu}}$ is independent of $\tilde{\nu}$. Qualitatively, this is because radiation with different wavenumbers within the band are depleted at different rates.

At some wavenumbers for which the medium is transparent, there is very little depletion even over long paths, and these wavenumbers ensure that the average band transmittance remains nonzero even at a great distance from the source. At other wavenumbers (e.g., at line centers), radiation is depleted rapidly, contributing to a sharp decrease in band transmission over a short distance. But once those wavenumbers are gone, they can't be depleted further, and so the transmission ceases to decrease as rapidly with further distance along the beam.

Problem 10.1: Imagine that between wavenumbers $\tilde{v}_1$ and $\tilde{v}_2$, the atmosphere is perfectly transparent, whereas between $\tilde{v}_2$ and $\tilde{v}_3$, the absorption coefficient β_a is constant and nonzero.

(a) Find an expression for the average transmittance $\mathcal{T}$ over a pathlength s for the spectral band $\Delta\tilde{v} = \tilde{v}_3 - \tilde{v}_1$.

(b) Sketch a graph of $\mathcal{T}(s)$ for the case that $\tilde{v}_2$ is the midpoint of the interval, being sure to show the asymptotic behavior of $\mathcal{T}$ for large s.

(c) Assuming that the radiation incident at point $s=0$ is "white", compute the fraction that is absorbed by the time it reaches $s = 1$ km, if $\beta_a = 3$ km^{-1}.

(d) Assume that the radiation that survives the transit in (c) goes on to traverse the path from $s = 1$ km to $s = 2$ km. What fraction of the radiation that begins this second leg is absorbed by the time it reaches the end?

(e) Explain why the fraction absorbed over the first kilometer is substantially different than the fraction absorbed over the second kilometer.

We will now consider the problem of band transmission in a more quantitative fashion. To start with, it is instructive to consider the band-averaged transmission and absorption properties in the idealized case of a single isolated absorption line. We will use this example to gain some basic insight and to introduce some definitions that can later be applied to more complex cases.

10.2.1   Absorption by an Isolated Line

Recall that the band-averaged path transmission in spectral interval $\Delta\tilde{\nu}$ is defined as

$$\mathcal{T} = \frac{1}{\Delta\tilde{\nu}} \int_{\Delta\tilde{\nu}_i} e^{-\tau_{\tilde{\nu}}} \, d\tilde{\nu} \tag{10.15}$$

from which we can also define the *band-averaged absorption*

$$\mathcal{A} = 1 - \mathcal{T}. \tag{10.16}$$

For the special case of a single isolated absorption line and a homogeneous path

$$\tau_{\tilde{\nu}} = S f(\tilde{\nu}) u, \tag{10.17}$$

where S is the line strength, $f(\tilde{\nu})$ is the line shape function, and u is the mass path:

$$u = \int_{s_1}^{s_2} \rho(s) \, ds, \tag{10.18}$$

where s is the distance along the line-of-sight.

Equivalent Width

Since we're only considering a single line embedded somewhere inside the spectral interval $\Delta\tilde{\nu}$, the band transmission is obviously a function of how wide an interval we choose; the more clear spectrum we include on either side of the line, the higher $\mathcal{T}$. It is therefore convenient to define a more fundamental property (for a given mass path u) called the line's *equivalent width* W:

$$W \equiv \int_{\Delta\tilde{\nu}_i} 1 - e^{-\tau_{\tilde{\nu}}} \, d\tilde{\nu}, \tag{10.19}$$

which doesn't depend on $\Delta\tilde{\nu}$ as long as it's large enough to encompass all significant contributions from the line's wings.

The physical interpretation of W is straightforward: it is the spectral width of a hypothetical "square," completely opaque line that absorbs the same total amount of radiation in the band as the actual (non-square, non-opaque) line. Therefore, the band-averaged absorption can be conveniently written

$$\mathcal{A} = \frac{W}{\Delta\tilde{\nu}}. \tag{10.20}$$

Of fundamental interest is the manner in which W increases with increasing mass path u under different assumptions. We will look at a few important limiting cases.

Weak Line (Linear) Limit

For the special case that $\tau_{\tilde{v}} \ll 1$ for all $\tilde{v}$ (even at the line center), we can use the approximation $\exp(x) \approx 1 - x$ to evaluate (10.19):

$$W = \int_{\Delta \tilde{v}_i} 1 - e^{-\tau_{\tilde{v}}} \, d\tilde{v} \approx \int_{\Delta \tilde{v}_i} \tau_{\tilde{v}} \, d\tilde{v} = \int_{\Delta \tilde{v}_i} S f(\tilde{v}) u \, d\tilde{v} , \qquad (10.21)$$

or, taking S and u out of the integral and using the normalization property of $f(\tilde{v})$,

$$W = Su . \qquad (10.22)$$

In other words, in the so-called *weak line limit*, also known as the *linear regime*, total path absorption is proportional to the line strength and the mass path u, *irrespective of line shape*.

The corresponding band absorption and transmission are then given by

$$\mathcal{A} = 1 - \mathcal{T} = \frac{Su}{\Delta \tilde{v}} . \qquad (10.23)$$

Simple Case: Ideal Square Line

Let's now consider an ideal square line with the property that

$$f(\tilde{v}) = \begin{cases} \dfrac{1}{W_0} & \text{for } \left(\tilde{v}_0 - \dfrac{W_0}{2} \right) < \tilde{v} < \left(\tilde{v}_0 + \dfrac{W_0}{2} \right) \\[2ex] 0 & \text{otherwise.} \end{cases}$$

$$(10.24)$$

In this case,

$$\begin{aligned} W &= \int_{\Delta \tilde{v}_i} 1 - e^{-\tau_{\tilde{v}}} \, d\tilde{v} \\ &= W_0 \left(1 - e^{-Su/W_0} \right) . \end{aligned} \qquad (10.25)$$

The corresponding band absorption and transmission are

$$\mathcal{A} = 1 - \mathcal{T} = \frac{W_0}{\Delta \tilde{v}} \left(1 - e^{-Su/W_0} \right) . \qquad (10.26)$$

The square line is of course an extreme and unrealistic case, as real lines have wings that extend indefinitely outward from the line center. Nevertheless, this example is useful as a simple illustration of the effects of non-gray absorption within a band. More importantly, the square line model is as far from being gray as you can get, so it defines an upper bound on the radiative effects of non-grayness.

Specifically, we find that the band absorption for large mass path has a limiting value of $W_0/\Delta\tilde{v}$. Since our square line has no wings, it can never absorb a larger fraction of the incident (white) radiation than the ratio of the line width to the width of the spectral band.

For any realistic line shape — i.e., for one with tails extending to infinity, we expect that the reduction in transmission with increasing mass path will be

1. slower than that predicted by Beer's Law for a gray medium, but

2. faster and more complete than that expected from a square line of the same width.

Lorentz Line

Let's now look at the absorption behavior of a realistic line, as described by the Lorentz shape

$$f(\tilde{v}) = \frac{\alpha_L}{\pi[(\tilde{v} - \tilde{v}_0)^2 + \alpha_L^2]} \, , \tag{10.27}$$

for which the equivalent width when integrated over the entire spectrum is

$$W = \int_{-\infty}^{\infty} \left[1 - \exp\left(\frac{-Su\alpha_L}{\pi[(\tilde{v} - \tilde{v}_0)^2 + \alpha_L^2]} \right) \right] d\tilde{v} \, . \tag{10.28}$$

We have extended the lower limit of integration in the above from zero to $-\infty$ for the sake of being able to obtain an analytic solution. To simplify the integral into a standard form that can be looked up in a table, we further define the nondimensional mass path

$$\tilde{u} \equiv \frac{Su}{2\pi\alpha_L} \, , \tag{10.29}$$

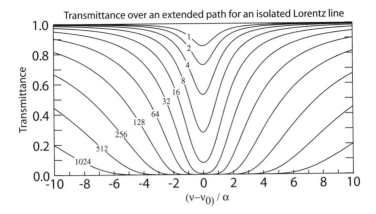

Fig. 10.1: The evolution of transmittance with increasing mass path for an isolated Lorentz line. For each curve, the line center optical path $\tilde{u}$ is equal to the label value divided by 2π.

which is nothing more than one-half of the optical path τ at the line center. The above integral can then be written

$$W = \int_{-\infty}^{\infty} \left[1 - \exp\left(\frac{-2\tilde{u}\alpha_L^2}{(\tilde{v} - \tilde{v}_0)^2 + \alpha_L^2} \right) \right] d\tilde{v} , \tag{10.30}$$

which has the solution

$$W = 2\pi\alpha_L L(\tilde{u}) , \tag{10.31}$$

where the *Ladenberg-Reiche function* $L(\tilde{u})$ can be expressed in terms of modified Bessel functions of the first kind of order 0 and 1:

$$L(\tilde{u}) = \tilde{u}e^{-\tilde{u}} \left[I_0(\tilde{u}) + I_1(\tilde{u}) \right] . \tag{10.32}$$

Admittedly, you won't find the modified Bessel functions on your pocket calculator, but apart from that minor inconvenience, they are standard mathematical functions. Here we will confine our attention to the behavior of $W(u)$ in the limit of very small and very large mass path. But wait: we already know what happens in the first case from (10.22), which is valid for *any* line shape — absorption in the weak line limit is simply proportional to u.

In the limit of large mass path (or, more precisely, large $\tilde{u}$), it can be shown that

$$W \approx 2\alpha_L \sqrt{2\pi\tilde{u}} = 2\sqrt{S\alpha_L u} . \tag{10.33}$$

In other words, in the *strong line limit*, an isolated Lorentz line absorbs in proportion to the square root of the mass path.

The average transmission for a spectral band $\Delta \tilde{v}$ is, as usual,

$$\mathcal{T} = 1 - \frac{W}{\Delta \tilde{v}} , \qquad (10.34)$$

where W is given by (10.31), *provided* that $\Delta \tilde{v}$ is large enough to encompass all significant absorption by the wings of the Lorentz line. If this condition is not satisfied, then the limits of integration employed in (10.28) are not applicable, and no closed-form solution exists. However, it is easy to convince yourself that the use of a narrower band $\Delta \tilde{v}$ will have the following consequences:

- The equivalent width W will be reduced relative to (10.31), because contributions from the far wings of the line are lost;

- The band-averaged transmittance $\mathcal{T}$ will be reduced, because the clearest portions of the spectrum furthest away from the line center are excluded.

The behavior of an isolated Lorentz line with varying $\tilde{u}$ is depicted graphically in Fig. 10.1. For the spectral interval depicted, the band transmittance is equal to the area under any given curve (labeled with values proportional to $\tilde{u}$), expressed as a fraction of the total area of the plot.

For small values of $\tilde{u}$, the transmission is close to unity everywhere, even at the line center. This represents the linear or weak line regime, for which $W = Su$. For large values ($\tilde{u} \gg 10$), the line becomes saturated in the center, so that those wavelengths can no longer contribute to further increases in $\mathcal{A}$ with increasing $\tilde{u}$. Instead, the width of the saturated zone increases, though at a slower rate than $\tilde{u}$ itself; this represents the strong line limit or square root regime (as noted above, this description is strictly valid only when the edges of the spectral window are far enough from the line center).

Unfortunately, we rarely have the luxury of dealing with isolated lines; rather, in the usual scenario we have dozens, if not hundreds of lines in our spectral interval. If the lines don't overlap (as might be the case at high altitudes), then their contributions to the band absorption $\mathcal{A}$ can be determined individually as for isolated lines, above, and then summed to give the total absorption. More commonly, we have to deal with lines that at least partly overlap, which is the subject of the next subsection.

10.2.2 Defining a Band Model

When setting out to characterize the transmission T of a band containing numerous lines, we don't want to have to perform a complete line-by-line calculation over all of the actual lines present — that would defeat the purpose of a band model. Rather, we want to be able to specify, in fairly generic terms, some key characteristics of the lines present in the band and then derive a suitable analytic approximation for $T(u)$. The characteristics that matter most include the following:

- *The average spacing δ between the lines,* defined as $\delta = \Delta\tilde{v}/N$, where N is the total number of lines in the spectral interval $\Delta\tilde{v}$.

- *The manner in which the lines are distributed throughout the spectral interval.* There are two common choices: (1) *random,* and (2) *regular* (or periodic). A random model (a.k.a. Goody model) might be an appropriate description of a portion of a water vapor band in which there is no apparent relationship beween the location of one line and those of its fellow lines (Fig. 9.11). A regular (periodic) model might be more appropriate in the P or R branch of a vibration/rotation band for a linear molecule, such as CO_2 (Fig. 9.13a). The difference matters because it determines how many of the lines present are likely to overlap other lines, all other factors being equal. In a regular distribution, the occurrence of overlap is minimized.

- *The line widths α.* Typically, band transmission models are derived under the assumption that α is the same for all lines present, as this simplifies the problem of finding closed-form approximations.

- *The statistical distribution of line strengths S.* Do they all have the same strength, or is there a wide range of different strengths present? If the latter, what is the relative proportion of lines of different strengths?

Line Strength Distributions

The last item in the previous list is dealt with by specifying a distribution function $p(S)$ that characterizes the relative proportion of lines with strength S. By definition, $p(S)$ is nonnegative and satisfies the normalization condition

$$\int_0^\infty p(S)\, dS = 1 \,. \tag{10.35}$$

The mean line strength is given by

$$\overline{S} = \int_0^\infty S p(S)\, dS \,. \tag{10.36}$$

Common models for $p(S)$ include the following:

1) δ-distribution $p(S) = \delta(S - \overline{S})$ (equal strength)
2) Exponential distribution $p(S) = (1/\overline{S}) \exp(-S/\overline{S})$
3) Godson distribution $p(S) = \overline{S}/(S_{\max}S)$ for $S < S_{\max}$
4) Malkmus distribution $p(S) = (1/S) \exp(-S/\overline{S})$

Although all of the above line strength distribution models have their uses, we will consider only two: the δ-distribution in conjunction with a regular line model, and the Malkmus distribution in conjunction with the random line model. The first of these combinations is known as the *Elsasser band model*, after the scientist who first studied its characteristics.

10.2.3   The Elsasser Band Model

A few absorption bands reveal a fairly regular repeating pattern of lines of similar strength. As discussed in Chapter 9, this property is what you would expect for the rotation spectrum (including P- and R-branches of a vibration/rotation band) of a simple linear molecule like CO_2. Therefore, in the Elsasser model of a simple absorption band, we imagine the structure to be represented by a periodic array of identical lines of strength S separated by spacing δ:

$$k(\tilde{\nu}) = \sum_{n=-\infty}^{n=+\infty} S f(\tilde{\nu} - n\delta) \,. \tag{10.37}$$

Elsasser Band Model

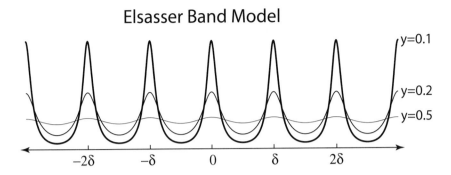

Fig. 10.2: Schematic depiction of the absorption coefficient k in the Elsasser (regular) band model, for three different values of the grayness parameter $y \equiv \alpha_L/\delta$.

With substitution of the Lorentz line shape, we have

$$k(\tilde{v}) = \sum_{n=-\infty}^{n=+\infty} \frac{S}{\pi} \frac{\alpha_L}{\left[(\tilde{v} - n\delta)^2 + \alpha_L^2\right]} \ . \tag{10.38}$$

Elsasser showed that this is mathematically equivalent to

$$k(\tilde{v}) = \frac{S}{\delta} \frac{\sinh(2\pi y)}{\cosh(2\pi y) - \cos(2\pi x)} \ , \tag{10.39}$$

where

$$y \equiv \frac{\alpha_L}{\delta}, \qquad x \equiv \frac{\tilde{v}}{\delta} \ . \tag{10.40}$$

y can be regarded as a "grayness parameter": if y is large, then adjacent lines strongly overlap and blur together, so that the line structure is increasingly obscured; for small y, the lines are well separated and resemble isolated lines for small to moderate mass paths (Fig. 10.2).

Because the pattern of lines is periodic, the band transmission $\mathcal{T}$ over a large spectral range can be obtained by integrating the monochromatic transmission over just a single interval δ, which is equivalent to one unit of the nondimensional wavenumber parameter x:

$$\mathcal{T} = \int_{-1/2}^{1/2} \exp[-k(x)u] \, dx \ , \tag{10.41}$$

or

$$\mathcal{T} = \int_{-1/2}^{1/2} \exp\left[-\frac{2\pi \tilde{u} y \sinh(2\pi y)}{\cosh(2\pi y) - \cos(2\pi x)}\right] dx \ , \tag{10.42}$$

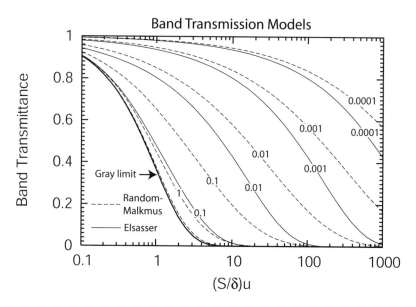

Fig. 10.3: Comparison of the Elsasser (solid curves) and random-Malkmus (dashed curves) band models for varying values of the grayness parameter y (labels on curves). For both models, curves approach the gray limit (Beer's Law) when $y \gg 1$.

where the nondimensional mass path $\tilde{u}$ is as defined in (10.29).

Unfortunately, the above integral cannot be solved in closed form. However, there are important limiting cases. The first is when y is large (order 10 or greater), in which case the line width is much greater than the spacing between lines. In this case, the medium is effectively gray, and the band transmission reduces to

$$\mathcal{T} = \exp(-2\pi y \tilde{u}) = \exp(-Su/\delta) . \qquad (10.43)$$

In other words, we're back to Beer's law, with mass absorption coefficient $k = S/\delta$.

The second limiting case of interest is for $\tilde{u} \gg 1$. The band transmission then has the asymptotic form

$$\mathcal{T} \approx 1 - \mathrm{erf}\left[\pi y \sqrt{2\tilde{u}}\right] , \qquad (10.44)$$

where $\mathrm{erf}(x)$ is the so-called *error function*, defined as

$$\mathrm{erf}(x) \equiv \frac{2}{\sqrt{\pi}} \int_0^x e^{-t^2} \, dt . \qquad (10.45)$$

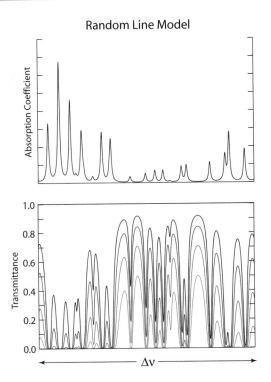

Fig. 10.4: Example of the distribution of line locations and strengths according to a random/Malkmus model. Upper panel shows the absorption coefficient (arbitrary units); lower panel depicts the spectrum of transmittance for four different mass paths.

The behavior of Elsasser band transmission $\mathcal{T}(u)$ is depicted as solid curves in Fig. 10.3 for various values of y. The main thing to take away from this plot is that when the spacing between lines is substantial ($y \ll 1$), the transmission decreases in a sub-exponential fashion.

10.2.4 The Random/Malkmus Band Model

Line spectra for important nonlinear molecules like water vapor, ozone, methane, etc. do not exhibit any of the regularity assumed by the Elsasser model. Even the P- and R-branches of a linear molecule like CO_2 band are more complicated in reality than might be expected based on our simplified discussion in Chapter 9. Consequently, the Elsasser band model is not widely used in actual band transmission calculations.

Examination of Fig. 9.11 reveals that the line spectrum for water vapor, one of the most important atmospheric absorbers, is highly irregular in nature. Line positions would be better described as random rather than regular. Also, the line strengths are quasi-random — in any given spectral interval there is a mix of relatively strong and weak lines.

A better match to reality in many cases is therefore offered by the random model, in which line positions are assumed to be scattered perfectly randomly throughout the chosen interval $\Delta\tilde{v}$. Furthermore, the line strengths are allowed to vary according to a prescribed distribution $p(S)$, as discussed earlier. One of the best general purpose models for $p(s)$ is the Malkmus distribution $p(S) = (1/S)\exp(-S/\overline{S})$.

As before, the average line spacing is given by $\delta \equiv \Delta\tilde{v}/N$, where N is the number of lines in spectral interval $\Delta\tilde{v}$. The definitions of y and $\tilde{u}$ are the same as for the Elsasser model, except that we use $\overline{S}$ in place of S. It can then be shown (see L02 4.4.3) that

$$\mathcal{T} = \exp\left[-\frac{\pi\alpha_L}{2\delta}\left\{\sqrt{1 + \frac{4\overline{S}u}{\pi\alpha_L}} - 1\right\}\right]$$

$$= \exp\left[-\frac{\pi y}{2}\left\{\sqrt{1 + 8\tilde{u}} - 1\right\}\right]. \tag{10.46}$$

The band transmission for this model is plotted as dashed curves in Fig. 10.3, where they can be compared with the results for the Elsasser model. For both models, the limiting behavior for large y is equivalent to Beer's law transmittance ('gray limit'). But because of the unevenness of the spacing of the lines, the transmission is greater for any given value of y than is the case for the Elsasser model.

10.2.5 The HCG Approximation

We now need to generalize from a homogeneous to inhomogeneous (vertical) path, allowing for the fact that pressure, and therefore linewidth α_L varies substantially over any significant vertical path in the atmosphere.

One appealing approach is to try to find an expression for an "effective" mass path $\bar{u}$ and pressure $\bar{p}$ such that the homogeneous path transmission with those values is equal to the correct inhomogeneous path transmission between two pressure levels p_1 and p_2:

$$\mathcal{T}_{\text{inhom}}(u) = \mathcal{T}_{\text{hom}}(\bar{u}, \bar{p}) . \tag{10.47}$$

The van de Hulst/Curtis/Godson (HCG) approximation, which was derived under the assumption of uniform temperature and constituent mixing ratio over the path, offers such a solution: let

$$\bar{p} = \frac{1}{2}(p_1 + p_2), \qquad \bar{u} = u . \tag{10.48}$$

That is, the effective mass path is the same as the actual mass path, and the effective pressure is just the average of the pressures at the endpoints of the path. It seems almost too simple, and yet this is the accepted method for using band transmission models in a vertically inhomogeneous atmosphere.

10.3 The *k*-Distribution Method

The narrow-band transmission models discussed in the previous section are based on finding analytic approximations to the band-averaged transmittance over a finite path, assuming a reasonable statistical model for the distribution of line positions and strengths in the spectral interval.

More recently, the so-called *k*-distribution method has emerged as a very effective and flexible way of dealing with the integration over a spectral interval. It is based on the idea that the integration over frequency (or wavenumber) of a complex line spectrum can be replaced with an equivalent integration over a much smoother function. In the latter case, much larger discretization steps (and therefore greatly reduced computational effort) can be used in the numerical integration without sacrificing accuracy. An extremely important property of the *k*-distribution method, and one which distinguishes it from band transmission models, is that it is well-suited to problems involving scattering as well as absorption.

This section gives a brief conceptual overview of the *k*-distribution method without delving too much into the practical details, which are best left to an advanced course in radiation (see TS02 sections 10.4 and 10.5.4).

10.3.1   Homogeneous Path

Let's start with an absorption spectrum $k(\tilde{v})$ like that depicted in Fig. 10.5a. In this plot, we see approximately 30 Lorentz lines with random positions and strengths, and subject to a modest degree of pressure broadening. If we undertake a "brute force" line-by-line calculation of the average transmittance of the band over a finite mass path u, we have to evaluate the following integral:

$$T(u) = \frac{1}{\tilde{v}_2 - \tilde{v}_1} \int_{\tilde{v}_1}^{\tilde{v}_2} \exp[-k(\tilde{v})u]\, d\tilde{v} \,. \qquad (10.49)$$

To numerically evaluate such an integral, we typically approximate it as a sum of the following form

$$T(u) \approx \sum_{i=1}^{N} \alpha_i \exp[-k(\tilde{v}_i)u] \,, \qquad (10.50)$$

where N is the number of wavenumbers $\tilde{v}_i$ at which $k(\tilde{v})$ is evaluated within the interval, and the coefficients α_i are weights which depend on the specific quadrature method used (e.g., the trapezoidal rule, Simpson's rule, etc.). In the simplest possible method (which we will assume for the sake of the present illustration) the frequencies $\tilde{v}_i$ are equally spaced and separated by an interval $\delta\tilde{v} = (\tilde{v}_2 - \tilde{v}_1)/N$, and $\alpha_i = 1/N$, so that T is simply the arithmetic average of $\exp[-k(\tilde{v}_i)u]$. In order to accurately resolve the shapes of individual lines, $\delta\tilde{v}$ must generally be at least an order of magnitude smaller than the linewidths, so N may be rather large.

Note, however, that the end result of the summation in (10.50) does not in any way depend on the *order* in which the terms are summed. Furthermore, if you draw any straight horizontal line across your absorption spectrum (e.g., the dotted line in Fig. 10.5a), you'll find that the same value of k occurs for $2M$ values of $\tilde{v}_i$, where M is the number absorption lines encountered along the way. This observation suggests that you could kill $2M$ birds with one stone in the evaluation of $\exp[-k(\tilde{v}_i)u]$, if you just knew what M was for each different value of k.

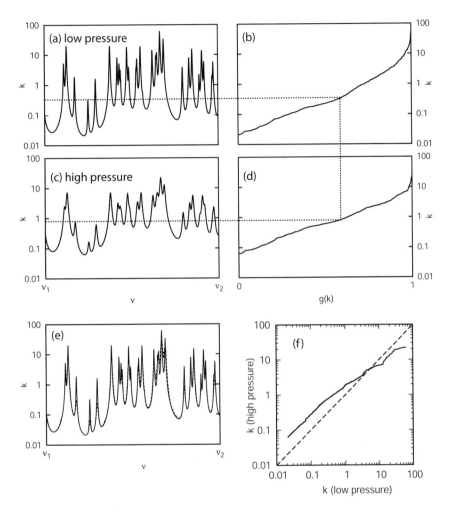

Fig. 10.5: Illustration of the k-distribution method and its extension, the correlated-k method. (a) A hypothetical spectrum of absorption coefficient k at relatively low pressure. (b) By sampling the spectrum at fine intervals and then sorting the results so that k increases monotonically, we define the function $0 \leq g(k) \leq 1$ (horizontal axis). Panels (c) and (d) are the same as (a) and (b) except with stronger pressure broadening. (e) Comparison of the actual spectrum for low pressure [from panel (a)] (solid curve) with one estimated from the spectrum at higher pressure [panel (c)] (dotted curve), using the mapping in panel (f). (f) The mapping between k values at the two pressure levels, based on equal values of g.

The essence of the k-distribution method is that you can take all N of your values of $k(\tilde{\nu}_i)$ and sort them so that they are arranged in ascending order. The result can be treated as a function of a new variable g that ranges from $g = 0$ for the smallest value of k present to $g = 1$ for the largest value. Fig. 10.5b shows the results of this process for the absorption spectrum in Fig. 10.5a. In striking con-trast to the original $k(\tilde{\nu})$, *the new $k(g)$ is a rather smooth, monotonically increasing function on the interval* $[0, 1]$. By working with $k(g)$ rather than the much more complicated $k(\tilde{\nu})$, we are able to replace the nasty integral (10.49) with the much nicer one

$$T(u) = \int_0^1 \exp[-k(g)u]\, dg \,. \tag{10.51}$$

Now, if you are only going to perform the calculation once, then nothing is gained by this procedure, because you still need to first evaluate $k(\tilde{\nu})$ for each of your N frequencies $\tilde{\nu}_i$. But if your purpose is set things up so that you can efficiently recompute T for a variety of different mass paths u (though all still at the same constant pres-sure, for now), then the ability to work with the simple function $k(g)$ is a decided advantage: whereas at least 1000 data points are needed to adequately characterize the shape of $k(\tilde{\nu})$ in Fig. 10.5a, a mere 5–10 points or so would probably suffice for the $k(g)$ in Fig. 10.5b. Not only storage requirements but also the computational effort needed to evaluate (10.51) are reduced by up to a couple of orders of mag-nitude.

We can summarize the main difference between the band mod-els covered in the previous section and the k-distribution method as follows:

- Band transmission models are based on specific simple sta-tistical models of the line positions and strengths, such as the random/Malkmus model. Since real line spectra almost never obey such a model exactly, the convenient analytic expressions derived for band models are almost guaranteed to be a bit rough in terms of how accurately they describe $T(u)$.

- In contrast to band models, the k-distribution method makes no prior assumption about the distribution of the line strengths or positions in the band; you simply take what na-ture gives you in a particular spectral interval and evaluate

$k(\tilde{v})$ and, from there, $k(g)$. In this regard, the k-distribution may be thought of as a data compression scheme rather than as a transmission model: you are keeping the information you really need for computing $\mathcal{T}$, namely, the relative frequency of different values of k, and throwing out the information that doesn't matter, which is how those different values of k are ordered with respect to $\tilde{v}$.

10.3.2   Inhomogeneous Path: Correlated-k

The above discussion of the k-distribution method assumes a homogeneous path — i.e., one over which the pressure and temperature is essentially constant so that $k(\tilde{v})$ is the same at every point along the path. In practical terms, this implies that we are restricted to relatively short horizontal paths in the atmosphere. We have to find a way to generalize the k-distribution method so that it can be used for extended vertical atmospheric paths over which pressure, and therefore linewidths, can vary drastically. In the case of the narrow band models discussed earlier, the HCG approximation gave us a basis for treating an inhomogeneous path as an equivalent homogeneous path. Can we come up with something analogous for the k-distribution method?

The answer is of course "yes," and the applicable approximation is known as the correlated-k method. First, let's simply write down the applicable equation, and then take a moment to understand what it's letting us get away with:

$$\mathcal{T}(u) = \int_0^1 \exp\left[-\int_0^u k(g, u')\, du' \right]\, dg . \qquad (10.52)$$

In one sense at least, the above equation makes sense. For each value of g, we are simply computing the transmittance over the path between our location $u' = 0$ and the remote location $u' = u$. We are then averaging this transmittance over the interval $0 < g < 1$ to get the band transmittance. What could be more straightforward?

But there is a serious flaw in the above reasoning: The above equation makes physical sense *only* if a given value of g corresponds to the same wavenumber $\tilde{v}$ at every point along the path. After all, a vertically propagating photon can't adjust its frequency along the way so as to preserve its original value of g! Recall that our definition of $k(g)$ at a particular pressure (in the homogeneous case) entailed a scrambling of the frequency information in the absorption spectrum. Indeed, any given value k is likely to be associated with not just one single frequency but rather with many different frequencies. For example, in Fig. 10.5a, the horizontal dotted line, corresponding to a single value of k intersects the plot of $k(\tilde{v})$ at 24 distinct frequencies! The absorption coefficient at all of these frequencies is associated with a single value of g, as indicated by the intersection of the horizontal dotted line with the $k(g)$ curve in Fig. 10.5b.

Note that as you move vertically through the atmosphere, pressure broadening substantially alters the spectrum $k(\tilde{v})$. In Fig. 10.5c, we see the absorption spectrum at a pressure that is three times greater than that assumed in Fig. 10.5a. Broadening of the individual lines leads to an absorption spectrum that is smoother and for which the extreme values of k are moderated – the peaks are reduced and the valleys are filled. The corresponding plot of $k(g)$ is shown in Fig. 10.5d. Although the shape is fairly similar to that in Fig. 10.5b, the curves are in fact different. There is no *a priori* reason to expect the "scrambling" of frequency information to be identical for both pressures. Therefore, picking a single value of g and integrating along a path that experiences changing pressure is *not* guaranteed to give you a meaningful estimate of the vertical transmittance at any particular frequency.

It turns out that *for an isolated Lorentz line*, there is, in fact, a unique mapping between g and $\tilde{v}$ that is independent of pressure. For this special case, the correlated-k method represented by (10.52) can be used with complete confidence. Unfortunately, we are rarely dealing with isolated lines, and when we are, we don't need a band model! We must face the fact that the correlated-k method conceals a rather daring assumption for any realistic line spectrum.

As is often the case, heated arguments over whether a given method is theoretically defensible eventually give way to the simple practical question: does it appear to work *well enough* in most common situations? In fact, it does. We can demonstrate this in two ways:

Consider again the horizontal dotted line in Fig. 10.5a. This represents a fixed value of k for our lower pressure spectrum. Follow the line to where it intersects the curve in Fig. 10.5b. This intersection determines the value of g that corresponds to our chosen k. Now follow the vertical dotted line down to where it intersects the curve in Fig. 10.5c. This intersection determines a new value of k *at the higher pressure level* for which $g(k)$ has the same value as for our original k at low pressure. Now follow the horizontal dotted line back to the left and note where it crosses $k(\tilde{v})$. These intersections define the new set of frequencies at high pressure that were determined by our particular choice of k at low pressure. For the most part, these frequencies are very close to those determined by the intersections in Fig. 10.5a. The correspondence is not perfect — for example, the fifth line from the left has two intersections in the top panel that have no counterparts in the lower panel.

More generally, we can determine the complete mapping between k at the two pressure levels, based on the requirement of equal values of g. The results for this example are shown in Fig. 10.5f. Using this mapping, we can test how well we are able to predict $k(\tilde{v})$ at one pressure based on $k(\tilde{v})$ at the other pressure. Fig. 10.5e depicts both the original $k(\tilde{v})$ at low pressure (solid curve) and the predicted $k(\tilde{v})$, based on applying the mapping in panel (f) to the high pressure $k(\tilde{v})$ in panel (c). Over most of the spectral interval, the agreement is nearly perfect. Only in the vicinity of a few line centers (e.g., that fifth line from the left) does the agreement break down noticably. However, these isolated errors occupy such a small fraction of the spectral band that they don't introduce much error into the calculation of $\mathcal{T}(u)$.

The bottom line is that the correlated-k method, while not perfect, typically allows fluxes and heating rates to be calculated with overall errors of less than 1%. Most importantly, it does so with at least three orders of magnitude less computational effort than a brute-force LBL calculation. If you ever have occasion to work with a modern model for computing band-averaged IR radiances or fluxes in the atmosphere, there's a good chance that you can find a correlated-k procedure lurking somewhere inside.

10.4 Applications to Meteorology, Climatology, and Remote Sensing

The previous section outlined the methods used to compute broadband upwelling and downwelling fluxes in a cloud-free atmosphere. Of course hardly anyone computes fluxes just for the fun of it; rather, they do it because it is an essential part of modeling the energy budget of the atmosphere.

10.4.1 Fluxes and Radiative Heating/Cooling

Radiative Heating Equations

In Section 2.7, we defined the net flux as

$$F^{net}(z) \equiv F^{\uparrow}(z) - F^{\downarrow}(z) \,. \tag{10.53}$$

Depending on the context, we might be interested in the net flux computed (or measured) for all wavelengths, for just the shortwave or longwave band, or even for a narrow spectral interval. In any of these cases, F^{net} represents the corresponding net upward flow of radiative energy, measured in watts per meter squared, through a unit horizontal area at level z.

Now consider a thin layer of the atmosphere with its base at altitude z and its upper boundary at $z + \Delta z$. The net flux $F^{net}(z)$ represents the rate at which radiative energy enters the bottom of this layer; likewise, $F^{net}(z + \Delta z)$ gives the rate at which energy leaves at the top of the layer. If the two fluxes are equal, then there is no net change over time in the internal energy of the layer. If they are not equal, then the layer must be experiencing a net gain or loss of energy.

It follows that the *radiative heating rate* at level z is given by

$$\mathcal{H} \equiv -\frac{1}{\rho(z)C_p}\frac{\partial F^{net}}{\partial z}(z) \,, \tag{10.54}$$

where $\rho(z)$ is the air density at level z and $C_p = 1005 \, \text{J}/(\text{kg K})$ is the specific heat capacity of air at constant pressure. The minus sign is needed because an *increase* in F^{net} with height implies a net *loss* of energy from level z. Traditionally, $\mathcal{H}$ is expressed in units of $°C/day$. When the value of $\mathcal{H}$ is negative (as it is more often than not), one might prefer to speak instead of positive *radiative cooling rate*.

In order to utilize the band model machinery we developed earlier, let's confine our attention to the heating/cooling rate associated with a particular spectral interval $\Delta\tilde{\nu}_i$. The complete expressions for upwelling and downwelling flux, including boundary contributions, are then

$$F_i^{\uparrow}(z) = F_i^{\uparrow}(0)\mathcal{T}_i(0,z) + \Delta\tilde{\nu}_i \int_0^z \pi\overline{B}_i(z')\frac{\partial\mathcal{T}_i(z',z)}{\partial z'}\,dz'\,, \qquad (10.55)$$

$$F_i^{\downarrow}(z) = F_i^{\downarrow}(\infty)\mathcal{T}_i(z,\infty) - \Delta\tilde{\nu}_i \int_z^{\infty} \pi\overline{B}_i(z')\frac{\partial\mathcal{T}_i(z,z')}{\partial z'}\,dz'\,, \qquad (10.56)$$

where, as usual, $\mathcal{T}_i(z,z')$ is the band-averaged flux transmittance between levels z and z'. Note that we are using $\overline{B}_i(z)$ as a shorthand notation for the average value of $B[T(z)]$ in the ith spectral interval.

Let's use the above expressions to evaluate F^{net} and, from there, $\partial F^{net}/\partial z$, as required for the heating rate in (10.54):

$$F_i^{net}(z) = F_i^{\uparrow}(0)\mathcal{T}_i(0,z) - F_i^{\downarrow}(\infty)\mathcal{T}_i(z,\infty)$$
$$+ \Delta\tilde{\nu}_i \int_0^z \pi\overline{B}_i(z')\frac{\partial\mathcal{T}_i(z',z)}{\partial z'}\,dz' \qquad (10.57)$$
$$+ \Delta\tilde{\nu}_i \int_z^{\infty} \pi\overline{B}_i(z')\frac{\partial\mathcal{T}_i(z,z')}{\partial z'}\,dz'\,,$$

$$\frac{\partial F_i^{net}(z)}{\partial z} = F_i^{\uparrow}(0)\frac{\partial\mathcal{T}_i(0,z)}{\partial z} - F_i^{\downarrow}(\infty)\frac{\partial\mathcal{T}_i(z,\infty)}{\partial z}$$
$$+ \Delta\tilde{\nu}_i\frac{\partial}{\partial z}\left[\int_0^z \pi\overline{B}_i(z')\frac{\partial\mathcal{T}_i(z',z)}{\partial z'}\,dz'\right. \qquad (10.58)$$
$$\left.+ \int_z^{\infty} \pi\overline{B}_i(z')\frac{\partial\mathcal{T}_i(z,z')}{\partial z'}\,dz'\right]\,.$$

To evaluate the partial derivatives of the integral terms, in which z appears both as one of the limits of integration *and* as an argument to the integrand itself, we invoke the following mathematical identity:

$$\frac{\partial}{\partial x}\int_{x_0}^x f(x,y)\,dy \equiv \int_{x_0}^x \frac{\partial f(x,y)}{\partial x}\,dy + f(x,x)\,, \qquad (10.59)$$

so that the heating rate $\mathcal{H}$ at level z is proportional to

$$\mathcal{H}(z)\rho(z)C_p = -F_i^{\uparrow}(0)\frac{\partial T_i(0,z)}{\partial z} + F_i^{\downarrow}(\infty)\frac{\partial T_i(z,\infty)}{\partial z}$$

$$+ \Delta\tilde{v}_i\left[-\int_0^z \pi\overline{B}_i(z')\frac{\partial^2 T_i(z',z)}{\partial z'\partial z}\,dz' - \int_z^{\infty} \pi\overline{B}_i(z')\frac{\partial^2 T_i(z,z')}{\partial z'\partial z}\,dz'\right.$$

$$\left. - \pi\overline{B}_i(z)\frac{\partial T_i(z',z)}{\partial z'}\bigg|_{z'=z} + \pi\overline{B}_i(z)\frac{\partial T_i(z,z')}{\partial z'}\bigg|_{z'=z}\right].$$

$$(10.60)$$

Before we make further adjustments, let's take a second to interpret the terms in the above equation.

The first term is the contribution of the upward flux at the surface to heating at level z. Note that $\partial T(0,z)/\partial z$ (which is negative) plays exactly the same role as the "absorption weighting function" we derived in (7.51), except that it now applies to the band-integrated flux rather than the monochromatic intensity. The second term is of course the same as the first, except that it represents the absorption of radiation incident at the top of the atmosphere. Both the first and the second terms are always greater than zero and represent positive heating terms.

The two integrals in the second line of the equation represent the contributions of emission at all other levels z' to heating at level z. These are also positive terms.

The final two terms,[4] respectively, represent *losses* of energy due to upward and downward emission of radiation by the atmosphere at level z. Note that both terms are equal and negative, because

$$\frac{\partial T_i(z',z)}{\partial z'}\bigg|_{z'=z} = -\frac{\partial T_i(z,z')}{\partial z'}\bigg|_{z'=z}. \qquad (10.61)$$

Although we could combine the last two terms in (10.60) using the above identity, we will leave them separate in order to make the next steps clearer.

Although (10.60) is certainly an accurate and complete statement of how local heating depends on the profile of transmission and temperature (via $\overline{B}(z)$), we're less interested here in computational

---

[4]These terms are omitted in Equation (11.29) of TS02.

validity than we are in physical insight. Watch carefully while we rearrange our equation into a new form that clarifies some aspects of the relationship between local heating and the surrounding environment.

We will start with an expression that has the form we are seeking and show that it is mathematically equivalent to, and can be substituted for, part of (10.60).

$$
\int_0^z \pi \left[\overline{B}_i(z') - \overline{B}_i(z) \right] \frac{\partial^2 T_i(z',z)}{\partial z' \partial z} \, dz'
$$

$$
= \int_0^z \pi \overline{B}_i(z') \frac{\partial^2 T_i(z',z)}{\partial z' \partial z} \, dz' - \int_0^z \pi \overline{B}_i(z) \frac{\partial^2 T_i(z',z)}{\partial z' \partial z} \, dz'
$$

$$
= \int_0^z \pi \overline{B}_i(z') \frac{\partial^2 T_i(z',z)}{\partial z' \partial z} \, dz' - \pi \overline{B}_i(z) \int_0^z \frac{\partial^2 T_i(z',z)}{\partial z' \partial z} \, dz'
$$

$$
= \int_0^z \pi \overline{B}_i(z') \frac{\partial^2 T_i(z',z)}{\partial z' \partial z} \, dz' - \pi \overline{B}_i(z) \left[\frac{\partial T_i(z',z)}{\partial z} \right]_{z'=0}^{z'=z}
$$

$$
= \int_0^z \pi \overline{B}_i(z') \frac{\partial^2 T_i(z',z)}{\partial z' \partial z} \, dz' - \pi \overline{B}_i(z) \frac{\partial T_i(z',z)}{\partial z} \bigg|_{z'=z} + \pi \overline{B}_i(z) \frac{\partial T_i(0,z)}{\partial z}
$$

$$
= \int_0^z \pi \overline{B}_i(z') \frac{\partial^2 T_i(z',z)}{\partial z' \partial z} \, dz' + \pi \overline{B}_i(z) \frac{\partial T_i(z',z)}{\partial z'} \bigg|_{z'=z} + \pi \overline{B}_i(z) \frac{\partial T_i(0,z)}{\partial z}
$$

$$
, \quad (10.62)
$$

or, if we subtract the right side of the above equality from the left side,

$$
\int_0^z \pi \left[\overline{B}_i(z') - \overline{B}_i(z) \right] \frac{\partial^2 T_i(z',z)}{\partial z' \partial z} \, dz' - \int_0^z \pi \overline{B}_i(z') \frac{\partial^2 T_i(z',z)}{\partial z' \partial z} \, dz'
$$

$$
- \pi \overline{B}_i(z) \frac{\partial T_i(z',z)}{\partial z'} \bigg|_{z'=z} - \pi \overline{B}_i(z) \frac{\partial T_i(0,z)}{\partial z} = 0. \quad (10.63)
$$

Using similar reasoning, we can show that

$$
\int_z^\infty \pi \left[\overline{B}_i(z') - \overline{B}_i(z) \right] \frac{\partial^2 T_i(z,z')}{\partial z' \partial z} \, dz' - \int_z^\infty \pi \overline{B}_i(z') \frac{\partial^2 T_i(z,z')}{\partial z' \partial z} \, dz'
$$

$$
+ \pi \overline{B}_i(z) \frac{\partial T_i(z,\infty)}{\partial z} + \pi \overline{B}_i(z) \frac{\partial T_i(z,z')}{\partial z'} \bigg|_{z'=z} = 0. \quad (10.64)
$$

Since the expressions on the left-hand sides of both (10.63) and (10.64) are equal to zero, we can subtract both expressions from inside the square brackets of (10.60) without changing the latter's validity. After considerable manipulation and cancellation of terms, we get

$$
\mathcal{H}(z) = \frac{1}{\rho(z)C_p} \Bigg\{
$$

$$
- \left[F_i^{\uparrow}(0) - \Delta\tilde{v}_i \pi \overline{B}_i(z) \right] \frac{\partial \mathcal{T}_i(0, z)}{\partial z} \qquad (A)
$$

$$
+ \left[F_i^{\downarrow}(\infty) - \Delta\tilde{v}_i \pi \overline{B}_i(z) \right] \frac{\partial \mathcal{T}_i(z, \infty)}{\partial z} \qquad (B)
$$

$$
- \Delta\tilde{v}_i \pi \int_z^{\infty} \left[\overline{B}_i(z') - \overline{B}_i(z) \right] \frac{\partial^2 \mathcal{T}_i(z, z')}{\partial z' \partial z} \, dz' \qquad (C)
$$

$$
- \Delta\tilde{v}_i \pi \int_0^z \left[\overline{B}_i(z') - \overline{B}_i(z) \right] \frac{\partial^2 \mathcal{T}_i(z', z)}{\partial z' \partial z} \, dz' \qquad (D)
$$

$$
\Bigg\} .
$$

(10.65)

Equation (10.65) certainly looks different than the mathematically equivalent (10.60), and it tells a different kind of story as well. Each of the partial derivatives represents the degree of *radiative coupling* between level z and some other part of the column. It characterizes the degree to which radiation *emitted* by one component is *absorbed* by the the atmosphere at z *and vice versa*.

Thus, for each of the lines (A)–(D), the difference inside the square brackets represents the imbalance between (a) radiation emitted from the remote location and reabsorbed at level z, and (b) energy lost by emission from level z and reabsorbed at the remote location. If the difference is positive, then the contribution to heating at level z is positive; negative implies cooling. I will emphasize the word **exchange** wherever it appears below in order to reinforce this idea of a *two-way* process.

Let's now interpret each line in turn:

Term (A) represents net heating/cooling through radiative **exchange** with the lower boundary. In the thermal IR band, we can usually take the surface to be black, in which case we can replace $F_i^\uparrow(0)$ with $\Delta\tilde{\nu}_i\pi\overline{B}_i(T_s)$, where T_s is the surface temperature. Since T_s is usually greater than $T(z)$, Term A usually represents a heating term.

Term (B) represents heating/cooling through radiative **exchange** with the top of the atmosphere (TOA). If we're working in the thermal IR band, then $F_i^\downarrow(\infty)$ is usually taken to be zero, in which case the exchange is strictly one-way. In the LW band, therefore, term (B) describes *cooling to space*. If, on the other hand, we're working with solar radiation, then $F_i^\downarrow(\infty)$ represents the incident flux of solar radiation at the TOA, and $\overline{B}(z) = 0$, so that term (B) describes heating through the direct absorption of solar radiation.

Terms (C) and (D) collectively represent radiative **exchanges** between level z and all other levels in the atmosphere z'. In order for the net effect of this exchange to be significant, there must be a large temperature difference between the two levels, *and* the radiative coupling (represented by the second derivatives of $\mathcal{T}$) must be strong. The coupling is strongest when the transmission $\mathcal{T}$ changes rapidly in response to changes in both z and z'. In regions of the spectrum for which the atmosphere is strongly absorbing (e.g., the middle of the CO_2 15 μm band), the coupling is strongest with levels z' that are very close to z and where the temperature difference is small; therefore the contribution of these wavelengths to local heating at z is negligible.

Note further that (C) represents **exchanges** between z and higher levels of the atmosphere; (D) represents **exchanges** with lower altitudes. In the middle of the troposphere, the temperature generally decreases in a quasi-linear fashion with increasing z. This implies that the cooling contribution by (C) will usually be offset to a large degree by heating from (D). The reverse applies in the stratosphere, where temperature tends to increase with height. It follows, therefore, that heating/cooling due to exhanges with other levels will be strongest where there is a minimum or maximum in $T(z)$. In particular, the tropopause level "sees" radiation arriving from the warmer stratosphere (term C) as well as from warmer levels of the troposphere (term D); hence, the tropopause experiences positive heating contributions from both (C) and (D).

In the longwave band, every term except (B) represents radiative exchanges between levels having temperatures falling somewhere in the range 190–310 K. The typical temperature *difference* between two levels that are strongly coupled is on the order of 10s of K or less. Furthermore, as noted above, terms (C) and (D) tend to partly cancel each other, except in the vicinity of the tropopause.

Term (B), by contrast, represents a direct loss of radiation to space, with no compensating return radiation. This term is therefore always negative, and it is quite often the largest term overall in the longwave radiation budget, especially at altitudes for which the atmosphere rapidly becomes more transparent with increasing height (e.g., due to the rapid narrowing of absorption lines). *To a very good approximation in many cases, radiative cooling profiles in the atmosphere can be estimated from term (B) alone.* This is called the *cooling-to-space approximation.*

Model Atmospheres

It's nice to have an equation like (10.65) to tell you *how* heating or cooling at a particular level is physically related to profiles of temperature and band transmittance. But simply staring at it won't tell you much about the actual magnitude of the heating or cooling to expect at any particular level z. You have to write a program to numerically evaluate the various terms in the equation using suitable band transmittance models, and you then have to apply your program to a particular profile of atmospheric temperature, humidity, and trace gas composition.

Although you could, in principle, pull any old radiosonde sounding off the Internet and run your program on it (although some assumptions would still be required concerning ozone profiles and the like), atmospheric scientists usually like to start by running their radiative transfer codes on idealized profiles called *model atmospheres.* These don't represent actual observations but are designed to reflect typical atmospheric conditions for a particular location and season. The use of standard model atmospheres has

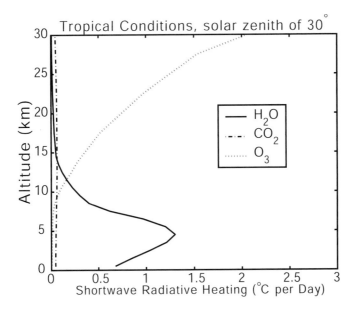

Fig. 10.6: Typical heating profiles due to solar absorption in a cloud-free tropical atmosphere, segregated according to the responsible atmospheric constituents ozone (O_3), carbon dioxide (CO_2), and water vapor (H_2O). *(Figure courtesy of S. Ackerman.)*

two advantages:

- It facilitates the comparison of different radiative transfer codes. If results differ significantly for two methods using the exact same model atmosphere, then at least one of them (perhaps both) must be doing something wrong!

- The results of a radiative transfer calculation for a model atmosphere can be regarded as typical, in some sense, for the region and season and question it represents, even if it is understood that actual conditions will vary from day to day and location to location. Thus a model atmosphere will usually be employed in a calculation any time an actual sounding is not available but you need representative radiative transfer results.

There are at least seven standard model atmospheres in circulation that radiation and remote sensing scientists tend to rely on for the above purposes: (1) tropical, (2) midlatitude summer, (3) mid-latitude winter, (4) subarctic summer, (5) subarctic winter, (6) arctic summer, and (7) arctic winter. Although the associated temperature and humidity profiles are highly idealized, they vary in the ways you'd expect: the tropical model atmosphere is warm and humid with a high, cold tropopause; the arctic winter atmosphere is extremely cold with low humidity and a very low tropopause, and the other five models fall somewhere in between these two extremes.

It's worth keeping in mind that variations in water vapor mixing ratio are often even more important for radiative heating profiles than are variations in the temperature profiles themselves. This is because of water vapor's relative opacity over much of the SW and LW bands.

Shortwave Heating

Figure 10.6 depicts heating profiles due to the absorption of solar radiation in a cloud-free tropical atmosphere. The heating rate is given in degrees per day. Separate profiles are shown for the three major contributors to atmospheric absorption in the solar band: water vapor, ozone, and carbon dioxide. The first two of these constituents are clearly the dominant absorbers in the solar band, with water vapor being responsible for the bulk of the absorption (up to 1.3 K/day) in the troposphere ($z < 15$ km in this model atmosphere) and ozone dominating in the stratosphere, with heating rates in excess of 2 K/day.[5] Carbon dioxide plays a minor role, being responsible for around 0.05 K/day of heating at all levels.

To first order, the differences between the shapes of the heating profiles for different constituents mirrors the difference in constituent mixing ratios:

- Water vapor is most abundant at the warm altitudes in the lower troposphere, because it condenses to liquid water or ice and precipitates out when it is transported to higher, colder altitudes.

- Ozone is concentrated primarily in the stratosphere, where it

---

[5]The heating rate continues to increase with altitude above 30 km, peaking at an altitude high in the upper stratosphere.

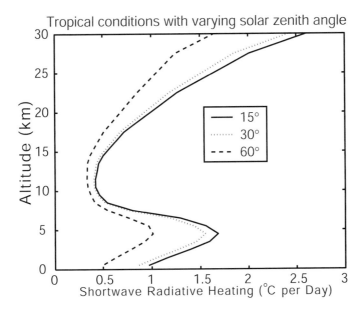

Fig. 10.7: Typical heating profiles due to solar absorption in a cloud-free tropical atmosphere at three different solar zenith angles. The heating profile for $\theta_s = 30°$ corresponds to the sum of the three profiles in Fig. 10.6. *(Figure courtesy of S. Ackerman.)*

is created by the action of UV-C radiation on molecular oxygen. In fact, the stratosphere itself, which is *defined* by the general increase of temperature with height starting around 10–15 km owes its very existence to the absorption of solar radiation by ozone. *If there were no molecular oxygen in the atmosphere, there would be no ozone layer. Without ozone, there would be very little solar heating of the middle atmosphere and therefore no stratosphere!*

- Carbon dioxide is evenly mixed throughout the atmosphere, because atmospheric sources and removal mechanisms for CO_2 operate very slowly in comparison to those for water vapor and ozone.

Problem 10.2: Actual water vapor mixing ratios in the standard tropical atmosphere continue to increase all the way to the surface.

Yet the heating rate associated with water vapor peaks at an altitude near 5 km and then decreases sharply below that level. Explain why.

Total shortwave heating rates are of course the sum of those contributed by the individual constituents. Profiles of total heating due to the absorption of solar radiation in a tropical atmosphere are shown in Fig. 10.7. The different profiles correspond to different solar zenith angles. Not surprisingly, when the sun is lower in the sky, overall heating rates are reduced.

Of course, the heating profiles described above include only contributions due to *direct* absorption of shortwave radiation. In the absence of clouds, solar radiation not absorbed by the atmosphere reaches the surface, where a fraction equal to one minus the surface albedo gets absorbed. Much of that energy *indirectly* heats the atmosphere by way of three mechanisms: (1) emission and reabsorption of longwave radiation (discussed below), (2) direct conduction of heat from the surface to the overlying air, followed by convective mixing, and (3) evaporation of water from the surface, followed by latent heat release in clouds.

Longwave Cooling

In the longwave band, each part of the atmosphere is simultaneously emitting and absorbing radiation. Where absorption dominates, there is net heating; where emission dominates, there is net cooling. Profiles of heating/cooling in the longwave band are more difficult to interpret because all four of the terms in (10.65) are potentially significant.

Fig. 10.8 shows longwave heating profiles for a tropical atmosphere, again segregated according to the responsible constituent. Water vapor is actually represented here by two curves, one for the heating contribution due to its rotation/vibration bands near 6.3 μm and beyond 15 μm; the other due to the relatively weak but pervasive continuum component that dirties up the spectral "windows" between conventional absorption bands.

Here is a brief rundown of the major features seen in this plot:

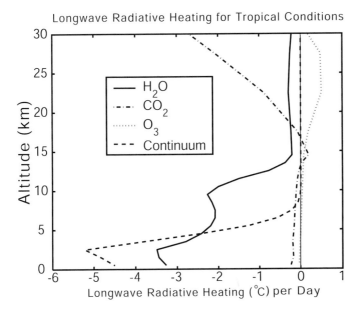

Fig. 10.8: Typical heating rate profiles due to longwave (thermal IR) radiative transfer in a cloud-free tropical atmosphere, segregated according to the responsible atmospheric constituents ozone (O_3), carbon dioxide (CO_2), water vapor resonant absorption (H_2O), and water vapor continuum. Negative values represent cooling. *(Figure courtesy of S. Ackerman, with modifications.)*

CO_2 Because of the high opacity of the pressure broadened 15 μm band, carbon dioxide contributes rather little to net radiative heating in the troposphere. Radiation emitted at one level is reabsorbed at nearby level having almost the same temperature. Only at the tropopause (near 15 km), where the temperature profile has a minimum, is there a small amount of net heating. At higher altitudes, pressure broadening is much weaker and the band "opens up," allowing emitted radiation to escape to space with little compensating radiation downward from higher levels. This is of course the *cooling to space* previously discussed in connection with term (B) in (10.65).

H_2O Because water vapor is concentrated at low altitudes, the cooling-to-space effect kicks in strongly between 3 and 10 km altitude, with maximum cooling rates between 2 and 3.5 K/day. The two peaks in the profiles are associated with different absorption bands, the stronger of these being associated with the higher altitude peak. Above the tropopause near 15 km, there is very little water vapor present and so its contribution to cooling at those altitudes is very modest – about 0.2 K/day.

H_2O continuum One of the unique characteristics of continuum absorption is that it is very sensitive to pressure. The mass absorption coefficient of water vapor falls off rapidly with height. Consequently, the atmosphere in the upper troposphere and above is effectively transparent in this spectral band, while lower altitudes see fairly strong absorption. Once again, cooling-to-space is the dominant radiative exchange term at the rather sharp transition between the two zones, with peak cooling of 5 K/day occurring at the relatively low altitude of 3 km. Above 10 km, the continuum contribution to cooling is essentially zero.

O_3 Ozone is responsible for the sole instance of significant LW *warming* in the atmosphere below 30 km, with the peak warming of 0.5 K/day occurring between 20 and 30 km. This heating is due to the absorption at the base of the ozone layer of radiation emitted by the ground in the 9.6 μm band — i.e., term (A) in (10.65). If the plotted profiles in Fig. 10.8 were extended to higher altitude, you would see the heating due to term (A) disappear and get replaced with fairly strong cooling-to-space at the top of the ozone layer.

The above discussion applies to a tropical atmosphere. Different model atmospheres have different profiles of temperature and LW absorption and therefore different profiles of LW heating/cooling. Fig. 10.9 shows total LW heating profiles for a tropical, midlatitude summer, and subarctic summer atmosphere. Qualitatively they are similar; only the details differ, mainly due to differences in the water vapor contribution and in the gross features of the temperature profile.

Note that the LW radiative exchanges in the cloud-free atmosphere have a net cooling effect at almost all levels of the atmosphere, whereas the effect of SW absorption was exclusively warming. In fact, in the stratosphere, SW warming and LW cooling nearly

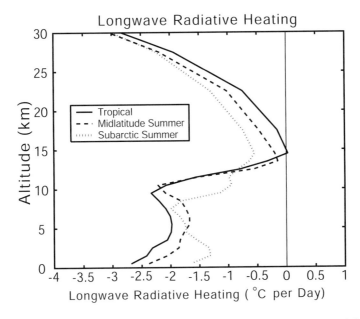

Fig. 10.9: Total longwave heating rate profiles for three different model atmospheres. *(Figure courtesy of S. Ackerman, with modifications.)*

cancel. This is because there are few other effective energy exchange mechanisms at work in the stratosphere; therefore the temperature of the stratosphere must necessarily approach that required for radiative equilibrium. In the troposphere, a variety of other processes are available to compensate for any radiative imbalance; therefore we don't expect the SW and LW heating profiles to be mirror images of one another.

CHAPTER 11

The Radiative Transfer Equation With Scattering

Throughout this book so far, we have discussed scattering primarily as one of two mechanisms for *extinguishing* radiation, the other mechanism being absorption. Thus, the extinction coefficient β_e could be decomposed into the sum of the absorption coefficient β_a and scattering coefficient β_s. The single scatter albedo $\tilde{\omega}$, defined as β_s / β_e, was introduced as a convenient parameter describing the relative importance of absorption and scattering: when $\tilde{\omega} = 0$, extinction of radiation is entirely by way of absorption; when $\tilde{\omega} = 1$, then there is no absorption, only scattering.

When radiation is extinguished via scattering, its energy is not converted to another form; rather, the radiation is merely redirected. The *loss* of radiation along one line-of-sight due to scattering is therefore always associated with a *gain* in radiation along other lines-of-sight passing through the same volume.

You can easily observe the above phenomenon with the help of a powerful, narrow beam of light, such as that from a searchlight, an automobile headlight or a laser pointer. When the air is very clear —i.e., free of smoke, dust, haze, or fog—then the beam can pass directly in front of you and you will not see it, because essentially none of the radiation is scattered out of the original path into the direction toward your eyes. But if the air contains suspended particles, then these particles will scatter some fraction of the beam into all directions, including toward your eyes, and the path of the beam will be clearly apparent, especially against a dark background. In this case, scattering clearly serves as a *source* of radiation, as seen from your vantage point. Of course the original beam is depleted by the same process. For example, if a fog is thick enough, the headlights of an oncoming car can't be seen at all until it is relatively close to you.

This chapter introduces the terminology and mathematical notation required to account for scattering as a *source* of radiation in the radiative transfer equation.

11.1   When Does Scattering Matter?

When scattering is important as a source of radiation along a particular line-of-sight, then the complexity of calculations of radiative transfer along that line-of-sight greatly increases compared with the nonscattering case. This is because one must, in the worst case, solve for the intensity field not just in *one direction* along a *one-dimensional path* but for *all directions* simultaneously in *three-dimensional space*! You would therefore like to be able to neglect scattering (as a source, at least) whenever you can get away with it.

In fact, you can safely ignore scattering as a source whenever gains in intensity due to scattering along a line-of-sight are negligible compared with (a) losses due to extinction *and* (b) gains due to thermal emission. In the atmosphere, these conditions are *usually* satisfied for radiation in the thermal IR band and for microwave radiation when no precipitation (e.g., rain, snow, etc.) is present. In addition, if one is concerned only with the depletion of *direct* radiation from an isolated, point-like source, such as the sun, then the above conditions are usually satisfied to reasonable accuracy.

For virtually any problem involving the interaction of short-wave (ultraviolet, visible, and near-IR) radiation with the atmosphere, scattering is the dominant atmospheric source of radiation along any line-of-sight other than that looking directly at the sun. The blue sky, white or gray clouds, the atmospheric haze that reduces the visual contrast of distant objects — all of these make their presence known primarily by way of scattered radiation.

11.2   Radiative Transfer Equation with Scattering

11.2.1   Differential Form

Previously, we derived Schwarzschild's Equation (8.4) under the assumption that scattering was unimportant and that therefore $\beta_e = \beta_a$. Under that assumption, we found that the change in intensity dI along an infinitesimal path ds could be written as

$$dI = dI_{abs} + dI_{emit} , \qquad (11.1)$$

where the depletion due to absorption is given by

$$dI_{abs} = -\beta_a I \, ds , \qquad (11.2)$$

and the source due to emission is

$$dI_{emit} = \beta_a B(T) \, ds . \qquad (11.3)$$

In order to generalize the equation to include scattering, we must recognize that depletion occurs due to both absorption and scattering, so that β_e rather than β_a must appear in the depletion term. Moreover, we must now add a source term that describes the contribution of radiation scattered *into* the beam from other directions, so that

$$dI = dI_{ext} + dI_{emit} + dI_{scat} , \qquad (11.4)$$

where

$$dI_{ext} = -\beta_e I \, ds . \qquad (11.5)$$

The term dI_{scat} requires more thought. First, we know it must be proportional to the scattering coefficient β_s, since without scattering there can be no contribution from this term. Second, we recognize that radiation passing through our infinitesimal volume from *any* direction $\hat{\Omega}'$ can potentially contribute scattered radiation in the direction of interest $\hat{\Omega}$. Moreover, these contributions from all directions will sum in a linear fashion — that is, the path taken by a photon arriving from one direction is not influenced by the presence of, or paths taken by, other photons.

Mathematically, these ideas are expressed as follows:

$$dI_{scat} = \frac{\beta_s}{4\pi} \int_{4\pi} p(\hat{\Omega}', \hat{\Omega}) I(\hat{\Omega}') \, d\omega' \, ds , \qquad (11.6)$$

where the integral is over all 4π steradians of solid angle, and the scattering *phase function* $p(\hat{\Omega}', \hat{\Omega})$ is required to satisfy the normalization condition

$$\frac{1}{4\pi} \int_{4\pi} p(\hat{\Omega}', \hat{\Omega}) \, d\omega' = 1 . \tag{11.7}$$

The complete differential form of the radiative transfer equation can thus be written

$$dI = -\beta_e I ds + \beta_a B ds + \frac{\beta_s}{4\pi} \int_{4\pi} p(\hat{\Omega}', \hat{\Omega}) I(\hat{\Omega}') \, d\omega' \, ds . \tag{11.8}$$

Dividing through by $d\tau = -\beta_e ds$, we can write

$$\frac{dI(\hat{\Omega})}{d\tau} = I(\hat{\Omega}) - (1 - \tilde{\omega}) B - \frac{\tilde{\omega}}{4\pi} \int_{4\pi} p(\hat{\Omega}', \hat{\Omega}) I(\hat{\Omega}') \, d\omega' , \tag{11.9}$$

where, in the interest of clarity, we make the dependence of I on direction $\hat{\Omega}$ explicit.

This is the most general and complete form of the radiative transfer equation that we will normally have to deal with in this book.[1]

Note that it is often convenient to lump all sources of radiation into a single term, so that (11.9) may be written in shorthand form as

$$\frac{dI(\hat{\Omega})}{d\tau} = I(\hat{\Omega}) - J(\hat{\Omega}) , \tag{11.10}$$

where the *source function* is given by

$$J(\hat{\Omega}) = (1 - \tilde{\omega}) B + \frac{\tilde{\omega}}{4\pi} \int_{4\pi} p(\hat{\Omega}', \hat{\Omega}) I(\hat{\Omega}') \, d\omega' . \tag{11.11}$$

---

[1]We have defined $d\tau$ here to be negative for translation toward the detector. This means that negative terms on the right hand side are source terms, and positive terms imply depletion. Some textbooks use the opposite convention, in which case the signs of all terms on the right hand side are reversed.

We see that the total source is a weighted sum of thermal emission and scattering from other directions, with the single scatter albedo controlling the weight given to each. If $\tilde{\omega} = 0$, the scattering term vanishes; if $\tilde{\omega} = 1$, the thermal emission component vanishes.

11.2.2 Polarized Scattering[†]

Throughout most of this book, we have ignored the role of polarization in atmospheric radiative transfer and considered the effects of transmission, absorption and scattering only on the *scalar* intensity I. Although this is almost always an approximation, it is often a very good one. There are times, however, when it is necessary to revert to a more accurate *fully polarized* treatment of radiative transfer, which requires us to consider changes not only in I but in all elements of the four-parameter Stokes vector $\mathbf{I} = (I, Q, U, V)$ that was introduced in (2.52). The fully polarized version of the differential radiative transfer equation (11.9) can be written

$$\frac{d\mathbf{I}(\hat{\Omega})}{d\tau} = \mathbf{I}(\hat{\Omega}) - (1 - \tilde{\omega})B\mathbf{U} - \frac{\tilde{\omega}}{4\pi} \int_{4\pi} \mathbf{P}(\hat{\Omega}', \hat{\Omega})\mathbf{I}(\hat{\Omega}') \, d\omega' \,, \quad (11.12)$$

where $\mathbf{P}(\hat{\Omega}', \hat{\Omega})$ is a 4×4 scattering *phase matrix*, and $\mathbf{U} \equiv (1, 0, 0, 0)$ when $\tilde{\omega}$ is considered to be independent of polarization. The latter assumption is not guaranteed to be valid; indeed, for some problems involving preferentially oriented particles, such as might be encountered in ice clouds or snowfall, even $\tilde{\omega}$ and the extinction coefficient β_e (implicit in τ) may each depend on both polarization and direction.

You are most likely to encounter the fully polarized RTE in the context of certain remote sensing problems. A more comprehensive discussion of polarized radiative transfer (though still with some simplifications, such as polarization-independent extinction and optical path) is given by L02 (Section 6.6). For the remainder of this book, we will continue to rely on the scalar form of the RTE given by (11.9) unless otherwise noted.

11.2.3 Plane Parallel Atmosphere

Although we know that the atmosphere is far from horizontally homogeneous, especially where clouds are concerned, most analytic solutions and approximations to the radiative transfer equation with scattering have been derived for the plane parallel case. Why? There are three basic reasons:

- Plane-parallel geometry is really the only semi-realistic case that lends itself to straightforward analysis and/or numerical solution (e.g., in climate and weather forecast models).

- There are indeed problems (e.g., the cloud-free atmosphere, horizontally extensive and homogeneous stratiform cloud sheets) for which the plane-parallel assumption usually seems quite reasonable as an approximation to reality.

- Even where it is not reasonable, there remains considerable doubt about the best way(s) to handle three-dimensional inhomogeneity, especially when computational efficiency is essential. Therefore investigators tend to fall back on plane-parallel geometry (with minor embellishments, such as the so-called *independent pixel approximation*), knowing that it is not perfect but believing it to be better than nothing at all (this is fine, as long as the potential for large errors is understood by all concerned!).

To adapt (11.10) to a plane-parallel atmosphere, we reintroduce the optical depth τ, measured from the top of the atmosphere, as our vertical coordinate, and we will henceforth use $\mu \equiv \cos\theta$ to specify the direction of propagation of the radiation measured from zenith.[2] We then have

$$\mu \frac{dI(\mu,\phi)}{d\tau} = I(\mu,\phi) - J(\mu,\phi) , \qquad (11.13)$$

where the source function for both emission and scattering is

$$J(\mu,\phi) = (1-\tilde{\omega})B + \frac{\tilde{\omega}}{4\pi} \int_0^{2\pi} \int_{-1}^1 p(\mu,\phi;\mu',\phi')I(\mu',\phi')\, d\mu'd\phi' . \qquad (11.14)$$

---

[2]Some textbooks, such as L02 and S94, specify that $\mu \equiv \cos\theta$. Others, such as TS02, instead define $\mu \equiv |\cos\theta|$, as I also did in an earlier chapter of this book. When writing the equations of radiative transfer with scattering, each convention has its own advantages and disadvantages. Here I have chosen the definition that permits the same equation to be used for both upward and downward radiation.

There is only a relatively small class of applications in which it is necessary to consider both scattering and emission at the same time. Two examples include (1) microwave remote sensing of precipitation, and (2) remote sensing of clouds near 4 μm wavelength, for which scattered solar radiation may be of comparable importance to thermal emission. Except where noted, the rest of this book will focus on problems involving scattering of solar radiation only, without the additional minor complication of thermal emission.

11.3   The Scattering Phase Function

One way to give physical meaning to the scattering phase function is to regard $\frac{1}{4\pi}p(\hat{\Omega}', \hat{\Omega})$ as a probability density: Given that a photon arrives from direction $\hat{\Omega}'$ and is scattered, what is the probability that its new direction falls within an infinitesimal element $d\omega$ of solid angle centered on direction $\hat{\Omega}$? The normalization condition (11.7) simply ensures that energy is conserved when there is no absorption ($\tilde{\omega} = 1$); i.e., the new direction of a scattered photon is guaranteed to fall *somewhere* within the available 4π steradians of solid angle, and you can't get more (or fewer) photons out than you put in.

The functional dependence of the phase function on $\hat{\Omega}$ and $\hat{\Omega}'$ can be quite complicated, depending on the sizes and shapes of the particles responsible for the scattering. Nevertheless, an important simplification can be made when particles suspended in the atmosphere are either spherical or else randomly oriented. For example, cloud droplets are spherical, and small aerosol particles and air molecules, while generally not spherical, have no preferred orientation.[3] In such cases, the scattering phase function for a volume of air depends only on the angle Θ between the original direction $\hat{\Omega}$ and the scattered direction $\hat{\Omega}'$, where

$$\cos\Theta \equiv \hat{\Omega}' \cdot \hat{\Omega} . \qquad (11.15)$$

---

[3]Falling ice crystals, snowflakes, and raindrops generally *do* have a preferred orientation due to aerodynamic forces, and this directional anisotropy must sometimes be considered in radiative transfer calculations.

The ability to replace $p(\hat{\Omega}', \hat{\Omega})$ with $p(\hat{\Omega}' \cdot \hat{\Omega}) \equiv p(\cos\Theta)$ is very helpful, inasmuch as the number of independent directional variables needed to fully characterize p is reduced from four (two each for $\hat{\Omega}$ and $\hat{\Omega}'$) to only one. The normalization condition (11.7) then reduces to

$$\frac{1}{4\pi} \int_0^{2\pi} \int_0^{\pi} p(\cos\Theta) \ \sin\Theta d\Theta d\phi = 1 \ , \qquad (11.16)$$

or

$$\frac{1}{2} \int_{-1}^{1} p(\cos\Theta) \ d\cos\Theta = 1 \ . \qquad (11.17)$$

Except where noted, this simplified notation for the phase function will be utilized throughout the remainder of this book.[4]

11.3.1   Isotropic Scattering

The simplest possible scattering phase function is one that is constant; i.e.

$$p(\cos\Theta) = 1 \ . \qquad (11.18)$$

Scattering under this condition is known as *isotropic*. It describes the case that all directions $\hat{\Omega}$ are equally likely for a photon that has just been scattered. Thus, the new direction the photon takes is in no way predictable from the direction it was traveling prior to being scattered; in other words, the photon "forgets" everything about its past.

An example of the random path of a single photon experiencing isotropic scattering is shown in Fig. 11.1a. Note that once the photon passes into the interior of the cloud layer it wanders aimlessly, often changing directions quite sharply with each scattering. Eventually, its "drunkard's walk" takes it back to the cloud top, where it emerges and, in this case, contributes to the albedo of the cloud. A different random turn at any point in its path could have instead taken it to the cloud base, where it would have then contributed

---

[4]It sometimes necessary, however, to recast a phase function that is inherently of the form $p(\cos\Theta)$ in terms of the absolute directions $(\hat{\Omega}', \hat{\Omega})$ in order to facilitate integration over zenith and/or azimuth angles θ and ϕ.

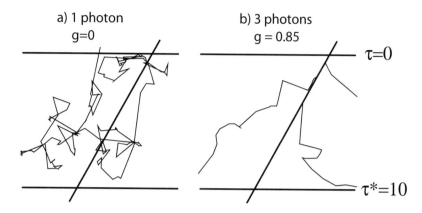

Fig. 11.1: Examples of the random paths of photons in a plane-parallel scattering layer with optical thickness $\tau^* = 10$. Photons are incident from above with $\theta = 30°$. Heavy diagonal lines indicate the path an unscattered photon would take. (a) The trajectory of a single photon when scattering is isotropic. (b) The trajectories of three photons when asymmetry parameter $g = 0.85$, which is typical for clouds in the solar band.

to the diffuse transmittance. Note that because of the large optical depth, the *direct* transmittance of the layer is vanishingly small; therefore there is virtually no chance that the photon could have passed all the way through to cloud base without first being scattered numerous times.

For isotropic scattering, the scattering source term in the radiative transfer equation simplifies to

$$\frac{\tilde{\omega}}{4\pi} \int_{4\pi} p(\hat{\Omega}', \hat{\Omega}) I(\hat{\Omega}') \, d\omega' \quad \rightarrow \quad \frac{\tilde{\omega}}{4\pi} \int_{4\pi} I(\hat{\Omega}') \, d\omega' \, . \quad (11.19)$$

That is, the source is independent of both $\hat{\Omega}$ and $\hat{\Omega}'$ and is simply equal to the single scatter albedo times the spherically averaged intensity.

Scattering by real particles in the atmosphere is never even approximately isotropic. Nevertheless, because the assumption of isotropic scattering leads to important simplifications in the analytic solution of the radiative transfer equation, it is frequently employed in theoretical studies in order to gain at least qualitative insight into the behavior of radiation in a scattering medium.

Furthermore, for some kinds of radiative transfer calculations, it is possible to find approximate solutions to a problem involving nonisotropic scattering by recasting it as an equivalent isotropic scattering problem, for which analytic solutions are easily obtained. Such so-called *similarity transformations* will be discussed in a later chapter.

11.3.2 The Asymmetry Parameter

In order compute scattered intensities to a high degree of accuracy, it is necessary to specify the functional form of the phase function $p(\cos \Theta)$. As will be seen in Chapter 12, the phase functions of real atmospheric particles can be complex and don't lend themselves to simple mathematical descriptions. Often, however, we don't care about intensities at all but only fluxes. In such cases, it is not necessary to get bogged down with details of the phase function; rather, it is sufficient to know the relative proportion of photons that are scattered in the forward versus backward directions. The scattering *asymmetry parameter* g contains this information and is defined as

$$g \equiv \frac{1}{4\pi} \int_{4\pi} p(\cos \Theta) \cos \Theta \, d\omega . \qquad (11.20)$$

The asymmetry parameter may be interpreted as the average value of $\cos \Theta$ for a large number of scattered photons. Thus

$$-1 \leq g \leq 1 . \qquad (11.21)$$

If $g > 0$, photons are preferentially scattered into the forward hemisphere (relative to the original direction of travel), while $g < 0$ implies preferential scattering into the backward hemisphere. If $g = 1$, this is the same as scattering into exactly the same direction as the photon was already traveling, in which case it might as well not have been scattered at all! A value of -1, on the other hand, implies an exact reversal of direction with every scattering event, a special case that is imaginable but physically unlikely.

For isotropic scattering, as discussed in the previous subsection, we expect $g = 0$, since scattering into the forward and backward hemispheres is equally likely. This can be shown explicitly by substituting $p = 1$ into (11.20), expanding $d\omega$ in spherical polar coordinates as $\sin\theta d\theta d\phi$, and choosing $\hat{\Omega} = \hat{z}$ so that the scattering angle Θ is the same as the zenith angle θ. Thus,

$$
\begin{aligned}
g &= \frac{1}{4\pi} \int_0^{2\pi} \int_{-\pi/2}^{\pi/2} \cos\theta \sin\theta \, d\theta \, d\phi \\
&= \frac{1}{2} \int_{-\pi/2}^{\pi/2} \cos\theta \sin\theta \, d\theta \\
&= \frac{1}{2} \int_{-1}^{1} \mu \, d\mu \\
&= 0 \, .
\end{aligned}
\tag{11.22}
$$

Note that while $g = 0$ for isotropic scattering, other phase functions can also have $g = 0$ and not be isotropic. The best example is the Rayleigh phase function derived in section 12.2, which describes the scattering of radiation by particles much smaller than the wavelength.

For many problems of interest, such as scattering of solar radiation in clouds, the asymmetry parameter g falls in the range 0.8–0.9. In other words, cloud droplets are strongly *forward scattering* at solar wavelengths. Fig. 11.1b shows examples of photon paths for $g = 0.85$. Although the average distance traveled by a photon between scattering events is the same as for isotropic scattering (Fig. 11.1a), the photon is now far more likely to be scattered into a direction that is not too different from its previous direction of travel. As a result, the photon's path, while still random, is far less chaotic than the isotropic case. Statistically, the photon travels a much greater distance before experiencing a sharp reversal in course. It is therefore also more likely to reach the cloud base and less likely to exit at cloud top. In other words, we expect the diffuse transmittance to increase and the cloud-top albedo to decrease when the asymmetry is large.

11.3.3 The Henyey-Greenstein Phase Function

The scattering phase functions of particles are often rather complicated (we will return to this subject in Chapter 12). As already

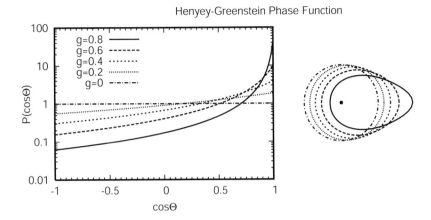

Fig. 11.2: The Henyey-Greenstein phase function plotted versus $\cos(\Theta)$ (left) and as a log-scaled polar plot (right).

pointed out, it is not always necessary to use a complete and accurate description of $p(\cos\Theta)$ in a radiative transfer calculation, as long as we know the asymmetry parameter g. For some types of calculations, we might want to employ a "stand-in" phase function that satisfies the following criteria:

- It should have a convenient mathematical form, ideally one that is an explicit function of the desired asymmetry parameter g.

- It should bear at least some resemblance to the shape of real phase functions, even if it doesn't have details like the rainbow, corona, etc. (See Chapter 12.)

- In order to be physically meaningful, the value of the phase function should be nonnegative for all values of Θ.

The *Henyey-Greenstein* phase function is the most widely used "model" phase function that satisfies all of the above criteria. It is given by

$$p_{\text{HG}}(\cos\Theta) = \frac{1 - g^2}{(1 + g^2 - 2g\cos\Theta)^{3/2}} \; . \tag{11.23}$$

As you can see from Fig. 11.2, the HG phase function is isotropic for $g = 0$. For positive g, the function peaks increasingly in the forward direction but remains quite smooth. In other words, it captures the asymmetry of real phase functions rather well but not the higher order details.

> **Problem 11.1:** Show that the parameter g appearing in (11.23) equals the asymmetry parameter as defined by (11.20).

Although the HG phase function with $g > 0$ does a good job of reproducing the observed forward peak in the phase functions of real particles, there is often also a pronounced (but somewhat smaller) backward peak which is *not* captured. Therefore, you will sometimes see the use of a *double* HG function, with one of the two terms serving to represent the backward peak:

$$p_{HG2}(\cos\Theta) = bp_{HG}(\cos\Theta; g_1) + (1 - b)p_{HG}(\cos\Theta; g_2), \quad (11.24)$$

where $g_1 > 0$, $g_2 < 0$, and $0 < b < 1$.

> **Problem 11.2:** (a) Given g_1, g_2, and b, find the asymmetry parameter g of the double Henyey-Greenstein phase function.
> (b) For marine haze particles in the visible band, it has been found that good values for the above parameters are $b = 0.9724$, $g_1 = 0.824$, and $g_2 = -0.55$. Find g.
> (c) Plot the phase function $p(\cos\Theta)$ described in part (b), using a logarithmic vertical axis.

11.4   Single vs. Multiple Scattering

When a solar photon enters the atmosphere or a cloud layer from the top, it will eventually either exit again (top or bottom) or else get absorbed. There are no other possibilities. Before either one happens, however, the photon may experience anywhere from zero to a very large number of scatterings from atmospheric particles.

Recall that if the photon passes entirely through the layer without getting either scattered or absorbed, then it is said to be *directly transmitted.* The probability of this happening to any particular photon is given by the direct transmittance t_{dir}, which we already know how to compute from Beer's Law. If, on the other hand, the photon exits the layer after having been scattered at least once, then it contributes to either the diffuse transmittance or the albedo of the layer, depending on whether it exits at the bottom or the top, respectively.

It is helpful now to distinguish between two general classes of problems: those in which *single scattering* dominates and those in which *multiple scattering* is the rule. In the first case, almost all of the photons contributing to the albedo and/or diffuse transmittance were scattered exactly once. Single scattering prevails whenever the layer is optically thin — i.e., $\tau^* \ll 1$, because each photon that is scattered in the interior of the layer then has a high probability of exiting the cloud before getting scattered a second time. Single scattering is also favored whenever the layer is strongly absorbing ($\tilde{\omega} \ll 1$), since a photon is then much more likely to get absorbed than to get scattered a second time.

If, on the other hand, the layer is both optically thick ($\tau^* > 1$) *and* strongly scattering ($1 - \tilde{\omega} \ll 1$), then many or most of the photons that enter the layer will be scattered more than once, perhaps even hundreds of times, before reemerging at the base or top of the layer. It takes a fair amount of sophistication to solve multiple scattering problems accurately. In fact, whole textbooks have been devoted to just this subject. In this book, we will defer until Chapter 13 our own fairly rudimentary treatment of radiative transfer with multiple scattering.

RTE for Single Scattering

For now, let's focus on the much simpler single scattering problem. In the absence of thermal emission, (11.13) and (11.14) can be combined to give

$$\mu \frac{dI(\mu, \phi)}{d\tau} = I(\mu, \phi) - \frac{\tilde{\omega}}{4\pi} \int_0^{2\pi} \int_{-1}^{1} p(\mu, \phi; \mu', \phi') I(\mu', \phi') \, d\mu' d\phi' .$$

$$(11.25)$$

What makes the single scattering problem simple is that the intensity $I(\mu', \phi')$ inside the integral is then, by definition, the attenuated intensity from the direct source (e.g., the sun) with no significant contribution from radiation that has already been scattered. If we assume a parallel beam of incident radiation from a point source above the cloud (a good approximation for direct sunlight), then we can write

$$I(\mu', \phi') = F_0 \delta(\mu' - \mu_0)\delta(\phi' - \phi_0)e^{\frac{\tau}{\mu_0}}, \qquad (11.26)$$

where $\mu_0 < 0$ and ϕ_0 give the directions of the incident beam, F_0 is the solar flux normal to the beam, and the exponential term is just the direct transmittance from the layer top $\tau = 0$ to level τ within the cloud. The Dirac δ-function $\delta(x)$ is defined to be zero for all $x \neq 0$ and infinite for $x = 0$, and it is normalized so that $\int_{-\infty}^{\infty} \delta(x')\, dx' = 1$, and $\int_{-\infty}^{\infty} f(x')\delta(x' - x)\, dx' = f(x)$.

With the above substitutions, (11.25) reduces to

$$\mu \frac{dI}{d\tau} = I - \frac{F_0 \tilde{\omega}}{4\pi} p(\cos \Theta)e^{\tau/\mu_0}, \qquad (11.27)$$

where the dependence of I on μ, ϕ, and τ is understood, and where $\cos \Theta \equiv \hat{\Omega} \cdot \hat{\Omega}_0$ is the cosine of the angle between the incident sunlight and the direction of the scattered radiation.

Let's rearrange the above equation and multiply through by $e^{-\tau/\mu}$:

$$\frac{dI}{d\tau}e^{-\tau/\mu} - \frac{1}{\mu}Ie^{-\tau/\mu} = -\frac{F_0 \tilde{\omega}}{4\pi\mu} p(\cos \Theta)e^{\tau/\mu_0}e^{-\tau/\mu}. \qquad (11.28)$$

This allows us to rewrite the left hand side as a simple derivative of a single expression:

$$\frac{d}{d\tau}\left[Ie^{-\tau/\mu}\right] = -\frac{F_0 \tilde{\omega}}{4\pi\mu} p(\cos \Theta)e^{\tau\left(\frac{1}{\mu_0} - \frac{1}{\mu}\right)}. \qquad (11.29)$$

In order to compute the scattered intensity emerging from the top or bottom of the atmosphere, we just have to integrate the above equation from $\tau = 0$ to $\tau = \tau^*$. For simplicity, we will assume here that $\tilde{\omega}$ and the phase function are independent of height, so that we can take them outside the integral. We get

$$I(\tau^*)e^{-\frac{\tau^*}{\mu}} - I(0) = \frac{-F_0 \tilde{\omega}}{4\pi\mu \left(\frac{1}{\mu_0} - \frac{1}{\mu}\right)} p(\cos \Theta) \left[e^{\tau^*\left(\frac{1}{\mu_0} - \frac{1}{\mu}\right)} - 1\right].$$

$$(11.30)$$

It may surprise you to learn that the above equation is valid both for downwelling radiation at the bottom of the atmosphere and for upwelling radiation at the top of the atmosphere. In the first case, we're interested in $I(0)$ for the case that $\mu > 0$:

$$I(0) = I(\tau^*)e^{-\frac{\tau^*}{\mu}} + \frac{F_0\tilde{\omega}}{4\pi\mu\left(\frac{1}{\mu_0} - \frac{1}{\mu}\right)}p(\cos\Theta)\left[e^{\tau^*\left(\frac{1}{\mu_0} - \frac{1}{\mu}\right)} - 1\right].$$

(11.31)

In the second case, we want $I(\tau^*)$ for $\mu < 0$, which requires only a slight rearrangement:

$$I(\tau^*) = I(0)e^{\frac{\tau^*}{\mu}} - \frac{F_0\tilde{\omega}}{4\pi\mu\left(\frac{1}{\mu_0} - \frac{1}{\mu}\right)}p(\cos\Theta)\left[e^{\frac{\tau^*}{\mu_0}} - e^{\frac{\tau^*}{\mu}}\right]. \quad (11.32)$$

To summarize, the above equations give scattered radiances at the top and bottom of the atmosphere (or a thin cloud layer) for the special case that all of the above are satisfied: (a) multiple scattering is negligible, (b) $\tilde{\omega}$ and $p(\cos\Theta)$ are constant, and (c) the sole external illumination is a parallel beam source such as the sun. *It's important to recall the requirement that either $\tilde{\omega} \ll 1$ and/or $\tau^* \ll 1$ in order for the first of these requirements to be satisfied.*

Let's take things a step further. First, we'll focus only on the scattered atmospheric contribution to the radiance and drop the term that describes the direct transmission of radiation from the opposite side of the atmosphere (we can always add it back, if we want it). Second, we'll assume that the reason why we can neglect multiple scattering is that $\tau^* \ll 1$, and we'll further assume that μ_0 and μ are *not* much smaller than one. Taking advantage of the fact that, for small x, $e^x \approx 1 + x$, we can then simplify our equations to

$$\left.\begin{array}{ll}\text{For } \mu > 0, & I(0) \\ \text{For } \mu < 0, & I(\tau^*)\end{array}\right\} = \frac{F_0\tilde{\omega}\tau^*}{4\pi|\mu|}p(\cos\Theta).$$

(11.33)

The interpretation of the above equation is straightforward — so straightforward in fact, that we probably could have guessed it without going through all the previous steps. First, the quantity $F_0\tau^*$ tells us the magnitude of the extinguished solar flux (recall that this is valid only in the limit of small τ^*). Second, the quantity $(\tilde{\omega}/4\pi)p(\cos\Theta)$ tells us how much of the intercepted flux contributes to the scattering source term in a given new direction $\hat{\Omega}$. Finally, the factor $1/\mu$ accounts (to first order) for the fact that you are looking through less atmosphere if you view it vertically than if you look toward the horizon; consequently the path-integrated contribution of scattering to the observed intensity increases toward the horizon.

Problem 11.3: If you have access to a decent plotting program, set things up so that you can conveniently plot $I(\tau^*)$ versus $-1 < \mu < 0$ using both (11.33) and (11.32) on the same graph. Assume no extraterrestrial source of radiation from direction $\mu \neq \mu_0$. Assume isotropic scattering. Determine the range of μ, μ_0, and τ^* for which the second equation is a good approximation to the first. When the two disagree significantly, describe the nature of the disagreement. Focus on values of $\tau^* \leq 0.1$, since we know that neither equation is valid unless the atmosphere is optically thin. Note also that (11.32) cannot be directly evaluated when $\mu_0 = \mu$, though it gives physically reasonable values in the limit as $\mu \rightarrow \mu_0$.

11.5 Applications to Meteorology, Climatology, and Remote Sensing

11.5.1 Intensity of Skylight

We imposed several seemingly drastic restrictions in deriving (11.33): $\tau^* \ll 1$, $\tilde{\omega}$ and $p(\cos\Theta)$ independent of τ, μ and μ_0 not too small. In fact, these assumptions are reasonably well justified for molecular scattering of visible and near-IR sunlight in the cloud- and haze-free atmosphere, as long as (a) you stay away from the blue and violet end of the spectrum, and (b) you don't get too close to the horizon.

Therefore, to evaluate the radiant intensity of the sky (apart from the direct rays of the sun itself) you need only specify the optical depth τ^* of the cloud-free atmosphere at the wavelength in question, supply a suitable phase function $p(\Theta)$, and substitute these into (11.33) for arbitrary μ and μ_0.

As will be shown in Chapter 12, the scattering phase function of air molecules in the visible band is

$$p(\Theta) = \frac{3}{4}(1 + \cos^2 \Theta) . \qquad (11.34)$$

This so-called *Rayleigh* phase function is quite smooth and is perfectly symmetric with respect to forward and backward scattering ($g = 0$). The factor-of-two variation in intensity implied by the above phase function is relatively minor and is unlikely to be obvious to the eye, especially since it is such a smooth function of the scattering angle Θ. Consequently, we expect the radiant intensity of the sky to appear rather uniform, punctuated only by the narrow spike of high intensity associated with the directly transmitted light of the sun.

Although $p(\Theta)$ has the same shape for molecular scattering at all visible wavelengths, the optical depth τ^* of the cloud free atmosphere is a strong function of wavelength. In fact, it is shown in the next chapter that $\tau^* \propto \lambda^{-4}$. Thus, (11.33) implies that the intensity of skylight due to molecular scattering should also be proportional to λ^{-4} and, indeed, it is precisely this dependence that gives us the blue sky. It is also because τ^* stops being "small" at shorter wavelengths that we can't trust (11.33) to give us accurate sky intensities in the blue and ultraviolet part of the spectrum.

Of course, even the cleanest air found in nature contains not only molecules, but other kinds of particles called aerosols. There are typically many thousands of aerosol particles in every cubic centimeter of air. Those of interest to us here have sizes ranging from 10^{-2} μm to ~ 1 μm or larger. The scattering of visible light by such comparatively large particles (compared to molecules, that is!) is not as strongly dependent on wavelength as is molecular scattering; furthermore the scattering phase function for aerosols is not symmetric like the Rayleigh phase function but rather exhibits fairly strong forward scattering.

We can summarize the comparative scattering behavior of air molecules and aerosols in the solar band as follows:

	Molecules	**Aerosol**
Wavelength dependence:	λ^{-4}	weak
$p(\Theta)$:	smooth, symmetric	strongly asymmetric
Time/location dependence:	nearly constant	highly variable

Problem 11.4: Based on the above information, explain how the presence of scattering aerosols (e.g., haze) would be expected to visibly affect both (a) the color of the sky and (b) the angular dependence of the intensity of scattered sunlight. Is your analysis consistent with everyday experience?

11.5.2 Horizontal Visibility

Every hour, at tens of thousands of locations around the globe, detailed weather observations are made by trained observers or automated weather instruments. It is no coincidence that a large majority of these stations are associated with airports. It was the need for timely local weather observations in support of aviation, more than any other single factor, that led to the emergence of a dense global weather observing network during the twentieth century.

Although pilots care about a lot of weather variables, the two that are most often of critical concern are (a) cloud ceiling height and (b) horizontal *visibility*. Both affect pilots' ability to safely land at airports and to see and avoid other air traffic. It is the latter variable we will address here, since it is closely tied to the subject of this chapter.

Visibility is defined as the maximum horizontal distance over which the eye can clearly discern features like runways, obstacles, navigation lights, etc. On a clear day in the desert, visibility often exceeds 100 km. But in a pea-soup fog on the California coast, visibility may be measured in meters rather than kilometers.

On first confronting this problem, your initial assumption might be that visibility is controlled entirely by the extinction coefficient β_e along the line-of-sight. After all, the transmittance over a distance s is just

$$t = e^{-\beta_e s} . \tag{11.35}$$

One might argue, therefore, that there is some minimum transmittance t_{min} associated with the limit of human perception, so that the visibility V should be related to β_e as follows:

$$V = -\frac{1}{\beta_e} \log(t_{min}) . \tag{11.36}$$

But such an analysis is too simple. Consider the following examples:

- Translucent ("two-way") mirrors are often used in department stores to facilitate the detection of shoplifters by security personnel. The transmittance is the same for light traveling in either direction through the mirror, but a shopper in a brightly lit room viewing the mirror from the reflective side can't normally see what's on the other side and probably doesn't even realize that it transmits at all. The person (or camera) viewing from the nonreflective side, however, can see through easily, especially if they are situated in a darkened room.

- If you let the windshield on your car get moderately dusty, its transmittance is somewhat reduced, but normally this reduction is fairly minor. In fact, when driving away from the sun during daytime, it may be scarcely noticeable. But if you turn in the direction of the setting sun, you may suddenly find it almost impossible to see! What has changed? Not the transmittance, but rather the glare of light scattered in your direction by the coating of dust particles.

From the above examples, we can perhaps begin to appreciate that it's not *transmittance* but rather *visual contrast* that determines what we can and can't see. We will define the contrast here as the fractional difference between the apparent brightness (radiant intensity) I of an object and the brightness I' of its surroundings:

$$C \equiv \frac{I' - I}{I'} . \tag{11.37}$$

In a purely absorbing atmosphere, a mere reduction in transmittance along a line-of-sight has no impact on the visual contrast between two objects at the same distance, and therefore relatively little on visibility (up to the limit imposed by your eyes' sensitivity to light), as long as the fractional reduction in brightness is the same for both.

Atmospheric scattering reduces contrast by adding a source of radiation to the line-of-sight that is independent of the brightness of whatever is at the far end of the path. Since this source is integrated along the line-of-sight, a long path produces a greater reduction in contrast than a short path. The distance at which the contrast of an object is reduced to the minimum level required for visual detection defines the visibility.

Let's analyze the visibility problem quantitatively, by considering the contribution of single-scattered radiation to the radiance along a finite horizontal path s. Because of the latter condition, we can't use the plane-parallel form of the RTE but must start with an adaptation of (11.9):

$$\frac{dI}{d(\beta_e s)} = -I + J , \tag{11.38}$$

where I is the intensity measured horizontally in azimuthal direction ϕ, J is the scattering source function given by

$$J = \frac{\tilde{\omega}}{4\pi} \int_{4\pi} p(\mu_0, \phi_0; 0, \phi) I(\hat{\Omega}') \, d\omega' , \tag{11.39}$$

and s is the distance in the direction *toward* the observer.

For this problem, we can assume a horizontally homogeneous atmosphere, so that both the extinction coefficient β_e and the scattering source function J are constant along the line-of-sight. With these assumptions, we can integrate (11.38) to get

$$I(S) = I(0)e^{-\beta_e S} + \left(1 - e^{-\beta_e S}\right) J , \tag{11.40}$$

where $I(0)$ is the "intrinsic" radiance of the remote scene as seen without any intervening atmosphere, and $I(S)$ is the brightness of the same scene at the observer's distance S. We see that the observed intensity is just a weighted average of the intrinsic brightness of the distant object and the scattering source function, with the weight being the path transmittance $t = e^{-\beta_e S}$ for the first term and $1 - t$ for the second. Obviously, if $t = 0$, we see only the atmospheric scattering and no trace of the object at $s = 0$.

> **Problem 11.5:** Fill in the steps of the derivation of (11.40) from (11.38). Hint: Multiplying both sides by an integrating factor $e^{\beta_e s}$ will allow you to recast the differential equation into a form that can be directly integrated.

Now let's use the above equation to compute the contrast of a black object with $I(0) = 0$ viewed against a white background with intensity $I'(0)$:

$$C = \frac{I'(S) - I(S)}{I'(S)} = \frac{I'(0)t}{I'(0)t + (1-t)J} . \tag{11.41}$$

We are interested in the distance S corresponding to the minimum contrast that still permits the human eye to distinguish the object from its background, so we invert the above equation to get

$$S = \frac{1}{\beta_e} \ln \left[\frac{I'(0)(1-C)}{CJ} + 1 \right] . \tag{11.42}$$

Now all that is left is to make reasonable assumptions about $I'(0)$, C, and J.

For the background, we assume an intensity $I'(0) = \alpha F_0$, where α depends on the reflective properties of the background for the particular viewing geometry and direction of the incident sunlight. For example, if the background is a nonabsorbing Lambertian reflector, then $\alpha \leq 1/\pi$, with the equality applying in the case of normal solar incidence.

As before, we'll assume that the atmosphere is optically thin in the vertical and that the sun is high in the sky, so the scattering source function can be approximated as

$$J \approx \frac{F_0 \tilde{\omega}}{4\pi} p(\mu_0, \phi_0; 0, \phi) , \tag{11.43}$$

where μ_0 is the cosine of the solar zenith angle. We'll assume that the phase function can be expressed in terms of the cosine of the scattering angle alone, with

$$\cos \Theta = \hat{\Omega}_0 \cdot \hat{\Omega}$$

$$= \left(\sqrt{1 - \mu_0^2} \cos \Delta\phi, \sqrt{1 - \mu_0^2} \sin \Delta\phi, \mu_0 \right) \cdot (1, 0, 0) \quad (11.44)$$

$$= \sqrt{1 - \mu_0^2} \cos \Delta\phi$$

where $\Delta\phi = \phi - \phi_0$ is the angle between the viewing azimuth and the solar azimuth.

We can now substitute the above expressions for J and $I'(0)$, with $\alpha \approx \mu_0 / \pi$ and $C \approx 0.02$, to get

$$S \approx \frac{1}{\beta_e} \ln \left[\frac{200\mu_0}{\tilde{\omega} p(\cos \Theta)} + 1 \right]. \quad (11.45)$$

Problem 11.6: Use (11.45) together with the phase function for marine haze given in Problem 11.2 to plot the visibility in km versus azimuth $\Delta\phi$ relative to the sun's direction for two cases: $\mu_0 = 1$ and $\mu_0 = 0.5$. For both cases assume $\beta_e = 1.0 \text{ km}^{-1}$ and $\tilde{\omega} = 1$. Explain the differences between the two curves. Are your results consistent with your experience?

CHAPTER 12

Scattering and Absorption By Particles

In the previous chapter, we introduced the mathematical framework and terminology needed to account for radiative scattering in the atmosphere. It is safe to say that whenever you find yourself struggling with a thorny problem involving radiative scattering at microwave and shorter wavelengths, some kind of *particles* are to blame, whether they be molecules or hailstones.[1]

Formally, the scattering component of the radiative transfer equation (11.9) depends on the local extinction coefficient β_e (since $d\tau = \beta_e ds$), single scatter albedo $\tilde{\omega}$ and the scattering phase function $p(\cos \Theta)$. These in turn depend both on wavelength and on the size, composition, shape and number of suspended particles, in addition to any absorption contributions by atmospheric gases. The purpose of this chapter is to examine some basic aspects of the relationship between a particle's physical and geometric properties and its absorption and scattering properties.

---

[1]Weak scattering can also occur at radio wavelengths due solely to turbulent fluctuations in the index of refraction of air and/or due to the presence of electrically conducting ionized gases.

Table 12.1: Examples of atmospheric particle types, with representative dimensions and number concentrations. Note that actual values can vary far more widely than indicated here.

Type	Size	Number
Gas molecule	$\sim 10^{-4}\ \mu m$	$< 3 \times 10^{19}\ cm^{-3}$
Aerosol, Aitken	$< 0.1\ \mu m$	$\sim 10^4\ cm^{-3}$
Aerosol, Large	$0.1\text{--}1\ \mu m$	$\sim 10^2\ cm^{-3}$
Aerosol, Giant	$>1\ \mu m$	$\sim 10^{-1}\ cm^{-3}$
Cloud droplet	$5\text{--}50\ \mu m$	$10^2\text{--}10^3\ cm^{-3}$
Drizzle drop	$\sim 100\ \mu m$	$\sim 10^3\ m^{-3}$
Ice crystal	$10\text{--}10^2\ \mu m$	$10^3\text{--}10^5\ m^{-3}$
Rain drop	$0.1\text{--}3\ mm$	$10\text{--}10^3\ m^{-3}$
Graupel	$0.1\text{--}3\ mm$	$1\text{--}10^2\ m^{-3}$
Hailstone	$\sim 1\ cm$	$10^{-2}\text{--}1\ m^{-3}$
Insect	$\sim 1\ cm$	$< 1\ m^{-3}$
Bird	$\sim 10\ cm$	$< 10^{-4}\ m^{-3}$
Airplane	$\sim 10\ m$	$< 1\ km^{-3}$

12.1 Atmospheric Particles

12.1.1 Overview

The variety of particles encountered in the atmosphere is enormous. Examples include individual gas molecules, haze, smoke, dust and pollen particles, cloud droplets and ice crystals, rain drops, snowflakes, hailstones, insects, birds, and airplanes. Every one of these examples has at least some practical significance as a scatterer of EM radiation in the atmosphere.[2] Table 12.1 gives representative dimensions and number concentrations for some common atmospheric particles.

For the scattering of radiation by particles, *size matters*. The size of a particle is in fact its most important defining characteristic. In general, particles that are far smaller than the wavelength will scatter only very weakly, though they may still *absorb* radiation (e.g., the gas molecules discussed in Chapter 9). We will revisit the question of what "far smaller" means in a moment.

---

[2]The last three of these are significant mainly for radar.

At the other extreme, if the particle is *very large* compared to the wavelength of the radiation, then the laws of reflection, refraction, and absorption presented for homogeneous media in Chapter 4 can be used to evaluate σ_e, $\tilde{\omega}$, and $p(\Theta)$ for the particle via the approximate technique known as *ray-tracing* or *geometric optics*.[3]

Unfortunately, many particles in the atmosphere fall in between the two extremes cited above. For these particles, more complex methods are needed in order to compute their scattering and absorption properties. Such methods generally have to consider the effects of diffraction, constructive and destructive interference and other wave-related phenomena.

In this book, we will discuss only those methods applicable to very small randomly oriented particles (Rayleigh theory) or to spheres of arbitrary size (Mie theory). Fortunately, a great many atmospheric particles, from molecules to haze droplets to cloud droplets to rain drops to hailstones, are reasonable (though not always perfect) candidates for one or both of these methods, so we can cover a fair amount of ground.

12.1.2 Relevant Properties

As already mentioned, the relationship between the size of a particle and the wavelength of the radiation of interest is of crucial importance to particle's optical properties as well as to the choice of a suitable method for calculating those properties. We therefore define the nondimensional *size parameter* as

$$x \equiv \frac{2\pi r}{\lambda} \, , \qquad (12.1)$$

where r is the radius of a spherical particle. In the case of nonspherical particles, r might represent the radius of a sphere having the same volume or surface area, depending on the context.

---

[3]Even for large particles, geometric optics gives results that are seemingly at odds with exact theories. The discrepancy is due to the inability of ray tracing alone to account for subtle bending of light waves passing *near* the particle. However, because the bending is slight, it is often acceptable to treat this radiation as if it had never been scattered at all, in which case the geometric optics approximation yields perfectly acceptable results.

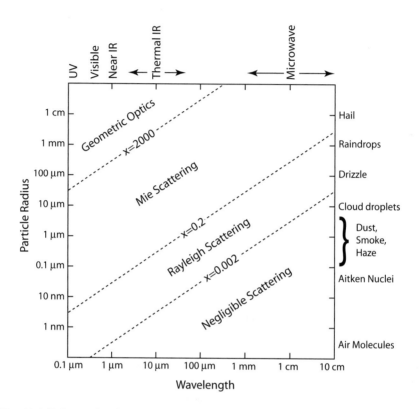

Fig. 12.1: Relationship between particle size, radiation wavelength and scattering behavior for atmospheric particles. Diagonal dashed lines represent rough boundaries between scattering regimes.

Given the value of x, one can immediately determine whether scattering by the particle is likely to be significant and, if so, which broad *scattering regime* — Rayleigh, Mie, or geometric optics — is most applicable. Figure 12.1 shows how various combinations of particle type and EM wavelength relate to these regimes.

Another key property is the relative index of refraction m, which was defined in (4.19) as

$$m \equiv \frac{N_2}{N_1},$$

where N_2 and N_1 are complex refractive indices of the particle and the surrounding medium, respectively. At the risk of slightly over-simplifying, the real part $n_r = \Re(N)$ governs the phase speed of propagation of a wave within the material and the imaginary part $n_i = \Im(N)$ governs absorption. N_1 is usually taken to be equal to one for particles suspended in air, so that $m \approx N_2$. N_2 depends on both the composition of the particle and on the wavelength. The dependence of the refractive index of water and ice on wavelength was shown in Fig. 4.1.

Finally, the *shape* of a particle may potentially play a large role in determining its radiative properties. It is convenient, and therefore common, to assume that particles are spheres for radiative purposes, even when this assumption is not entirely appropriate. Ice crystals, snowflakes, and solid-phase aerosols (e.g., soot) are good examples of particles that are far from spherical and therefore should really not be treated as such, at least not without prominently posted disclaimers. Unfortunately, computational methods appropriate for nonspherical particles are far more difficult to work with and have only recently come into common use with the advent of fast computers. We will not consider them here.

12.2 Scattering by Small Particles

12.2.1 Dipole Radiation

When a particle is sufficiently small relative to the wavelength — i.e., $|m|x \ll 1$ — every part of the particle simultaneously experiences the same externally imposed oscillating electric field. The response of the particle to the electric field is to become partially polarized. That is, there is a small displacement of positive charge within the particle in the direction of the electric field vector, while there is a displacement of negative charge in the opposite direction. In short, it becomes an electric *dipole*, with induced *dipole moment*

$\vec{p}$. The physical dimensions of $\vec{p}$ are charge times distance, which can be interpreted as the net amount of charge Q displaced times an effective displacement $\vec{x}$.

For most particles of interest to us, the dipole moment of a small spherical particle is proportional to the strength of the external electric field:

$$\vec{p} = \alpha \vec{E}_0 \exp(i\omega t) , \qquad (12.2)$$

where α is called the *polarizability* of the particle. It depends on the composition and the size of the particle, as well as on the frequency $\omega = 2\pi \nu$ of the incident wave. Note that α may be complex. Any nonzero imaginary part implies a phase difference between the real part of $\vec{p}$ and the real part of $\vec{E}$.

In summary, we have an oscillating dipole whose strength and orientation fluctuates in lockstep with the electric field due to the incident wave. But an oscillating dipole produces its own oscillating electric field, and these oscillations propagate outward at the speed of light. This is of course the origin of the scattered radiation.

Now imagine that the incident wave is traveling in direction $\hat{\Omega}$ and you are positioned at a large distance $R \gg r$ from the dipole, in direction $\hat{\Omega}'$. There are several facts we can jot down that will aid us in visualizing the relationship between the scattered wave at our location and the incident wave:

1. We know that in any EM wave, the electric field vector is perpendicular to the direction of propagation $\hat{\Omega}$.

2. We are assuming here that $\vec{p}$ is aligned with the electric field $\vec{E}_0$ of the incident wave,[4] so $\vec{p}$ is also perpendicular to $\hat{\Omega}$.

3. Because of the symmetry of the charge distribution in the dipole, the electric field vector $\vec{E}_{\text{scat}}$ of the scattered wave at any location must lie in the plane that contains both $\vec{p}$ and $\hat{\Omega}'$.

4. The *strength* of the electric field at your location is proportional to the *projection* of $\vec{p}$ as seen from your direction. Specifically,

---

[4]In other words, we are assuming that the polarizability α is a *scalar* rather than a 3×3 *tensor* which would alter the direction of $\vec{p}$ relative to $\vec{E}_0$. This is always valid for spherical particles composed of an electrically isotropic substance like water.

$\vec{E}_{scat}$ is zero if you are viewing the dipole "end on" and it is a maximum (for a given distance) when you are viewing it at right angles. We can put this in mathematical terms by saying that $\vec{E}_{scat} \propto \sin\gamma$, where γ is the angle between $\vec{E}_0$ (using Fact 2, above) and the scattered direction $\hat{\Omega}'$.

5. Less obvious, but equally important, is that the power radiated by the dipole is related to the *acceleration* of the electric charge in the dipole. That is to say, a stationary dipole will create a static electric field but no propagating EM wave, and it will therefore radiate no energy. A vibrating dipole, on the other hand, induces a vibrating electric field (and therefore an outward propagating EM wave) whose amplitude is proportional to the *square* of the frequency of the vibration.

Facts 4 and 5 together, combined with (12.2), give us the following proportionality:

$$|\vec{E}_{scat}| \propto \frac{\partial^2 \vec{p}}{\partial t^2} \sin\gamma \propto \omega^2 \sin\gamma . \tag{12.3}$$

As discussed in section 2.5, the *power per unit area*, and therefore the intensity I, is proportional to the *square* of the electric field amplitude. Therefore, the scattered intensity is given by the following proportionality:

$$I \propto \omega^4 \sin^2\gamma . \tag{12.4}$$

We now want to recast the above proportionality in terms of the scattering angles Θ and Φ, where Θ is the angle between $\hat{\Omega}$ and $\hat{\Omega}'$, and Φ is the polar angle about $\hat{\Omega}$ measured from an arbitrary starting point.

For convenience, we let the direction of incidence $\hat{\Omega}$ coincide with the x-axis, and the incident electric field vector $\vec{E}_0$ be aligned with the z-axis, consistent with Fact 2, above. We can then expand $\hat{\Omega}$ and $\hat{\Omega}'$ in Cartesian coordinates as follows:

$$\hat{\Omega} = (1, 0, 0) , \tag{12.5}$$

$$\hat{\Omega}' = (\cos\Theta, \sin\Theta \sin\Phi, \sin\Theta \cos\Phi) . \tag{12.6}$$

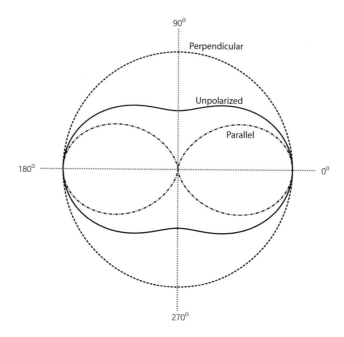

Fig. 12.2: Polar plot of the phase function for scattering by small particles (Rayleigh scattering). The outermost curve (dashed) represents the scattered intensity for directions $\hat{\Omega}'$ lying in a plane *perpendicular* to the electric field vector of the incident wave. The innermost curve (dot-dashed) corresponds to directions lying in a plane *parallel* to the electric field vector. The solid curve represents the scattered intensity for unpolarized incident radiation, as given by (12.10).

This allows us to write

$$\cos\gamma = \hat{\mathbf{z}} \cdot \hat{\mathbf{\Omega}}'$$
$$= (0,0,1) \cdot \hat{\mathbf{\Omega}}' \qquad (12.7)$$
$$= \sin\Theta\cos\Phi\,,$$

and

$$\sin^2\gamma = 1 - \cos^2\gamma \;\; = 1 - \sin^2\Theta\cos^2\Phi\,. \qquad (12.8)$$

Substituting into (12.4) gives

$$I \propto \omega^4 (1 - \sin^2\Theta\cos^2\Phi)\,. \qquad (12.9)$$

The above equation contains all of the essential features of what we will henceforth refer to as *Rayleigh scattering*. Before we continue, let's take a moment to interpret this result:

- The intensity of scattered radiation is proportional to the *fourth power* of the frequency of the incident radiation, assuming that the polarizability α is not a strong function of frequency (this may or may not be true for any given particle). You should mentally file this piece of information; we will return to it later.

- For Φ equal to either $90°$ or $270°$ — in other words, for any scattered ray lying in the plane perpendicular to $\vec{E}_0$, the scattered intensity is both constant and at its maximum value, irrespective of Θ (the outermost curve in Fig. 12.2).

- For Φ equal to either $0°$ or $180°$ *and* $\Theta = 90°$ — in other words, for either of the two directions along the axis of the dipole — the scattered intensity is zero (see the innermost curve in Fig. 12.2).

12.2.2 The Rayleigh Phase Function

The complete shape of the Rayleigh phase function for polarized incident radiation is shown in the top two panels of Fig. 12.3. For unpolarized incident radiation, the phase function $p(\Theta)$ is obtained by averaging (12.9) over Φ and normalizing according to (11.7) to get

$$p(\Theta) = \frac{3}{4}(1 + \cos^2 \Theta) \, . \tag{12.10}$$

The above expression is the one that we normally regard as describing the scattering phase function of very small particles. It is depicted as the solid curve in Fig. 12.2 and in the bottom panel of Fig. 12.3.

Problem 12.1: Verify the derivation of (12.10) from (12.9).

Problem 12.2: From (12.10), show that the asymmetry parameter g for Rayleigh scattering is zero.

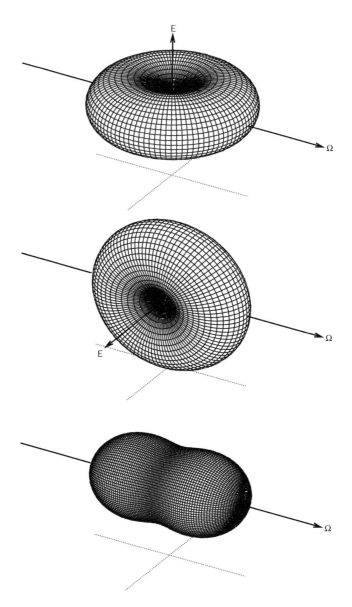

Fig. 12.3: Three-dimensional rendering of the Rayleigh phase function. The vector Ω indicates the direction of the incident radiation. The vector E indicates the orientation of the electric field vector in the incident wave. Top: Incident radiation is vertically polarized. Middle: Incident radiation is horizontally polarized. Bottom: Incident radiation is unpolarized.

12.2.3   Polarization

Equation (12.10) assumes that the incident radiation is unpolarized. But note that even if unpolarized light is incident on the particle, *the scattered light will, in general, be polarized.* You can convince yourself of this by imagining yourself positioned in the direction indicated by the ray labeled *E* in the *middle* panel of Fig. 12.3, which is to say, at a 90° angle to a horizontal beam of incident radiation (e.g., from the setting sun). At this position, you will observe no scattering of the horizontally polarized component of the incident radiation. You *will*, however, observe the maximum amount of scattering of the vertically polarized component of the incident radiation. Moreover, the scattered radiation in the latter case will itself be vertically polarized.

In short, viewing in any direction at 90° to the incident beam, you will see scattered radiation that is completely polarized. At most other angles, the scattered radiation is partially polarized, because neither component is zero. Only in the forward direction ($\Theta = 0°$) or the backward direction ($\Theta = 180°$), is the degree of scattering the same regardless of the polarization of the incident radiation; hence, unpolarized incident radiation gives rise to unpolarized scattered radiation in these two directions. In general, the degree of polarization of Rayleigh-scattered radiation is given by

$$P = \frac{1 - \cos^2 \Theta}{1 + \cos^2 \Theta}.$$
(12.11)

Radiation from the cloud- and haze-free sky is dominated by Rayleigh scattering by air molecules. According to the above equation, skylight will be unpolarized when looking directly toward or away from the sun, and 100% polarized when viewing the sky at a 90° angle from the sun.

In reality, the inevitable presence of aerosols, which are much larger than molecules and don't satisfy the Rayleigh criterion, reduces the polarization somewhat. Also, multiple scattering, which is weak but not negligible in this instance, further reduces the polarization slightly.

Nevertheless, wearing a pair of polarized sunglasses, you can easily verify the above effect by viewing a portion of the blue sky at right angles from the sun and rotating the sunglasses (or your head) about the line-of-sight. The sky will appear darker or lighter, depending on whether the sunglasses transmit or block the polarized radiation. The bluer the sky (and therefore the less haze present) the more pronounced the effect will be.

12.2.4   Scattering and Absorption Efficiencies

We were able to infer the scattering phase function for small particles based on relatively simple handwaving arguments. Let's now turn to the question of how *much* radiation a small particle scatters and/or absorbs. While it is possible to obtain this information directly based on the dipole model we developed above (see BH83, section 5.2), the complete derivation requires more space and explanation than seems warranted at this introductory level. Among other things, it would be necessary to explain the relationship between the (relative) complex index of refraction m of the particle and its polarizability α, as well as to show how the imaginary part of α bears on absorption of the incident electromagnetic wave by the particle.

An alternate way of getting at the same information is to take the general Mie solutions for spheres of arbitrary size, which I will briefly discuss in section 12.3, and find limiting expressions for $x \ll 1$. Specifically, you rewrite the solutions as power series in x and discard all but the first few terms. Here, I will give you the essential results without going through the derivations (see BH83, section 5.1).

General Relationships

To terms of order x^4, the extinction and scattering efficiencies, respectively, of a small spherical particle are

$$Q_e = 4x\Im \left\{ \frac{m^2 - 1}{m^2 + 2} \left[1 + \frac{x^2}{15} \left(\frac{m^2 - 1}{m^2 + 2} \right) \frac{m^4 + 27m^2 + 38}{2m^2 + 3} \right] \right\}$$
$$+ \frac{8}{3} x^4 \Re \left\{ \left(\frac{m^2 - 1}{m^2 + 2} \right)^2 \right\}, \quad (12.12)$$

and

$$Q_s = \frac{8}{3}x^4 \left| \frac{m^2 - 1}{m^2 + 2} \right|^2 . \tag{12.13}$$

The absorption efficiency is then $Q_a = Q_e - Q_s$. For sufficiently small x (see BH83, p. 136 for details), Q_a simplifies to

$$Q_a = 4x\Im\left\{ \frac{m^2 - 1}{m^2 + 2} \right\} . \tag{12.14}$$

We see that the absorption efficiency Q_a is proportional to x, while the scattering efficiency Q_s is proportional to x^4. It follows that, for sufficiently small x, and assuming that m has a nonzero imaginary part,

$$Q_s \ll Q_a \approx Q_e , \tag{12.15}$$

and the single scatter albedo

$$\tilde{\omega} \equiv \frac{Q_s}{Q_e} \propto x^3 . \tag{12.16}$$

The above relationships have a number of important practical implications for atmospheric radiation and remote sensing. We will highlight a few of these here.

Scattering Cross-Section

First of all, if we assume that we're in a part of the spectrum where m for our particle varies slowly with wavelength, then according to (12.13) the scattering efficiency Q_s of a particle in the Rayleigh limit is proportional to x^4, which is in turn proportional to $(r/\lambda)^4$ or, equivalently, to $(r\nu)^4$. [Recall that we already saw this proportionality in (12.9), since $\omega \equiv 2\pi\nu$.] The scattering *cross-section* σ_s, which is what actually determines how much radiation is scattered, is of course the product of Q_s with the particle cross-sectional area πr^2, so that

$$\sigma_s \propto \frac{r^6}{\lambda^4} . \tag{12.17}$$

This proportionality is well worth memorizing, as long as you also remember that it's only valid in the Rayleigh regime — i.e., for $x \ll 1$.

Single Scatter Albedo

The second relationship worth commenting on is (12.16), which tells us that the single scatter albedo for small particles goes with x^3. Of course this is only true for particles that are at least slightly absorbing; if the imaginary part of m is zero, then $\tilde\omega = 1$ no matter how small x.

What this means in practice is that for sufficiently small x you can pretty much forget about scattering and focus instead on just the absorption properties of the particles. This limiting behavior arises in at least two important cases: (1) molecular absorption (but not scattering) of thermal infrared radiation by atmsospheric gases (see Chapter 9), and (2) absorption (but not scattering) of microwave radiation by cloud droplets.

Mass Absorption Coefficient

Not only can you forget about *scattering* in the limit of small x, but a surprisingly convenient fact emerges concerning *absorption* by particles in this limit. Recall that the mass absorption coefficient k_a of a substance is defined as its absorption cross-section per unit mass. For a spherical particle of radius r and density ρ, we can write

$$k_a = \frac{Q_a \pi r^2}{\rho(4/3)\pi r^3} = \frac{3Q_a}{4\rho r} . \tag{12.18}$$

Substituting (12.14) and (12.1), we have

$$k_a = \frac{6\pi}{\rho\lambda} \Im\left\{ \frac{m^2-1}{m^2+2} \right\} . \tag{12.19}$$

Note that *there is no dependence here on the particle radius r!*

Imagine a volume V of air containing a number of spherical particles (e.g., cloud droplets) which may be of various sizes but which are in any case all much smaller than the wavelength of interest. We can write the volume absorption ($\approx$ extinction) coefficient (dimensions of inverse length) in terms of the sum of the particles' individual absorption cross-sections σ as follows:

$$\beta_a = \frac{1}{V} \sum_i \sigma_i . \tag{12.20}$$

But $\sigma_i = k_a M_i$, where M_i is the mass of the droplet, so we have

$$\beta_a = \frac{1}{V} \sum_i k_a M_i = k_a \frac{1}{V} \sum_i M_i \tag{12.21}$$

or, quite simply,

$$\boxed{\beta_a = k_a \rho ,} \tag{12.22}$$

where ρ is just the combined mass of the substance (e.g., cloud water) per unit volume of air. We therefore conclude that *for radiation passing through a cloud of sufficiently small absorbing particles, the total absorption is equal to k_a [as given by (12.19)] times the total mass path, regardless of the exact sizes of the constituent particles.*

Summary

Let us conclude this section by summarizing some **key facts** about scattering and absorption in the Rayleigh regime:

1. If you have a particle of fixed size and expose it to radiation with two different wavelengths $\lambda_1 < \lambda_2$, then it will scatter the shorter wavelength λ_1 more strongly by a factor of $(\lambda_2/\lambda_1)^4$.

2. If you have radiation of a fixed wavelength λ and use it to illuminate two particles of radius $r_1 < r_2$, the larger particle will scatter the radiation more strongly by a factor $(r_2/r_1)^6$.

3. For sufficiently small particles with complex (not pure real) refractive index m, scattering is negligible and absorption is proportional to mass path only, irrespective of particle size. In this limit, a cloud behaves radiatively like an absorbing gas rather than a collection of discrete scatterers.

The first of these facts is directly responsible for the blue sky and the reddish setting sun. The second fact is of central importance to weather radar. The third is relevant to microwave remote sensing of cloud water. We will revisit each of these topics in the Applications section at the end of this chapter.

12.3   Scattering by Spheres — Mie Theory

A brief outline of Mie theory for scattering and absorption by homogeneous spheres of arbitrary size parameter x and relative index of refraction m is given by S94 (pp. 235–243). Full derivations are given by BH83 (pp. 82–107) and L02 Section 5.2. In a nutshell, the Maxwell equations are used to derive a wave equation for electromagnetic radiation in three dimensional space, and these are expressed in spherical polar coordinates (r, ϕ, Θ), with appropriate boundary conditions at the surface of the sphere. The result is a separable partial differential equation, the solution of which is expressed as an infinite series of products of orthogonal basis functions, including sines and cosines (for the dependence on ϕ), spherical Bessel functions (for the dependence on r), and associated Legendre polynomials (for the dependence on $\cos \Theta$).

If you have already had a course in partial differential equations, then that last sentence will be at least vaguely intelligible. The bottom line is that the extinction and scattering efficiencies of a sphere may be written as

$$Q_e = \frac{2}{x^2} \sum_{n=1}^{\infty} (2n + 1)\Re(a_n + b_n) , \qquad (12.23)$$

$$Q_s = \frac{2}{x^2} \sum_{n=1}^{\infty} (2n + 1)(|a_n|^2 + |b_n|^2) , \qquad (12.24)$$

where the coefficients a_n and b_n are referred to as Mie scattering coefficients and are functions of x and m. The mathematical form of these coefficients is not particularly informative to the untrained eye, so they will not be reproduced here.

Similar summations are used to describe the wave scattering amplitudes as a function of scattering angle Θ. These are used to obtain expressions for the elements of the 4×4 scattering phase matrix $P_{ij}(\Theta)$ (see 11.2.2). The P_{11} element of this matrix is the same as our scalar phase function $p(\Theta)$ for unpolarized incident light.

As a practical matter, one cannot actually compute an infinite sum; therefore it is always necessary to truncate the series and keep only enough terms to yield a sufficiently accurate approximation. Generally speaking, the required number of terms N is a little larger than x; the criterion developed by BH83 based on extensive testing is that N should be the integer closest to $x + 4x^{1/3} + 2$. For a typical cloud droplet of 10 μm radius and a visible wavelength of 0.5 μm, the size parameter $x \approx 120$; thus the number of terms required in the summation is 127.

For much larger particles (e.g. raindrops in the visible band, with $x \sim 10^4$ or more) the number of terms that must be retained is rather large. Although the computer time required to evaluate these terms is no longer a huge issue for most applications, numerical precision begins to suffer due to the accumulation of roundoff error. There are therefore practical limits to the size of a sphere whose properties can be evaluated using Mie theory. Geometric optics (or ray tracing; see Section 4.3.1) becomes the preferred method in such cases.

12.3.1 Extinction Efficiency for Nonabsorbing Sphere

Figure 12.4 depicts the extinction efficiency Q_e as a function of x for a sphere with $m = 1.33$. This is a representative value for water in the visible band. Note that no imaginary part is assumed here, so the droplet is nonabsorbing ($\tilde{\omega} = 1$) for all x.

The top panel (Fig. 12.4a) shows the typical behavior of Q_e over a wide range of x. It starts out at zero for $x = 0$ and rises monotonically up to about $x = 6$, where Q_e achieves a maximum value of about 4. In other words, for this value of x, the droplet scatters four times as much radiation as one might surmise from its cross-sectional area alone! Thereafter, it exhibits an ever-dampening oscillation about a mean value of 2, which is the limiting value of Q_e for large x (recall that we already exploited this behavior in section 7.2.3).

At the other end of the range, we have the opportunity to com-

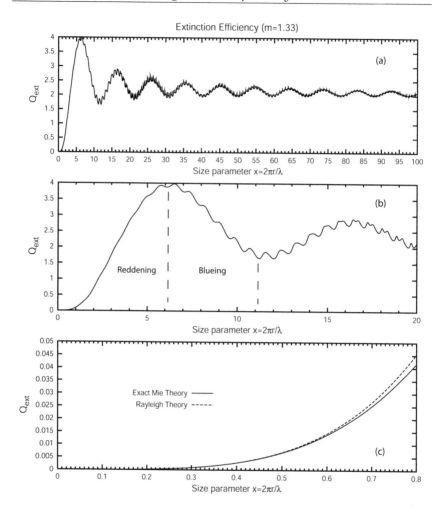

Fig. 12.4: The extinction efficiency Q_e as a function of size parameter x for a non-absorbing sphere with $m = 1.33$, for various ranges of x. (a) "Big picture" view, showing that $Q_e \to 2$ as $x \to \infty$. (b) Detail for $x < 20$, with examples of subranges for which extinction increases with x (reddening) or decreases with x (blueing). (c) Detail for $x < 0.8$, comparing the Rayleigh (small particle) approximation and exact Mie theory.

pare $Q_e (= Q_s)$ computed using the exact Mie theory with that obtained for the small-particle (Rayleigh) limit (Fig. 12.4c). We can see that the agreement is quite good up to about $x = 0.6$. Beyond that point, Q_e increases less rapidly than the x^4 dependence predicted by (12.13).

Reddening/Blueing

Let's now zoom in on the first couple of big wiggles in the curve (Fig. 12.4b). Let's further assume for the moment that r is fixed, so that variations in x are due to variations in the wavelength λ, not particle size — that is, increasing x implies decreasing λ, and vice versa. Despite allowing the wavelength to vary, we will pretend (somewhat unrealistically) that m also remains approximately constant, so that our Q_e curves are still valid.

With the above assumptions in mind, we find that in the region $0 < x < 6$, Q_e increases with x and therefore decreases with wavelength. This means that for radiation passing through a cloud of our fixed-size particles, the shorter wavelengths will be attenuated more strongly than the longer wavelengths. This phenomenon is known as *reddening*, and is responsible for the reddish color of the setting sun. In fact, we already found a similar phenomenon in connection with Rayleigh scattering in the previous section; those findings applied to particles with $x \ll 1$, which is of course a small portion of the range of x we are looking at right now.

For x between 6 and 11, on the other hand, extinction is stronger for longer wavelengths than for shorter, giving rise to *blueing* of the radiation passing through our particles. Blueing of sunlight or moonlight is only very rarely observed; it would require an unusual distribution of aerosol sizes in order for the blueing effect to dominate over the usual reddening by both air molecules and smaller aerosols.[5]

> **Problem 12.3:** Visible radiation spans the wavelength range from 0.4 μm to 0.7 μm. Assuming that atmospheric aerosols have approximately the same refractive index m as that used to produce Fig. 12.4b, determine the range of aerosol radii that would give rise to blueing.

We can look at the above phenomenon from a slightly different (and more realistic) perspective by plotting the extinction efficiency

---

[5]Large volcanic eruptions occasionally inject matter into the stratosphere that coalesces into aerosols of fairly uniform size; on rare occasions these may have a size that leads to blueing of visible light. Some authors have suggested that such rare events gave rise to the phrase "once in a blue moon."

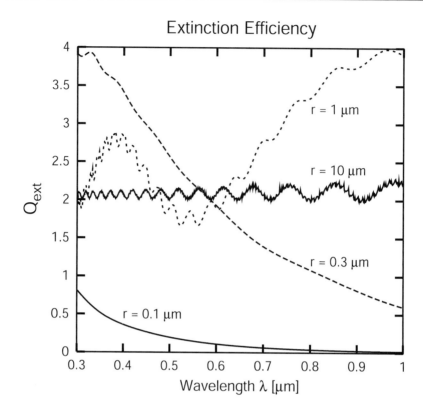

Fig. 12.5: The extinction efficiency as a function of wavelength for water droplets of the indicated sizes.

versus wavelength for selected water droplet radii, as in Fig. 12.5. For droplet radii of 0.1 and 0.3 μm, which are characteristic of small haze droplets, extinction is a strong function of wavelength, with short wavelengths (e.g., UV-A, violet, blue) being extinguished far more strongly than longer wavelengths (red, near IR). This is again the classic reddening behavior that we observe on a hazy day, especially when the sun is low in the sky.

At an intermediate radius of 1 μm, the extinction behavior is more complex. Near infrared wavelengths are fairly strongly attenuated, violet light (near 0.4 μm) and red light (near 0.7 μm) is attenuated slightly less strongly, and there is a pronounced minimum in extinction between 0.5 and 0.6 μm. We can conclude that if the aerosol population of the atmosphere consisted primarily of droplets of 1 μm radius, the setting sun would take on a rather unnatural greenish hue![6]

The largest radius for which Q_e is plotted in Fig. 12.5 is 10 μm, which is a typical radius for ordinary cloud droplets. Over the entire range of wavelength plotted, $Q_e \approx 2$. The lack of strong wavelength dependence is why the color of sunlight passing through thin clouds is not noticeably altered by the encounter. Even the obvious wiggles seen on this curve are actually irrelevant in practice, because cloud droplets never have exactly one size but rather are distributed over a fairly broad range of sizes. Even a fairly small 10% variability in droplet size would be enough to average away most of the wiggle structure in the Q_e curve.

12.3.2 Extinction and Scattering by Absorbing Spheres

Let's now broaden our perspective in the following two ways: (1) we will allow the imaginary part of m to be nonzero, and (2) we will look at not only Q_e but also the absorption efficiency Q_a, the single scatter albedo $\tilde{\omega}$, and the scattering asymmetry parameter g. Representative results are shown in Fig. 12.6. Based on these plots we can make the following general statements:

- Increasing absorption by the particle material (by increasing the imaginary part of m) has the effect of suppressing the wiggles in the curve of Q_e. Apart from that change, the curves are similar, all having a limiting value of approximately 2 for large x.

- In the limit as x goes to zero, the single scatter albedo also goes to zero, as predicted by (12.16). The sole exception is if $\Im(m) = 0$ (not shown), in which case $\tilde{\omega} = 1$ regardless of x.

- For $x > 10$, there is no completely predictable relationship between $\Im(m)$ and either Q_a or $\tilde{\omega}$. The absorption tends to increase with small increases in $\Im(m)$, as you might expect,

---

[6]It is tempting, though probably futile, to speculate on a possible role for 1 μm haze or cloud droplets in the sickly greenish light that is observed to accompany some severe thunderstorms. Various other physical mechanisms have been proposed; as of this writing none has been widely embraced as *the* definitive explanation for green thunderstorms, partly because of the scarcity of direct measurements that could be used to test the various theories.

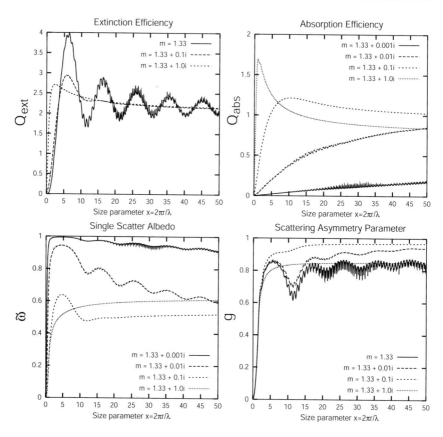

Fig. 12.6: Key optical properties of spheres as functions of x, for varying values of the imaginary part of m.

but the trend reverses when $\Im(m)$ is of order one — particles with large $\Im(m)$ scatter *more* effectively than those with smaller $\Im(m)$.

- For $\Im(m) = 0$, there is considerable fine ripple structure in the curves for both Q_e and g. The presence of even slight absorption (e.g., the case $m = 1.33 + 0.001i$) pretty much eliminates these ripples. But even for nonabsorbing particles, these fine ripples tend to be unimportant. This is because you never have particles all having the same exact value of x but rather a mix of particles of various sizes. When combining the contributions from various sizes, the small ripples quickly average away.

- For $x = 0$, the asymmetry parameter g is also zero, as expected for Rayleigh scattering. As x increases, g very rapidly increases as well, plateauing somewhere in the range from about 0.8 and 0.95.

Forward Scattering

The last item is worthy of particular attention. It indicates that *particles comparable to or larger than the wavelength tend to strongly forward scatter*, as contrasted with the case that $x \ll 1$, for which the backward and forward scattered components are about equal. It turns out that *this observation is generally applicable not only to spheres but to particles of all types and shapes*. This behavior is due to constructive interference in the forward direction by waves scattered by different parts of the particle, as discussed for example by S94 (Section 5.2.1).

12.3.3 Scattering Phase Function

The forward-scattering properties of larger particles becomes even more apparent as we turn our attention to the scattering phase function $p(\Theta)$ of our spheres, as depicted for example in Fig. 12.7.

For $x = 0.1$ (bottom), we have the classical Rayleigh phase function, which is symmetric in the forward and backward directions. For slightly larger x, there is a tendency for the phase function in the forward direction $\Theta < 90°$ to have larger amplitude than in the backward direction.

By the time we get to $x = 3$, we have a broad lobe of enhanced scattering for Θ between about $0°$ and $40°$. Within that range, the amplitude of $p(\Theta)$ is around a factor of 100 larger than it is for Θ between $120°$ and $180°$. Now watch this forward-scattering lobe carefully as we move upward on the figure — *it becomes both narrower and more intense with increasing x*. In fact, for very large x, this so-called *forward diffraction peak*, starts to resemble a δ-function and falls right on y-axis in Fig. 12.7, so that it can no longer be distinguished.

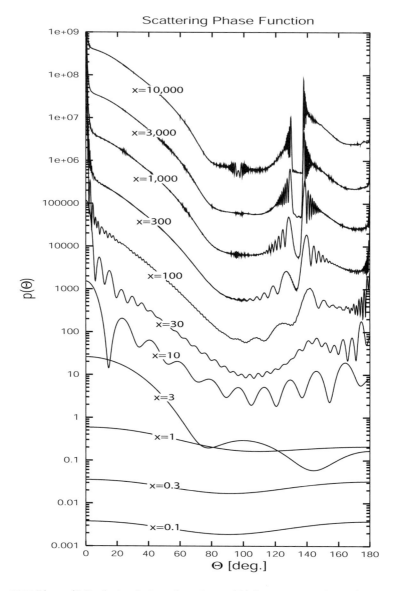

Fig. 12.7: Plots of Mie-derived phase functions $p(\Theta)$ for various values of x, assuming $m = 1.33$ (fine-scale oscillations in the curves for large x have been smoothed out by allowing x to vary over a narrow range). The vertical scale is logarithmic but otherwise arbitrary; each curve has been displaced upward from the previous one for clarity. Note increasing asymmetry and complexity of phase functions with increasing x. The topmost curve ($x = 10,000$) is very similar to that predicted by geometric optics except for the narrow forward and backward peaks at $0°$ and $180°$. See Figs. 12.8 and 12.9 for polar plots of some of these same curves.

Fig. 12.8: Polar plots of the Mie-derived scattering phase function $p(\Theta)$ for selected values of x.

At the same time as the forward scattering peak gets narrower with increasing x, the rest of the phase function becomes more complex, exhibiting an ever greater number of ripples. By the time we get to $x = 100$, we start to see unmistakable signs of an enhanced scattering feature near $\Theta = 140°$. This feature also sharpens and intensifies dramatically with increasing x, until there is nearly a hundred-fold difference between the amplitude of the peak at $\Theta = 137°$ and the "floor" of the valley at just a slightly smaller angle! This feature is the *primary rainbow* whose existence was previously explained in section 4.3.1 using the ray tracing method (Fig. 4.8) and assuming a single internal reflection of the ray. The slightly weaker peak at $\Theta = 130°$, just to the left of the primary rainbow, is the secondary rainbow, which is associated with rays undergoing two internal reflections in the sphere.

In summary, the Mie solution, which is based on an infinite series solution of the EM wave equation with suitable boundary conditions, yields results which basically converge to the geometric optics results, once we let x get large enough. In fact, for $x > 2000$ or so, we have crossed out of the range of x for which Mie theory is traditionally applied (see Fig. 12.1). Even for very large x, however, there are aspects of scattering by particles that geometric optics alone can never explain, such as the forward diffraction peak as well as the intensified scattering near $180°$ known as the *glory*.

The polar plots in Fig. 12.8 and Fig. 12.9 provide an alternative way of visualizing the evolution of the phase function with increasing x. In the first of these, the amplitude of the phase function is proportional to the distance along a particular radial at angle Θ, with $\Theta = 0$ pointing horizontally to the right. For $x = 0.1$ we again have the symmetric Rayleigh phase function; you'll probably recognize the shape from Figs. 12.2 and Figs. 12.3. For even modest increases in x, the asymmetry quickly becomes very pronounced. By the time we reach $x = 10$, the forward scattering lobe is already so intense that it no longer fits on the page!

For larger x, we can tame the extreme features of the phase function by making the radial amplitude proportional to the *logarithm* of $p(\cos \Theta)$ (Fig. 12.9). Among other things, these plots allow us to clearly see, for the first time, what's happening at $\Theta = 0°$ and $\Theta = 180°$. There are a few features that deserve special mention,

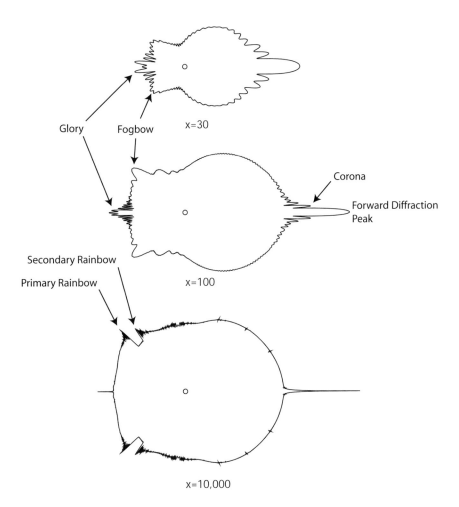

Fig. 12.9: Similar to Fig. 12.8, but plotted as $\log[p(\Theta)]$ so as to better accommodate the extreme variations in the amplitude of the phase function for large x. Commonly observed optical features associated with the phase function are indicated. Note the δ-function-like characteristic of the forward and backward peaks for the largest values of x.

because they are associated with commonly observed optical phenomena:

Forward Diffraction Peak

We have already mentioned the strong forward scattering that occurs in connection with larger particles, spherical or not. This phenomenon is readily observable in daily life. It is much harder to see through the glare of a dirty windshield when driving toward the sun than away. Dust particles settling through a shaft of sunlight in a room are easiest to spot when looking generally toward the source of the light. The rays of light from the setting sun emerging from a break in the clouds (so-called *crepuscular rays*) are most evident when viewed in the general direction of the sun.

Fig. 12.9 makes much clearer the profound narrowing of the diffraction peak with increasing x. For $x = 10,000$, the peak is so narrow that the scattered radiation it represents might as well be considered as never having been scattered at all. In the geometric optics approximation, this feature doesn't even exist! In fact, while Mie theory predicts $Q_e \approx 2$ in the limit of large x, geometric optics always predicts $Q_e = 1$. The forward diffraction peak is largely responsible for the discrepancy.

Corona

For intermediate values of the size parameter x, the forward diffraction peak is accompanied by number of weaker *sidelobes*. If you were to view the sun through a very thin cloud made up of identical spherical droplets with x of order 100 or less, you would see a series of closely spaced rings immediately surrounding the light source. Moreover, because the precise angular position of the rings depends on wavelength, the rings would be brightly colored. This optical feature is known as a *corona*.

Coronas observed in real clouds are more diffuse, and less brightly colored, than the corona you would expect from a cloud composed of identical droplets. In fact, one reason colored coronas are rarely observed at all is because few clouds have a sufficiently narrow distribution of drop sizes.[7]

Far more commonly you will just see a diffuse circular bright patch surrounding the sun with little if any coloration. This feature represents a blending of both the forward diffraction peaks and the sidelobes contributed by a variety of different drop sizes.

Glory

The *glory* is in many respects analogous to the forward diffraction peak and the corona, except that it is exactly on the opposite end of the phase function. It is called a "glory" because if you stand on a hill overlooking a fog bank with the sun at your back, you will see a bright patch or ring surrounding the shadow of your head in a manner reminiscent of medieval paintings of saints.

A much more predictable setting for observing glories is as a passenger in an airplane flying above a cloud layer, from whence a bright ring is often seen immediately surrounding the shadow of the airplane. If the airplane is high enough above the cloud layer, the shadow will be too indistinct to see but the glory will be visible nonetheless.

As was also the case for the corona, glories may involve multiple rings and vivid colors, provided only that the range of drop sizes is sufficiently narrow. More commonly, the glory is seen as a fairly indistinct white ring or circular bright patch.

For very large x, the glory narrows to a δ-function-like spike in the exact backscattering direction $\Theta = 180°$. Like the forward diffraction peak, the glory is a feature not predicted by geometric optics, at least for spheres with the index of refraction of water.[8]

---

[7]Another reason, of course, is that only true enthusiasts of optical phenomena take time each day — and risk their eyesight — in order to stare almost directly at the sun in the hope of spotting a spectacular corona!

[8]You have probably noticed that a lot of street signs, license plates, reflective leg straps for bicycle riders, etc., are intensely reflective when the light source is very close to being in line with the object and the observer. For example, when approaching a stop sign at night from a couple of blocks away, your own headlights cause the sign to light up brightly, whereas illumination by light sources in other directions doesn't have nearly as intense an effect. Close examination reveals the presence of *retroreflective* beads, which are simply small spheres with an index of refraction falling between approximately 1.5 and 2.0. For this range of index of refraction, geometric optics is able to explain the unusually strong backscatter as

Fogbow/Rainbow

We already mentioned the occcurence of sharp spikes in the scattering phase function corresponding to the primary and secondary rainbows. The positions of these features are noted on the polar plot for $x = 10,000$ in Fig. 12.9. For smaller x, the primary rainbow feature is still present but not nearly as sharp. Because the peak is much more diffuse, the separation of colors (due to varying n_r) will not be nearly as vivid as you find in a "normal" rainbow, and you will instead observe a more or less whitish ring centered on the point opposite the sun (i.e., centered on your own shadow). In this case, a better name for the feature is *fogbow*, because it arises (for visible light) when the water droplets have a size characteristic of fog and clouds rather than rain.

> **Problem 12.4:** Assuming a wavelength $\lambda = 0.5$ μm, which is near the middle of the visible band, determine the water droplet radii corresponding to each of the three phase functions depicted in Fig. 12.9.

12.4   Distributions of Particles

The atmosphere never contains particles of just one size. In performing radiation transfer calculations for clouds and aerosols, it is invariably necessary to start out by determining the combined optical properties of a distribution of particles of varying sizes and, possibly, shapes and compositions. We will limit our attention to the case of varying size only, though the formal extension to shape and composition is straightforward.

In Section 7.4.4, I already introduced the concept of a size distribution function $n(r)$ for cloud droplets. To refresh your memory,

$$n(r)\ dr = \begin{cases} \text{number of droplets (per unit volume of} \\ \text{air) whose radii fall in the range } [r, r + dr] \end{cases} . \quad (12.25)$$

The same concept is applicable to any particle type.

---

the result of rays that pass into the sphere and experience total internal reflection on the far side.

We already saw that the volume extinction coefficient for the distribution of particles described by $n(r)$ is

$$\beta_e = \int_0^\infty n(r)Q_e(r)\pi r^2 \, dr . \tag{12.26}$$

In other words, the total extinction β_e is equal to the extinction cross-section contribution from a single particle of radius r multiplied by the number of particles (per unit volume) having that radius and then integrated over all possible radii.

A completely analogous relationship gives the scattering coefficient

$$\beta_s = \int_0^\infty n(r)Q_s(r)\pi r^2 \, dr . \tag{12.27}$$

From there, we immediately have the single-scatter albedo of the distribution as $\tilde{\omega} = \beta_s/\beta_e$.

The combined scattering phase function is the *scattering cross-section weighted average* of the individual phase functions:

$$p(\cos\Theta) = \frac{1}{\beta_s} \int_0^\infty n(r)Q_s(r)\pi r^2 p(\cos\Theta; r) \, dr , \tag{12.28}$$

which also implies a combined asymmetry parameter of

$$g = \frac{1}{\beta_s} \int_0^\infty n(r)Q_s(r)\pi r^2 g(r) \, dr . \tag{12.29}$$

12.5 Applications to Meteorology, Climatology, and Remote Sensing

12.5.1 The Scattering Properties of Clouds

The radiative properties of clouds, including their ability to reflect and absorb both solar and thermal radiation, depend on their optical depth τ^*, their single scatter albedo $\tilde{\omega}$ and the scattering phase function $p(\cos\Theta)$. These properties in turn depend on the size parameter x and on the complex index of refraction m for the cloud's constituent particles. Both x and m depend on wavelength λ, and x also depends on the droplet radius r. The index of refraction m

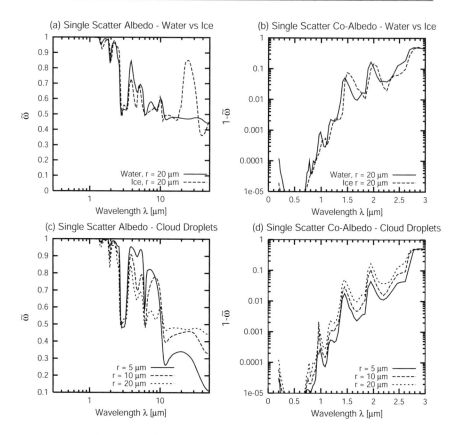

Fig. 12.10: Single scatter albedo (or co-albedo) as a function of wavelength for water and ice spheres of various sizes. The left column depicts $\tilde{\omega}$ over the entire visible, near IR and thermal IR range. The right column depicts the scattering co-albedo (defined as $1 - \tilde{\omega}$) for just the solar band. The top row compares water and ice for particle radius $r = 20$ μm; the bottom row compares water droplets of three different radii (5, 10, and 20 μm).

depends on composition and material phase as well, but for most clouds, there are only two possibilities: liquid water or ice.

For reasonably large x, we already saw that $Q_e \approx 2$, so that the optical thickness τ^* can often be taken to be almost independent of wavelength. The phase function $p(\Theta)$ is adequately characterized for many purposes by the asymmetry parameter g, which we saw tends to hover in the fairly narrow range 0.8–0.9 for x greater than around 10.

This leaves the single scatter albedo $\tilde{\omega}$ as the one variable that could potentially have a large influence on how cloud reflectivity/absorptivity varies with λ. And indeed this conjecture is validated by the plots of $\tilde{\omega}$ vs. λ shown in Fig. 12.10. This information is represented in two different ways. The first is by simply plotting $\tilde{\omega}$ on a linear vertical axis, as is done in the two panels in the left column. This is fine for showing the coarse variations of $\tilde{\omega}$ with wavelength but tends to obscure subtle deviations of $\tilde{\omega}$ from exactly one (pure scattering, no absorption), which can nevertheless be significant for absorption by clouds. Therefore, for the shorter wavelengths where absorption is comparatively weak, we plot the scattering *co-albedo*, defined as $1 - \tilde{\omega}$, on a logarithmic vertical axis.

Here are the basic points you should take away from these plots:

- The visible band (0.4 μm $< \lambda <$ 0.7 μm) coincides almost exactly with a surprisingly narrow portion of the EM spectrum for which absorption by cloud droplets is, for all practical purposes, zero. You can think of it as an astonishing coincidence that clouds (when viewed from the sunlit side) appear to our eyes as white rather than gray, black, or some other color! As soon as you move into either the UV or near-IR bands, $\tilde{\omega}$ quickly decreases to well below 1, settling into the range 0.5–0.8 for most of the IR band. For even $\tilde{\omega} = 0.8$, the albedo of a thick cloud is only around 15%.

- At several wavelengths, there is a significant difference between the single scatter albedo of a spherical ice particle and that of a water droplet of the same size (top row). For some of these wavelengths, ice particles are less absorptive than the water droplets; for others, the reverse is true. These differences can be exploited by satellite sensors to distinguish ice phase clouds (cirrus) from water clouds[9].

- For most wavelengths, there is a significant dependence of the single scatter albedo on the droplet radius in liquid water clouds (bottom row). As a general rule (although there are exceptions), a larger droplet has lower $\tilde{\omega}$ (i.e., is more absorptive) than a smaller droplet at the same wavelength.

---

[9]The fact that ice particles in clouds are generally *not* spheres complicates the problem somewhat, but the principle is still valid.

Once again, satellite remote sensing techniques can exploit this property to estimate the effective droplet radius r_{eff} in water clouds.

12.5.2　Radar Observations of Precipitation

Radar has become one of the most important observational tools of operational meteorologists as well as hydrologists. Weather radar allows severe weather systems to be tracked in real-time. It also allows the monitoring of rainfall with far more detail in both time and space than is possible with conventional rain gauges.

The basic principle of operation of a radar system is simple. A transmitter sends out a continuous series of short pulses of microwave radiation. A sensitive receiver then measures the intensity of the backscattered radiation as a function of the time elapsed following each transmitted pulse. The time elapsed Δt is of course just the round trip distance divided by the speed of light c, so that the one-way distance d to the target is given by

$$d = \frac{c\Delta t}{2} . \tag{12.30}$$

The backscattered power P_r received by the radar antenna is given by the following proportionality:

$$P_r \propto \frac{\eta}{d^2} , \tag{12.31}$$

where η (Greek letter *eta*) is the *backscatter cross-section per unit volume of air*. It is just the sum of the backscatter cross-sections σ_b of all particles in the sampled volume of air V, divided by V:

$$\eta = \frac{1}{V} \sum_i \sigma_{b,i} , \tag{12.32}$$

The backscatter cross-section σ_b is closely related to to the more familiar scattering cross-section σ_s, except that it only accounts for radiation scattered exactly backward toward the radar antenna, rather than radiation scattered into all directions. As a matter of fact,

$$\sigma_b \equiv \sigma_s \, p(\Theta)|_{\Theta=\pi} . \tag{12.33}$$

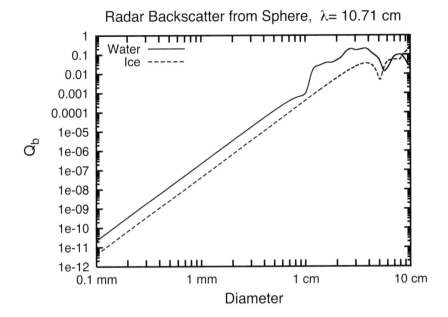

Fig. 12.11: Radar backscatter efficiency Q_b for water and ice spheres at the wavelength of the WSR-88D operational weather radar.

Now let's assume that we're dealing with particles that all have the same composition (e.g., liquid water), are spherical in shape, and are distributed in size according to a size distribution function $n(D)$, where D is the droplet diameter. The assumption of spherical shape, while approximate, is reasonable for raindrops that are "not too large."

We can then replace the summation in (12.32) with an integral involving $n(D)$ and $\sigma_b(D)$:

$$\eta = \int_0^\infty \sigma_b(D) n(D)\, dD \, , \tag{12.34}$$

or

$$\eta = \int_0^\infty Q_b(D) \left[\frac{\pi}{4} D^2 \right] n(D)\, dD \, , \tag{12.35}$$

where the term in square brackets is just the cross-sectional area of a sphere with diameter D, and Q_b is the *backscatter efficiency*.

If our spherical particles happen to have size parameters $x \ll 1$, then we're in the Rayleigh regime. This means that (a) the Rayleigh formula (12.13) for σ_s applies, and (b) the phase function is given by (12.10). Substituting these into (12.33) gives

$$Q_b = 4x^4 \left| \frac{m^2 - 1}{m^2 + 2} \right|^2 . \tag{12.36}$$

If our particles are too large, then Rayleigh theory no longer applies, and we have to calculate σ_b using Mie theory. Fig. 12.11 shows accurate calculations of Q_b for a wide range of sizes of water and ice spheres. The wavelength $\lambda = 10.71$ cm chosen for these calculations corresponds to that used by the current-generation operational weather radar network in the United States.

You can see that for liquid water spheres up to a diameter of about 6 mm (solid curve), the Rayleigh relationship (12.36) holds to a high degree of accuracy: each decade (factor ten) increase in D corresponds to a four decade (factor 10^4) increase in Q_b. In fact, 6 mm corresponds to a rough upper limit on the observed sizes of raindrops in heavy rain; beyond this size, raindrops tend to be broken up by aerodynamic forces as they fall.

Hailstones can of course become considerably larger than raindrops. It is therefore convenient that the Rayleigh approximation apparently holds up to a diameter of around 3 cm for a pure ice sphere (dashed curve). Note that for any given D in the Rayleigh regime part of the curve, Q_b for pure ice is only 20% of that for liquid water. This difference is due to the substantially smaller value of m for ice in the microwave band, as compared to liquid water[10].

> **Problem 12.5:** Based on the above information, compute the diameter of a spherical hailstone that has the same radar backscatter cross-section σ_b (not Q_b!) as a spherical raindrop with a diameter of 2 mm.

Let's assume that the hydrometeors (e.g. raindrops, hailstones, etc.) that are observed by a 10-cm weather radar all fall in the

---

[10]It is worth keeping in mind, however, that growing hailstones often have a coating of liquid water. Even a thin coating of water can drastically alter the radar backscattering properties of an ice particle.

Rayleigh regime. We can then substitute (12.36) into (12.35) to get

$$\eta = \frac{\pi^5}{\lambda^4} \left| \frac{m^2 - 1}{m^2 + 2} \right|^2 \int_0^\infty n(D)D^6 \, dD \; . \tag{12.37}$$

Substituting this expression back into (12.31), we find that the backscattered power measured by the radar receiver is

$$P_r \propto \left| \frac{m^2 - 1}{m^2 + 2} \right|^2 \frac{Z}{d^2} \; , \tag{12.38}$$

where Z is the *reflectivity factor*, defined as

$$Z = \int_0^\infty n(D)D^6 \, dD \; . \tag{12.39}$$

In other words, the reflectivity factor is numerically equal to *the sum of the sixth powers of the diameters of all of the drops in a unit volume of air.* The standard units of Z used by meteorologists are $[\text{mm}^6\text{m}^{-3}]$. *An estimate of the reflectivity factor Z at each range d along the beam is what most weather radars record and display.*

Because observed values of Z span an enormous range, meteorologists prefer to work with a logarithmic representation of Z, defining a nondimensional unit dBZ, which means "decibels with respect to one standard unit of Z." You convert the reflectivity factor from standard units to units of dBZ as follows:

$$Z\,[\text{dBZ}] = 10\log_{10}(Z) \; , \tag{12.40}$$

where Z on the right hand side is the numerical value of Z expressed in standard (dimensional) units of reflectivity. Thus, an increase in reflectivity by 10 dBZ corresponds to a factor ten increase in Z expressed in standard units. An increase of 30 dBZ implies a thousand-fold increase in reflectivity.

Problem 12.6: Depending on range, a typical weather radar can measure reflectivities from as low as −20 dBZ to as high as 70 dBZ. In terms of physical units, what is the ratio of the two reflectivity factors?

In converting the received power P_r to an estimate of the reflectivity factor Z, the radar processing software assumes a value of m appropriate to liquid water in (12.38). The displayed quantity is therefore actually better regarded as an *equivalent reflectivity factor* Z_e which may or may not be equal to the *true* reflectivity factor Z defined by (12.39), depending on whether the targets are liquid water or something else, like ice. If the particles are in fact ice, then

$$Z_e \approx 0.20Z .\qquad\qquad (12.41)$$

Problem 12.7: During a particular (and peculiar) rainstorm, each cubic meter of air contains 1000 falling drops, each of identical diameter D. (a) Compute the reflectivity factor Z, assuming $D = 1$ mm. (b) Repeat for $D = 2$ mm. (c) By what factor did Z increase on account of a mere two-fold increase in D? (d) Express your answers to (a)–(c) in units of dBZ. (e) If you replace the liquid raindrops with ice spheres of the same size, by how many dBZ will the radar-estimated effective reflectivity Z_e be reduced? (f) Notwithstanding Eq. (12.41), hailstorms are often recognized on radar displays by virtue of their anomalously *high* Z_e. Why?

In actual rainfall, drops do not all have one size but rather are distributed over a wide range of sizes. Because of the D^6 dependence in Z, observed reflectivities are heavily influenced by the few largest drops in the volume of air. A single drop with a diameter 5 mm reflects more microwave radiation than 15,000 drops of 1 mm diameter! And clouds, with their typical droplet diameters of around 20 μm, are completely invisible to all but the most sensitive radars, despite typical droplet concentrations in excess of 10^8 m^{-3}.

Problem 12.8: From the information given above concerning cloud droplets, find a typical reflectivity factor Z for clouds, expressed in dBZ.

Radar Rainfall Estimation

Raindrops passing through the air eventually reach the surface, and the rate at which water is deposited (depth per unit time) is known as the *rainfall rate R*. One of the most important applications of radar is the operational estimation of accumulated rainfall for agricultural and hydrological purposes.

Unfortunately, there is no unique relationship between the rainfall rate and the relative number of larger and smaller droplets present in the column of air. Consequently, there can be no unique relationship between radar reflectivity Z and rain rate R. However, we know from experience that heavier rainfall *tends* to be associated with a greater number of large raindrops, whereas light rain is *usually* characterized by smaller drops. *On average*, therefore, we expect heavy rain rates to be associated with large Z and light rain rates to give rise to correspondingly weaker radar echoes.

Field observations of raindrops have revealed that the dropsize distribution $n(D)$ for rain is often reasonably well approximated by

$$n(D) = N_0 \exp(-\Lambda D) , \qquad (12.42)$$

where N_0 and Λ are parameters that are functions of the rain rate R. In fact, the most widely used model of the above form is known as the *Marshall-Palmer size distribution*, after the researchers who developed it. In the Marshall-Palmer distribution, N_0 is a constant and $\Lambda = aR^b$, where the parameters a and b were chosen so as to maximize the agreement between the above size distribution function and a large number of actual observations of drop sizes at various rain rates.

It is beyond the scope of this text to discuss the M.-P. distribution in detail, except to note that, when it is substituted into (12.39) and combined with suitable assumptions about raindrop fall speed as a function of D, it is possible to obtain the following Z–R relationship:

$$Z = 200R^{1.6} , \qquad (12.43)$$

where R is assumed to be given in mm hr^{-1}, and Z is in standard units of mm^6 m^{-3}. Other assumed (or measured) drop size distributions usually lead to Z–R relationships having a similar form, but with different values for the two numerical coefficients.

Problem 12.9:   Use the Marshall-Palmer Z–R relationship above to estimate the rain rates R associated with displayed radar reflectivities of (a) 10 dBZ, (b) 30 dBZ, and (c) 50 dBZ.

12.5.3   Microwave Remote Sensing and Clouds

Microwave radiometers operating at various frequencies from 3 to 183 GHz are assuming an increasingly prominent role in the satellite remote sensing of the atmosphere. One of the main attractions of the microwave band is the relative transparency of clouds at these wavelengths, so that some properties of the surface and of the atmospheric column can be estimated under nearly all-weather conditions.

At even the high end of the frequency range given above, the wavelength λ is a relatively long 3 mm which, for typical 10 μm radius cloud droplets, gives size parameter $x \approx 0.02$. This is so small that we can ignore scattering, and the mass extinction (absorption) coefficient k_L of cloud liquid water is accurately given by (12.19). Figure 12.12 shows how k_a varies with frequency over the microwave band.

Consider a microwave radiometer at ground level viewing vertically incident radiation emitted by the atmosphere. In the microwave band, the Rayleigh-Jeans approximation allows us to work

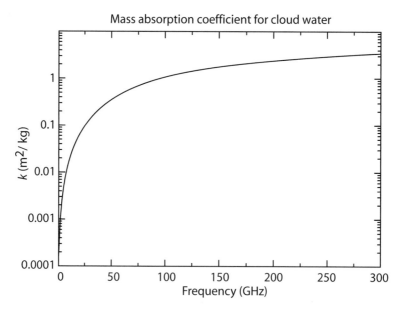

Fig. 12.12: The mass absorption coefficient for cloud water at microwave frequencies.

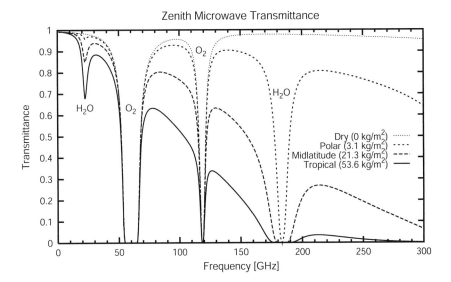

Fig. 12.13: Zenith microwave transmittance of the cloud-free atmosphere for different models of atmospheric temperature and humidity. The vertically integrated water vapor content associated with each model is given in parentheses.

with brightness temperature T_B as a convenient stand-in for radiant intensity, with $T_B = \varepsilon T$, where ε is the emissivity of a surface or atmospheric layer, and T is its physical temperature (see section 6.1.4).

If we assume for the moment that the cloud-free atmosphere is perfectly transparent (it is not) and that there is a single cloud layer with average temperature T and total vertically integrated cloud liquid water L, then the measured brightness temperature is given approximately by

$$T_B = \varepsilon T = [1 - t(L)] \, T = [1 - \exp(-k_L L)] \, T \,. \qquad (12.44)$$

You could then use your upward-looking microwave radiometer to estimate the cloud water path by simply (i) solving the above equation for L, (ii) assuming something reasonable for T, and (iii) plugging in the observed brightness temperature T_B.

The reality is of course slightly more complicated. In particular, there are two other atmospheric constituents that always contribute additional absorption and emission in the microwave band: water vapor, and oxygen (Fig. 12.13). If we stay well away from the 60 GHz and 118 GHz absorption bands due to oxygen, then the reduction in transmittance due to the dry atmosphere alone is only a few percent. Furthermore, since the surface air pressure at any given location, and therefore the total column oxygen content, varies only by about 5%, we can get away with assuming a fixed optical depth τ_O due to oxygen.

Water vapor is a bigger problem, because atmospheric column vapor content V varies from very low (~ 1 kg m^{-2}) in dry polar air masses to rather high (up to 60 kg m^{-2}) in humid tropical air masses. In order to limit the total optical depth due to water vapor, let's confine our attention to the spectrum below about 40 GHz, so that even in the worst case, we still have a zenith transmittance of at least 60% or so. That way, the atmosphere will never become so opaque due to water vapor that it becomes hard to see changes in opacity due to cloud water.

If we assume that the mean emitting temperature of the atmospheric water vapor and oxygen isn't *too* different from that of the cloud layer, then we can write

$$T_B \approx [1 - \exp(-\tau)]\, T \, , \qquad (12.45)$$

where the total atmospheric optical depth is approximated as

$$\tau \approx \tau_O + k_L L + k_V V \, , \qquad (12.46)$$

and k_V is the column-averaged mass absorption coefficient of water vapor. We can divide through by T, rearrange, and take the logarithm of both sides to get

$$y \equiv \log\left(\frac{T - T_B}{T}\right) \approx -k_L L - k_V V - \tau_O \, . \qquad (12.47)$$

Given a reasonable value for T, the new variable y is a known function of the observed T_B. The definition of y is convenient because it turns out to be a simple linear function of our two unknowns V and L. Unfortunately, we have one equation in two unknowns, and so a measurement of T_B at a single wavelength is not sufficient to uniquely determine both variables.

Let's therefore design our radiometer to measure T_B at two different frequencies ν_1 and ν_2. We can then write our equation in matrix form as

$$
\begin{bmatrix} y_1 \\ y_2 \end{bmatrix} = - \begin{bmatrix} k_{L,1} & k_{V,1} \\ k_{L,2} & k_{V,2} \end{bmatrix} \begin{bmatrix} L \\ V \end{bmatrix} - \begin{bmatrix} \tau_{O,1} \\ \tau_{O,2} \end{bmatrix} . \tag{12.48}
$$

We now have two linear equations in two unknowns. In principle, we can solve for L and V as follows:

$$
\begin{bmatrix} L \\ V \end{bmatrix} = - \begin{bmatrix} k_{L,1} & k_{V,1} \\ k_{L,2} & k_{V,2} \end{bmatrix}^{-1} \begin{bmatrix} y_1 + \tau_{O,1} \\ y_2 + \tau_{O,2} \end{bmatrix} , \tag{12.49}
$$

assuming that the inverse of the matrix of absorption coefficients $\mathbf{K}$ exists.

Mathematically speaking, the inverse exists if the determinant $\|\mathbf{K}\| \neq 0$, a condition that is almost guaranteed to be satisfied for any pair of distinct microwave frequencies. *Practically* speaking, however, the mere existence of an inverse is not enough! Why not?

Recall that (12.47) was presented as an *approximate* model of the dependence of y on L and V. This suggests that we should modify (12.49) to allow for the likelihood of errors ϵ_i in the relationship:

$$
\begin{bmatrix} L' \\ V' \end{bmatrix} = - \begin{bmatrix} k_{L,1} & k_{V,1} \\ k_{L,2} & k_{V,2} \end{bmatrix}^{-1} \left\{ \begin{bmatrix} y_1 + \tau_{O,1} \\ y_2 + \tau_{O,2} \end{bmatrix} - \begin{bmatrix} \epsilon_1 \\ \epsilon_2 \end{bmatrix} \right\} , \tag{12.50}
$$

where L' and V' are now *estimates* of the true L and V. The *estimation error* can then be written

$$
\begin{bmatrix} L' - L \\ V' - V \end{bmatrix} = \begin{bmatrix} k_{L,1} & k_{V,1} \\ k_{L,2} & k_{V,2} \end{bmatrix}^{-1} \begin{bmatrix} \epsilon_1 \\ \epsilon_2 \end{bmatrix} . \tag{12.51}
$$

The goal of a remote sensing technique, of course, is to make sure that the estimation errors are as small as possible. In this instance, it means ensuring that the matrix $\mathbf{K}^{-1}$ does not excessively "amplify" the model and/or instrument errors ϵ_i. Since the magnitude of $\mathbf{K}^{-1}$ is proportional to $1/\|\mathbf{K}\|$, it follows that we require not only that $\|\mathbf{K}\|$ be nonzero (the strict mathematical requirement for invertibility) but that it be as large as possible!

In plain English, we want our two sensor channels to respond in substantially different ways to L and V, so that the opacity contributions of each constituent can be separated with as little ambiguity as possible. Now, regardless of frequency, $k > 0$ for both L and V, so the most we can hope for is that one channel should have a pro-portionally larger response to V than to L, while for other channel the reverse should be true. Examination of Figs. 12.12 and 12.13 suggests the way to achieve this: Choose one channel to fall on or near the center of the water vapor absorption line at 22.235 GHz; choose the second channel to fall between 30 and 40 GHz, where water vapor absorption is much weaker than for the first channel but liquid water absorption is significantly stronger. This is in fact what is done in the design of commercial two-channel microwave radiometers, though the precise choice of frequencies depends on a more sophisticated analysis than we have offered here.

Several other subtleties have also been glossed over here with respect to the *optimal inversion* of radiometric measurements; these are best left to a course in remote sensing. Suffice it to say that an explicit matrix-inverse method, as described above, is usually less satisfactory than a statistical or semi-statistical method that is cho-sen so as to minimize the average squared error over the widest possible range of atmospheric conditions.

Problem 12.10: Assume that you have an upward-looking mi-crowave radiometer with channels at 23.8 GHz and 31.4 GHz. For the first frequency, take $k_{L,1} = 0.087$, $k_{V,1} = 0.0052$, and $\tau_{O,1} = 0.02$. For the second frequency, take $k_{L,2} = 0.15$, $k_{V,2} = 0.0021$, and $\tau_{O,2} = 0.03$. All values for k are in units of m^2/kg. Assume a mean atmospheric temperature $T = 280$ K.

(a) Approximately what brightness temperature T_B should each channel observe in a perfectly dry atmosphere, with $V = L = 0$?

(b) Repeat your calculation for $V = 60$ kg m^{-2}, which is typical of a humid tropical atmosphere. Leave $L = 0$ (i.e., no cloud).

(c) Repeat your calculation again, this time assuming $L = 0.3$ kg m^{-2}, which is typical of a fairly thick nonprecipitating stra-tocumulus layer.

(d) Derive a retrieval algorithm for the estimation of V. The final algorithm should have the form $V' = a_1 \log(T - T_{B,1}) + a_2 \log(T - T_{B,2}) + a_3$. Provide the coefficients a_i to four significant figures.

(e) Test your algorithm by applying it to your results from parts (a), (b), and (c). Do you recover the correct values of V in each case?

CHAPTER 13

Radiative Transfer with Multiple Scattering

We are now nearing the end of our introductory survey of radiative transfer in the atmosphere, and it is perhaps no surprise that we have saved the best — or at least the most challenging — for last. Every problem we have dealt with so far entailed either absorption and emission with no scattering, or else at most single scattering. These restrictions enabled us to solve the radiative transfer equation along a single line of sight without worrying about what was going on in other locations and directions.

Such simplifications are utterly useless for solar radiative transfer in clouds. Because most water clouds are both optically thick ($\tau \gg 1$) and are only weakly absorbing ($\tilde{\omega} \approx 1$), multiple scattering cannot be neglected. That is to say, at most points in the interior of the cloud, the majority of radiation incident on a cloud particle will have already been scattered at least once by some other particle. Photons incident at cloud top will typically be scattered numerous times before re-emerging from the cloud, either at the top or base in the plane parallel case, or even from the sides in the case of three-dimensional clouds. What this means in practice is that you cannot consider what is happening to the radiant intensity along one line-of-sight without simultaneously considering what it is doing everywhere else.

The full radiative transfer equation for a plane parallel atmosphere was given earlier as (11.13) and (11.14). If we neglect thermal emission, the two can be combined to give

$$\mu \frac{dI(\mu, \phi)}{d\tau} = I(\mu, \phi) - \frac{\tilde{\omega}}{4\pi} \int_0^{2\pi} \int_{-1}^{1} p(\mu, \phi; \mu', \phi') I(\mu', \phi') \, d\mu' d\phi' .$$

(13.1)

This integrodifferential equation tells us that in order to determine $I(\mu, \phi)$ at a particular level τ in a cloud, we must simultaneously determine $I(\mu', \phi')$ for all values of μ' and ϕ' and for all other values of τ.

In general, (13.1) cannot be solved exactly except under extremely restrictive (and inevitably unrealistic) assumptions about the scattering phase function, among other things. Therefore, radiation specialists have put much effort into

- studying closed form solutions to (13.1) for highly idealized cases (e.g., isotropic scattering, infinite cloud optical depth) with an eye toward gaining *qualitative* insight into radiative transfer in clouds, and

- developing computational techniques for obtaining reasonably accurate *numerical* solutions for real-world problems.

We will not delve deeply into such methods here, as they are mainly of interest to those who perform radiative transfer calculations for a living. If this book has piqued your own interest in atmospheric radiation, then you should plan to continue your education with advanced textbooks, such as L02 and TS02, that devote considerable space, and literally hundreds of equations, to computational methods.

Here, we will begin by trying to convey some insight into how multiple scattering "works" in a plane-parallel cloud layer. We will then walk through one of the simplest possible analytic solutions to (13.1) known as the *two-stream method*. The two-stream approximation is not terribly useful for computing accurate radiant intensities as a function of μ and ϕ, but it's not bad for estimating hemispherically averaged *fluxes* in plane parallel cloud layers. In fact, because it is relatively undemanding of computer resources, some variation on the two-stream method (or the slightly more sophisticated four-stream method) is usually at the heart of the shortwave radiative parameterization schemes found in virtually all climate models.

13.1 Visualizing Multiple Scattering

When radiation is incident on a plane-parallel scattering layer of the atmosphere (e.g., a cloud), we can visualize the radiative transfer process in terms of the fates of a large number of individual photons. When the radiation is due to a quasi-point source, like the sun, then each photon enters at cloud top ($\tau = 0$) traveling in the same initial direction $\hat{\Omega}_0$. The subsequent fate of each photon, however, is determined by its chance encounters with the scattering and/or absorbing particles in the layer, as summarized by the following sequence of events:

1. First, each photon travels a random distance before it encounters its first extinction event. Although the distance traveled by each photon individually is random, the *average* distance is dictated by Beer's Law. In fact, if the total cloud optical depth is τ^*, then we know that a fraction $t_{\text{dir}} = \exp(\tau^*/\mu)$ of the incident photons will reach the cloud base without being extinguished at all.

2. The fraction $1 - t_{\text{dir}}$ of the photons that do *not* make it all the way through the cloud on their first attempt get extinguished (i.e., scattered or absorbed). Of those photons, the fraction that gets absorbed is simply $1 - \tilde{\omega}$. For those photons, their long journey from the sun has come to an abrupt end; their energy $h\nu$ goes into warming the cloud.

3. Those photons that get scattered instead of being absorbed now have a new direction of propagation μ'. Along that direction, Beer's Law (applied to the new optical distance to the boundary) again determines the probability that a particular photon will reach the upper or lower boundary and exit the cloud.

4. For each photon, steps 2 and 3 are repeated until the photon has either been absorbed or exited the cloud layer. The albedo

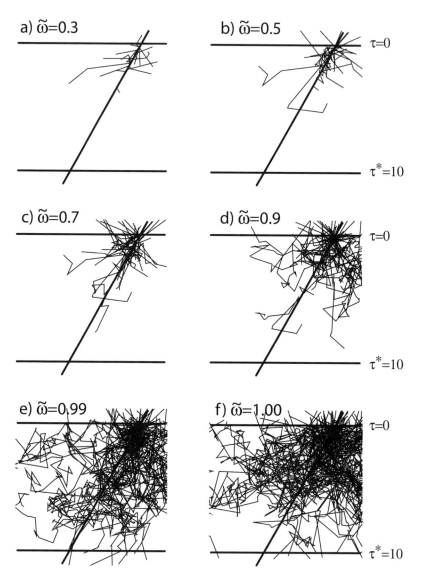

Fig. 13.1: Examples of the random paths of 100 photons in a plane-parallel, isotropically scattering layer ($g = 0$) with optical thickness $\tau^* = 10$ and variable single scatter albedo $\tilde{\omega}$. Photons are incident from above with $\theta = 30°$. Heavy diagonal lines indicate the path an unscattered photon would take.

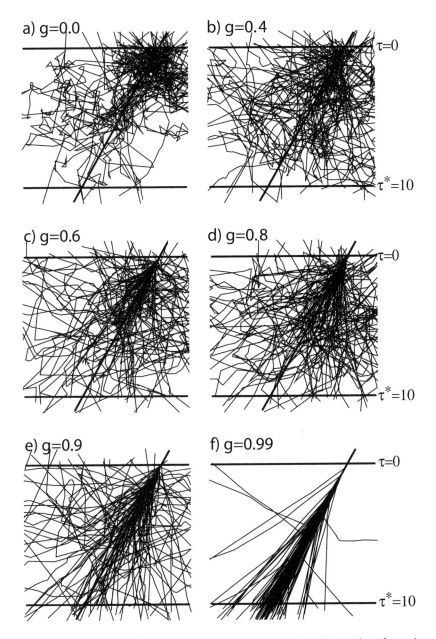

Fig. 13.2: Same as Fig. 13.1, but for conservative scattering ($\tilde{\omega} = 1$) and varying values of the asymmetry parameter g.

and diffuse transmittance of the cloud, respectively, describe the fraction of incident photons that exit the top or the bottom of the layer.

The above process is depicted graphically for a variety of combinations of $\tilde{\omega}$ and g in Figs. 13.1 and 13.2. Each photon trajectory is followed until either the photon gets absorbed or else it exits from the cloud. Note that even a slight chance of absorption in any single extinction event translates into a rather high probability of absorption by the time the photon has been extinguished numerous times on its passage through an optically thick cloud. Note also the degree to which the asymmetry parameter g influences the relative likelihood of the photon emerging from the base or the top of the cloud in the conservative scattering case (Fig. 13.2).

It is possible to numerically simulate radiative transfer in clouds using exactly the procedure described above. Such a method is called a *Monte Carlo model*, because the fate of each photon on each leg of its journey is simulated as random process, much like the spin of a roulette wheel or the roll of a pair of dice. Monte Carlo models are easy to understand and easy to implement. They are especially useful for handling non-plane parallel cloud geometries. The only real drawback to Monte Carlo methods is that a very large number of photon trajectories might have to be simulated in order to obtain statistically accurate results. For some problems, especially those involving very deep clouds with little or no absorption, Monte Carlo methods are inefficient, because each photon might undergo thousands of scattering events inside the cloud before finally emerging to be counted toward either the albedo or diffuse transmittance.

Other methods for solving multiple scattering problems do not simulate individual photon trajectories but rather seek mathematical or numerical solutions to the radiative transfer equation. We now turn our attention to the simplest such method.

13.2 The Two-Stream Method

13.2.1 Azimuthally Averaged RTE

Recall first of all that the contribution a beam of radiation makes to the horizontal flux doesn't depend on its azimuthal angle ϕ but only on the angle from vertical, as embodied in $\mu = \cos\theta$. This means that we needn't worry about the azimuthal dependence of I, as long as we get its dependence on μ and τ right.

Therefore, let's define the *azimuthally averaged intensity* as

$$I(\mu) \equiv \frac{1}{2\pi} \int_0^{2\pi} I(\mu, \phi) \, d\phi \, . \tag{13.2}$$

Also, if we assume an azimuthally isotropic scattering medium, so that $p(\mu, \phi; \mu', \phi')$ is equivalent to $p(\mu, \mu', \Delta\phi)$, where $\Delta\phi \equiv \phi - \phi'$, then we can also define the *azimuthally averaged phase function* as

$$p(\mu, \mu') \equiv \frac{1}{2\pi} \int_0^{2\pi} p(\mu, \mu', \Delta\phi) \, d(\Delta\phi) \, . \tag{13.3}$$

With these definitions, we can eliminate ϕ from (13.1) by taking the azimuthal average of all terms in (13.1) and simplifying to get

$$\mu \frac{dI(\mu)}{d\tau} = I(\mu) - \frac{\tilde{\omega}}{2} \int_{-1}^1 p(\mu, \mu') I(\mu') \, d\mu' \, , \tag{13.4}$$

This is the azimuthally averaged radiative transfer equation.[1]

Problem 13.1: Show that (13.4) indeed follows from (13.1)–(13.3).

13.2.2 The Two-Stream Approximation

Equation (13.4) is a reasonably general restatement of the full RTE and contains no indefensible assumptions or approximations. It therefore can be (and is) used as the starting point for other methods of solution as well. The specific "leap of faith" that is unique to the so-called two-stream method, which we will now derive, is

---

[1]The question of how you actually specify $p(\mu, \mu')$ in terms of the (usually) more fundamental $p(\cos\Theta)$ is addressed in section 6.1.2 of L02. The conversion depends on the expansion of the phase function as a sum of Legendre polynomials, as discussed in Appendix A.

Fig. 13.3: Assumed angular distribution of intensity in the two-stream approximation.

the assumption that the intensity $I(\mu)$ is approximately constant in each hemisphere. That is,

$$I(\mu) = \begin{cases} I^\uparrow & \mu > 0 \\ I^\downarrow & \mu < 0 \end{cases} \tag{13.5}$$

where $I^\uparrow$ and $I^\downarrow$ are constants. Schematically, this assumption is depicted in Fig. 13.3.

The assumption of constant intensity through each hemisphere sounds quite radical, but in fact, it's not as bad as you might think. Imagine, for example, that you are hovering in a balloon between a uniform, flat surface (e.g., the ocean, cornfield-covered Iowa, or snow-covered Greenland) and the base of heavy stratiform cloud layer. If you look at any point below the horizon ($\mu = 0$), you see the more or less uniform color and brightness associated with the surface. Everywhere above the horizon, you see the more or less uniform grayness of the cloud layer. The horizon itself presents a rather sharp discontinuity in intensity between the ground and the overlying cloud layer.

Within the cloud layer, the contrast between the lower and upper hemisphere is less dramatic, but the assumption of constant I for each hemisphere is still not patently ridiculous. And even if there is in fact some dependence of I on μ within each hemisphere, it's safe to say that this dependence will usually be monotonic (e.g., steady brightening from the horizon to zenith) and that you could always find an intermediate value of μ for which the intensity is close to the average for the entire hemisphere.

The Two-Stream Equations

So much for the rationalization; now for the math. We will set up separate equations for the upwelling and downwelling streams of radiation. The mechanics of the derivation are the same for each stream, so we'll save space by going through the details for only the upwelling stream $I^\uparrow$. We start by substituting the constants $I^\uparrow$ and $I^\downarrow$ for $I(\mu)$ in the appropriate locations in (13.4):

$$\mu \frac{dI^\uparrow}{d\tau} = I^\uparrow - \frac{\tilde{\omega}}{2} \int_0^1 p(\mu, \mu') I^\uparrow \, d\mu' - \frac{\tilde{\omega}}{2} \int_{-1}^0 p(\mu, \mu') I^\downarrow \, d\mu' . \quad (13.6)$$

Note that the integration of $p(\mu, \mu')I(\mu')$ is split into two pieces to allow us to separately treat the constant I in each hemisphere. $I^\uparrow$ and $I^\downarrow$ can be taken outside of the integrals, yielding

$$\mu \frac{dI^\uparrow}{d\tau} = I^\uparrow - \frac{\tilde{\omega}}{2} \left[\int_0^1 p(\mu, \mu') \, d\mu' \right] I^\uparrow - \frac{\tilde{\omega}}{2} \left[\int_{-1}^0 p(\mu, \mu') \, d\mu' \right] I^\downarrow . \quad (13.7)$$

It is convenient at this point to define a quantity called the *backscattered fraction b*, which will be used as a shorthand for integrals like those appearing above:

$$b(\mu) \equiv \begin{cases} \dfrac{1}{2} \displaystyle\int_{-1}^0 p(\mu, \mu') \, d\mu' = 1 - \dfrac{1}{2} \int_0^1 p(\mu, \mu') \, d\mu', & \mu > 0 , \\[3mm] \dfrac{1}{2} \displaystyle\int_0^1 p(\mu, \mu') \, d\mu' = 1 - \dfrac{1}{2} \int_{-1}^0 p(\mu, \mu') \, d\mu', & \mu < 0 . \end{cases} \quad (13.8)$$

$b(\mu)$ represents the fraction of radiation that is scattered into the opposite hemisphere, with new direction of propagation μ. In the case of (13.7), it characterizes the degree to which backscattering enhances $I^\uparrow$ at the expense of $I^\downarrow$. We can now rewrite (13.7) as

$$\mu \frac{dI^\uparrow}{d\tau} = I^\uparrow - \tilde{\omega}[1 - b(\mu)]I^\uparrow - \tilde{\omega} b(\mu) I^\downarrow . \quad (13.9)$$

This equation still contains an explicit dependence on μ, which just muddies the water, because we've already stipulated that I is independent of μ in each hemisphere. So let's eliminate μ by averaging (13.9) over the entire hemisphere:

$$\int_0^1 \left[\mu \frac{dI^\uparrow}{d\tau} = I^\uparrow - \tilde{\omega}[1 - b(\mu)]I^\uparrow - \tilde{\omega} b(\mu) I^\downarrow \right] d\mu . \quad (13.10)$$

The result can be written as

$$\frac{1}{2}\frac{dI^{\uparrow}}{d\tau} = I^{\uparrow} - \tilde{\omega}(1-\bar{b})I^{\uparrow} - \tilde{\omega}\bar{b}I^{\downarrow} , \qquad (13.11)$$

or

$$\boxed{\frac{1}{2}\frac{dI^{\uparrow}}{d\tau} = (1-\tilde{\omega})I^{\uparrow} + \tilde{\omega}\bar{b}(I^{\uparrow} - I^{\downarrow}) ,} \qquad (13.12)$$

where

$$\bar{b} \equiv \int_0^1 b(\mu)\, d\mu . \qquad (13.13)$$

Repeating the above steps for the downward stream yields the analogous equation

$$\boxed{-\frac{1}{2}\frac{dI^{\downarrow}}{d\tau} = (1-\tilde{\omega})I^{\downarrow} - \tilde{\omega}\bar{b}(I^{\uparrow} - I^{\downarrow}) .} \qquad (13.14)$$

Equations (13.12) and (13.14) are the so-called *two-stream equations for diffuse incidence.*[2] Since $I^{\uparrow}(\tau)$ and $I^{\downarrow}(\tau)$ are unknown and appear in both equations, we're evidently dealing with a coupled pair of ordinary linear differential equations. The usual way to solve such a system is to combine them into a single second-order differential equation, apply boundary conditions, and solve for the specific boundary conditions of interest. But before we do, let's take a closer look at the mean backscatter fraction $\bar{b}$.

The Backscatter Fraction and g

The mean backscatter fraction $\bar{b}$ is explicitly related to the scattering phase function $p(\mu, \mu')$ via (13.8) and (13.13). The properties of the phase function can in turn be partly characterized via the asymmetry parameter g, which was defined by (11.20). It follows that there could be some kind of systematic relationship between $\bar{b}$ and g that would allow us to replace $\bar{b}$ in (13.12) and (13.14) with a suitable

---

[2]With relatively little effort, one can generalize the above equations to accommodate illumination at the top of the atmosphere by a direct beam of radiation from the sun — see for example TS02, Ch. 6.

function of g. This possibility can be made clearer by considering three special cases.

If scattering is perfectly isotropic $[p(\cos\Theta) = p(\mu, \mu') = 1]$, then $g = 0$. In this case, regardless of the direction from which the radiation comes originally, it is equally likely to be scattered into either hemisphere, so clearly $\bar{b} = 1/2$.

If $g = 1$, this implies that all radiation is scattered in exactly the same direction as it was traveling before being scattered. Thus, absolutely no radiation can ever be scattered back into the opposite hemisphere; therefore $\bar{b} = 0$ for this case. Likewise, if $g = -1$, then all radiation is scattered into the opposite hemisphere, and $\bar{b} = 1$.

To summarize, we have the following known mappings between g and $\bar{b}$:

$$g = -1 \quad \rightarrow \quad \bar{b} = 1$$

$$g = 0 \quad \rightarrow \quad \bar{b} = \frac{1}{2}$$

$$g = 1 \quad \rightarrow \quad \bar{b} = 0$$

If we now *assume* that the relationship between g and $\bar{b}$ is linear,[3] then we can write

$$\bar{b} = \frac{1 - g}{2}. \tag{13.15}$$

Making this substitution in (13.12) and (13.14), we have

$$\frac{1}{2}\frac{dI^\uparrow}{d\tau} = (1 - \tilde{\omega})I^\uparrow + \frac{\tilde{\omega}(1 - g)}{2}(I^\uparrow - I^\downarrow), \tag{13.16}$$

$$-\frac{1}{2}\frac{dI^\downarrow}{d\tau} = (1 - \tilde{\omega})I^\downarrow - \frac{\tilde{\omega}(1 - g)}{2}(I^\uparrow - I^\downarrow). \tag{13.17}$$

---

[3]This is another approximation; see TS02 Section 7.5 for a full discussion of the relationship between $\bar{b}$ and g.

13.2.3   Solution

We start by adding and subtracting (13.16) and (13.17) to obtain

$$\frac{1}{2}\frac{d}{d\tau}(I^\uparrow - I^\downarrow) = (1 - \tilde{\omega})(I^\uparrow + I^\downarrow) , \qquad (13.18)$$

$$\frac{1}{2}\frac{d}{d\tau}(I^\uparrow + I^\downarrow) = (1 - \tilde{\omega}g)(I^\uparrow - I^\downarrow) . \qquad (13.19)$$

We then differentiate (13.19) to get

$$\frac{d^2}{d\tau^2}(I^\uparrow + I^\downarrow) = 2(1 - \tilde{\omega}g)\frac{d}{d\tau}(I^\uparrow - I^\downarrow) . \qquad (13.20)$$

But note now that the derivative on the right hand side can be replaced with an expression obtained from (13.18), yielding

$$\frac{d^2}{d\tau^2}(I^\uparrow + I^\downarrow) = 4(1 - \tilde{\omega}g)(1 - \tilde{\omega})(I^\uparrow + I^\downarrow) . \qquad (13.21)$$

Applying the same procedure as above to (13.18) gives

$$\frac{d^2}{d\tau^2}(I^\uparrow - I^\downarrow) = 4(1 - \tilde{\omega}g)(1 - \tilde{\omega})(I^\uparrow - I^\downarrow) . \qquad (13.22)$$

These two equations are the same, except that in the first one the independent variable is $I^\uparrow + I^\downarrow$ while in the second it's $I^\uparrow - I^\downarrow$. We can therefore kill two birds with one stone by solving the single equation

$$\frac{d^2y}{d\tau^2} = \Gamma^2 y , \qquad (13.23)$$

where

$$y \equiv (I^\uparrow + I^\downarrow) \quad \text{or} \quad y \equiv (I^\uparrow - I^\downarrow) , \qquad (13.24)$$

and

$$\boxed{\Gamma \equiv 2\sqrt{1 - \tilde{\omega}}\sqrt{1 - \tilde{\omega}g} .} \qquad (13.25)$$

The general solution is

$$y = \alpha e^{\Gamma\tau} + \beta e^{-\Gamma\tau} . \qquad (13.26)$$

It follows that the solutions for $I^\uparrow$ and $I^\downarrow$ are likewise sums of exponentials:

$$I^\uparrow(\tau) = Ae^{\Gamma\tau} + Be^{-\Gamma\tau}, \tag{13.27}$$

$$I^\downarrow(\tau) = Ce^{\Gamma\tau} + De^{-\Gamma\tau}, \tag{13.28}$$

where the coefficients A–D remain to be determined. Although there are four coefficients, they are not all independent. This can be seen by substituting (13.27) and (13.28) into (13.16), which yields

$$\begin{aligned}
\frac{dI^\uparrow}{d\tau} &= 2(1 - \tilde{\omega})\left(Ae^{\Gamma\tau} + Be^{-\Gamma\tau}\right) \\
&\quad + \tilde{\omega}(1 - g)\left[(A - C)e^{\Gamma\tau} + (B - D)e^{-\Gamma\tau}\right].
\end{aligned} \tag{13.29}$$

But differentiating (13.27) gives

$$\frac{dI^\uparrow}{d\tau} = A\Gamma e^{\Gamma\tau} - B\Gamma e^{-\Gamma\tau}, \tag{13.30}$$

so we can equate (13.29) and (13.30) to get

$$\begin{aligned}
&[2(1 - \tilde{\omega})A + \tilde{\omega}(1 - g)(A - C) - A\Gamma]\, e^{\Gamma\tau} = \\
&[-B\Gamma - 2(1 - \tilde{\omega})B - \tilde{\omega}(1 - g)(B - D)]\, e^{-\Gamma\tau}.
\end{aligned} \tag{13.31}$$

The above equation must be valid for all τ, which is only possible if the terms multiplying the exponentials are each zero. Solving for A and C in the first case and B and D in the second, we find

$$\frac{C}{A} = \frac{B}{D} = \frac{2 - \tilde{\omega} - \tilde{\omega}g - \Gamma}{\tilde{\omega}(1 - g)} = \frac{\sqrt{1 - \tilde{\omega}g} - \sqrt{1 - \tilde{\omega}}}{\sqrt{1 - \tilde{\omega}g} + \sqrt{1 - \tilde{\omega}}} \equiv r_\infty. \tag{13.32}$$

The reason for using r_∞ to denote this ratio will become apparent later. With this definition, we can write

$$C = r_\infty A \quad ; \quad B = r_\infty D, \tag{13.33}$$

which allows us to rewrite (13.27) and (13.28) as

$$I^\uparrow(\tau) = Ae^{\Gamma\tau} + r_\infty De^{-\Gamma\tau}, \tag{13.34}$$

$$I^\downarrow(\tau) = r_\infty Ae^{\Gamma\tau} + De^{-\Gamma\tau}. \tag{13.35}$$

Boundary Conditions

At this point we are nearly finished — only two coefficients in our solution remain undetermined. To find these coefficients, we need to supply two boundary conditions appropriate to the problem we wish to solve. Let's choose the following:

$$I^{\uparrow}(\tau^*) = 0 \quad ; \quad I^{\downarrow}(0) = I_0 , \tag{13.36}$$

which state that the lower boundary is black (no upward reflected radiation at $\tau = \tau^*$ and a known hemispherically averaged intensity I_0 is incident on the top of the atmosphere. With these boundary conditions, we have

$$0 = A e^{\Gamma \tau^*} + r_{\infty} D e^{-\Gamma \tau^*} , \tag{13.37}$$

and

$$I_0 = r_{\infty} A + D . \tag{13.38}$$

These are solved for A and D, which are then substituted back into (13.34) and (13.35) to get our final solutions

$$I^{\uparrow}(\tau) = \frac{r_{\infty} I_0}{e^{\Gamma \tau^*} - r_{\infty}^2 e^{-\Gamma \tau^*}} \left[e^{\Gamma(\tau^* - \tau)} - e^{-\Gamma(\tau^* - \tau)} \right] , \tag{13.39}$$

$$I^{\downarrow}(\tau) = \frac{I_0}{e^{\Gamma \tau^*} - r_{\infty}^2 e^{-\Gamma \tau^*}} \left[e^{\Gamma(\tau^* - \tau)} - r_{\infty}^2 e^{-\Gamma(\tau^* - \tau)} \right] . \tag{13.40}$$

Equations (13.39) and (13.40) give the general two-stream solution for the case of known uniform (diffuse) illumination I_0 at the top of a cloud layer and a completely absorbing lower boundary. We now look at the implications of this solution for a few specific examples.

13.3   Semi-Infinite Cloud

If you want to gain insight into how single scatter albedo $\tilde{\omega}$ and asymmetry parameter g influence the reflection and absorption properties of clouds, the interpretation of your results is easiest if there are no other variables to consider. If a cloud is optically thin, what you see from above the cloud layer is at least as sensitive to the radiative properties of the surface below the cloud as it is to the cloud properties themselves.

To exclude such influences, we will first consider the case of a *semi-infinite* cloud; i.e., a cloud layer with an upper boundary at $\tau = 0$ but which is effectively infinite in depth below that level. A cloud need not be semi-infinite in a literal sense in order to behave radiatively like a semi-infinite cloud; all that's necessary is for it be so thick that a photon incident on the cloud top has essentially zero chance of emerging from the bottom before either getting absorbed or else getting scattered back up through the cloud top.

We adapt (13.39) and (13.40) to the case of a semi-infinite cloud simply by letting $\tau^* \to \infty$, which gives us

$$I^{\uparrow}(\tau) = I_0 r_{\infty} e^{-\Gamma\tau} , \tag{13.41}$$

$$I^{\downarrow}(\tau) = I_0 e^{-\Gamma\tau} . \tag{13.42}$$

13.3.1 Albedo

Armed with (13.41) and (13.42), we can look at several interesting radiative properties of our cloud. Let's start by finding the albedo at cloud top, which is defined as the ratio of the reflected to incident radiation flux:

$$\text{Albedo} \quad = \quad \frac{\pi I^{\uparrow}(0)}{\pi I^{\downarrow}(0)} = \frac{I_0 r_{\infty} e^{-\Gamma\tau}}{I_0 e^{-\Gamma\tau}} , \tag{13.43}$$

which simplifies to

$$\boxed{\text{Albedo} = r_{\infty} .} \tag{13.44}$$

We discover that the albedo of a semi-infinite cloud is just r_{∞}, which explains (retroactively) why that particular function of $\tilde{\omega}$ and g was singled out for its own special symbol.

With that fact in mind, let's study the properties of r_∞ more closely. For convenience, its definition is repeated here:

$$r_\infty \equiv \frac{\sqrt{1 - \tilde{\omega}g} - \sqrt{1 - \tilde{\omega}}}{\sqrt{1 - \tilde{\omega}g} + \sqrt{1 - \tilde{\omega}}} . \qquad (13.45)$$

For starters, if $\tilde{\omega} = 1$, then $r_\infty = 1$, regardless of the value of g (as long as $g < 1$). This makes sense, because if there is zero absorption, then any photon incident on the top of a semi-infinite cloud must eventually emerge from the top again, no matter how many times it gets scattered first. It cannot get permanently lost deep inside the cloud, because no matter where it is, the photon is still closer to the top than it is to the (infinitely distant) bottom and therefore its random wanderings are statistically guaranteed to take it to the top eventually.

You can also see that if $g = 1$, then $r_\infty = 0$, regardless of the value of $\tilde{\omega}$ (as long as $\tilde{\omega} < 1$). Again, this makes sense, because in this case, every photon that is "scattered" continues traveling in exactly the same direction as before and can never change direction to return to the surface. However, this case is unrealistic for two reasons: (i) g is *always* less than one for any real scattering medium, and (ii) even if g *were* equal to one, then you might as well say that the medium doesn't scatter, since all "scattered" radiation continues traveling in its original direction as if it had never been scattered in the first place.

Having dealt with those two limiting cases, let's consider the more realistic situation in which $g < 1$ and $0 < \tilde{\omega} < 1$. Fig. 13.4 shows how r_∞ varies with $\tilde{\omega}$ for two different values of g, the larger value ($g = 0.85$) being typical of real clouds in the solar band. The albedo is zero for $\tilde{\omega} = 0$ and goes to one for $\tilde{\omega} \to 1$, as expected. The slighly less obvious point to note is that the overall absorptivity of the cloud, which is given in this case by one minus the albedo (since transmittance is zero for a semi-infinite cloud), is quite significant even for $\tilde{\omega}$ fairly close to one.

For example, $\tilde{\omega} = 0.999$ and $g = 0.85$ yields $r_\infty = 0.85$, corresponding to a cloud absorptivity of 15%. In other words, even though there is only a very slight chance for a photon to get absorbed in any *single* extinction event (in this example, that chance is

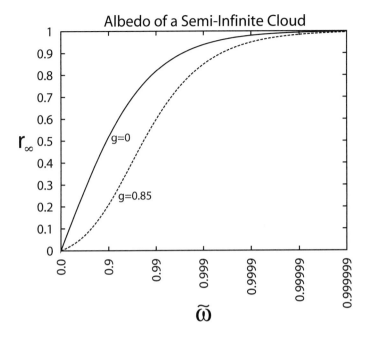

Fig. 13.4: The albedo of a semi-infinite cloud, as computed from (13.45).

only 0.1%), there is a much greater probability (15%) that a photon incident on the top of the cloud will get absorbed at some point in its wanderings before emerging from the cloud top again. The reason, of course, is that the photon's probability of survival is equal to $\tilde{\omega}^n$, where n is the number of scattering events it experiences inside the cloud. For a deep cloud with small scattering co-albedo (i.e., $1 - \tilde{\omega} \ll 1$), n can be a fairly large number.

Problem 13.2: Assume that $r_\infty = \tilde{\omega}^{\bar{n}}$, where $\bar{n}$ is the *effective mean number of scatterings* that photons incident on a semi-infinite cloud undergo inside the cloud before reemerging from the cloud top. (a) For the case that $\tilde{\omega} = 0.9999$ and $g = 0.85$, compute r_∞ and $\bar{n}$. (b) Repeat the above calculation, but with $\tilde{\omega} = 0.9$. (c) Explain why $\bar{n}$ is much different for the above two cases.

13.3.2 Flux and Heating Rate Profile

We can also look at the profile of the net flux $F^{net} = F^\uparrow - F^\downarrow$ within our semi-infinite cloud. Recall first of all that the two-stream method assumes uniform (isotropic) intensity within each hemisphere; hence the flux in each direction is just π times the relevant intensity:

$$F^{net} = \pi(I^\uparrow - I^\downarrow) . \tag{13.46}$$

Substituting (13.41) and (13.42), we have [4]

$$F^{net} = -\pi I_0(1 - r_\infty)e^{-\Gamma \tau} . \tag{13.47}$$

F^{net} in this case decays in exponential fashion, just as it would in a purely absorbing medium following Beer's Law. The *rate* of decay is proportional to Γ, which is equal to 2 for a purely absorbing medium ($\tilde{\omega} = 0$) and decreases with increasing scattering ($\tilde{\omega} \to 1$).

In fact, for the purely absorbing case, we can write

$$F^{net} = -\pi I_0 e^{-2\tau} = -\pi I_0 e^{-\tau/\bar{\mu}} , \tag{13.48}$$

where $\bar{\mu} = 1/2$. This is equivalent to Beer's Law for the case that a parallel beam of radiation is incident on the top of a purely absorbing layer at an angle of 60° from zenith.

For partially scattering cases ($0 < \tilde{\omega} < 1$), the parameter Γ is less than 2. In this case, scattering effectively reduces the optical depth of a cloud as compared to the purely absorbing case. If you measure the net flux at a position τ in the cloud, you will find that it is equivalent to the flux you would expect to find at a "flux optical depth" of $\tau_{flux} = \Gamma\tau/2$ in a purely absorbing cloud.

Recall from (10.54) that the heating rate at a level z in the atmosphere is given by

$$\mathcal{H} = -\frac{1}{\rho C_p}\frac{\partial F^{net}}{\partial z}(z) , \tag{13.49}$$

---

[4]Recall that I in this chapter is the *spectral* (i.e., monochromatic) radiance. Therefore, F^{net}, as used here, is the *spectral* net flux (units of W m^{-2} μm^{-1}). To obtain the broadband net flux, you would need to integrate F^{net} over a suitable range of wavelengths, with due allowance for the dependence of I_0, r_∞, Γ, and τ on λ. It follows that $\mathcal{H}$, as used in this section, is also a spectral rather than broadband heating rate.

where C_p is the heat capacity of air at constant pressure, and ρ is the air density at level z. Assuming that the volume extinction coefficient β_e is constant in our cloud, we have $\beta_e dz = -d\tau$, and we can write

$$\mathcal{H} = \frac{\beta_e}{\rho C_p} \frac{\partial F^{net}}{\partial \tau}(\tau) . \qquad (13.50)$$

Substituting (13.47) and letting $F_0 \equiv \pi I_0$ be the incident flux at the top of the cloud, we get

$$\mathcal{H} = \frac{\beta_e F_0 (1 - r_\infty) \Gamma}{\rho C_p} e^{-\Gamma\tau} . \qquad (13.51)$$

The maximum heating occurs at cloud top ($\tau = 0$) and decreases exponentially downward, exactly like the net flux itself. Not surprisingly, the rate is also proportional to β_e, since this parameter determines how much physical air mass is associated with a unit change in τ. If β_e is large, the same absorbed radiation heats a smaller mass of air and the temperature increase is therefore greater.

Problem 13.3: Assume that in the wavelength interval $0.5 \ \mu m < \lambda < 1.5 \ \mu m$, the scattering co-albedo of a water cloud is given approximately by $1 - \tilde{\omega} \approx (1.8 \times 10^{-8}) \exp[10.5\lambda]$, with λ given in units of μm (see Fig. 12.10). Also assume that, in the same wavelength range, the spectral flux (W m^{-2} μm^{-1}) from the sun incident normally on the top of a semi-infinite cloud is given by $F_0 = (5.9 \times 10^{-5}) B_\lambda(T)$, where $T = 6000$ K.

(a) For intervals of 0.2 μm or less, evaluate and graph the spectral heating rate $\mathcal{H}$ at cloud top ($\tau = 0$), assuming the following parameter values: $g = 0.85$, $\beta_e = 0.2$ m^{-1}, $C_p = 1004$ J/(kg K), and $\rho = 1.0$ kg/m^3. Give your results in units of K/(day μm). Hint: It might save time to write a short computer program to perform the above calculations.

(b) By estimating the average height of your plotted curve in (a) and multiplying that height by the appropriate interval $\Delta\lambda$, determine the total heating rate [K/day] contributed by absorbed solar radiation between 0.5 μm and 1.5 μm. If your results seem unreasonably large or small, check your units.

13.4   Nonabsorbing Cloud

Let's now abandon our semi-infinite cloud, and turn to the more realistic case of cloud layer with finite optical depth τ^*. We will initially consider the case that scattering is *conservative*; i.e., $\tilde{\omega} = 1$. This assumption sounds drastic, but in fact the single scatter albedo of cloud droplets is very close to one over most of the visible band (see Fig. 12.10), and absorption by clouds is indeed negligible for most purposes within that band.

Note that if we simply set $\tilde{\omega} = 1$ and then try to evaluate (13.39) and (13.40) we run into the problem that $\Gamma = 0$. Each equation then collapses to the ratio 0/0, which is undefined. The obvious workaround is to take the limit of each equation as $\tilde{\omega} \to 0$. But there is an easier way: let's go back to an earlier step in our original derivation, namely (13.18) and (13.19). We can now re-solve these from scratch, using $\tilde{\omega} = 1$. Equation (13.18) then becomes

$$\frac{1}{2}\frac{d}{d\tau}(I^\uparrow - I^\downarrow) = 0 , \tag{13.52}$$

which implies

$$I^\uparrow - I^\downarrow = \text{constant} \quad \to \quad \pi(I^\uparrow - I^\downarrow) = F^{\text{net}} = \text{constant} . \tag{13.53}$$

or

$$I^\uparrow - I^\downarrow = \frac{F^{\text{net}}}{\pi} = \text{constant} . \tag{13.54}$$

In other words, the net flux does not change with depth in the cloud. This is what you would expect, because a change of F^{net} would imply absorption (and heating), and there can be no absorption when $\tilde{\omega} = 1$. Similarly, (13.19) becomes

$$\frac{d}{d\tau}(I^\uparrow + I^\downarrow) = 2(1 - g)(I^\uparrow - I^\downarrow) = \frac{2F^{\text{net}}}{\pi}(1 - g) , \tag{13.55}$$

which integrates to

$$I^\uparrow + I^\downarrow = \frac{2F^{\text{net}}\tau}{\pi}(1 - g) + K , \tag{13.56}$$

F^{net} and K are constants of integration whose values will be determined by the boundary conditions. Solving (13.54) and (13.56) for

$I^\uparrow$ and $I^\downarrow$ gives

$$I^\uparrow = \frac{F^{net}}{2\pi}[1 + 2\tau(1 - g)] + \frac{K}{2} , \quad (13.57)$$

and

$$I^\downarrow = -\frac{F^{net}}{2\pi}[1 - 2\tau(1 - g)] + \frac{K}{2} . \quad (13.58)$$

We now apply the same boundary conditions as before: $I^\uparrow(\tau^*) = 0$, and $I^\downarrow(0) = I_0$, giving us

$$\frac{K}{2} = I_0 + \frac{F^{net}}{2\pi} , \quad (13.59)$$

and

$$F^{net} = \frac{-\pi I_0}{1 + (1 - g)\tau^*} . \quad (13.60)$$

The general solution of the two-stream equations for the case of conservative scattering is then

$$I^\uparrow(\tau) = \frac{I_0(1 - g)(\tau^* - \tau)}{1 + (1 - g)\tau^*} , \quad (13.61)$$

$$I^\downarrow(\tau) = \frac{I_0[1 + (1 - g)(\tau^* - \tau)]}{1 + (1 - g)\tau^*} . \quad (13.62)$$

From these, we can immediately find the cloud-top albedo

$$r = \frac{I^\uparrow(0)}{I^\downarrow(0)} = \frac{(1 - g)\tau^*}{1 + (1 - g)\tau^*}, \quad \tilde{\omega} = 1 , \quad (13.63)$$

and the transmittance

$$t = \frac{I^\downarrow(\tau^*)}{I^\downarrow(0)} = \frac{1}{1 + (1 - g)\tau^*}, \quad \tilde{\omega} = 1 . \quad (13.64)$$

The above expressions for r and t sum to one, as they must, since there is no absorption.

Not surprisingly, in the limit $\tau^* \to \infty$, the cloud-top albedo $r \to 1$, which also implies $t \to 0$. A bit more surprising, perhaps, is how large τ^* can become while still permitting significant transmission of radiation through a nonabsorbing cloud. For example, with $\tau^* = 100$, the transmittance t is still about 6%. All of this transmittance is associated with photons that have been scattered many hundreds of times on their journey through the cloud layer. It follows that if $\tilde{\omega}$ were even slightly less than one, the fraction of incident photons that would survive this journey would be substantially reduced.

Problem 13.4: A typical heavy stratocumulus cloud layer has an optical thickness $\tau^* = 50$, $\tilde{\omega} = 1$, and $g = 0.85$ in the visible band.
   (a) Compute its albedo and total transmittance.
   (b) If the cloud were perfectly absorbing rather than perfectly scattering, what optical thickness would yield the same transmittance as in (a), assuming $\bar{\mu} = 0.5$?

Problem 13.5: Repeat problem 7.12 but this time, for each case, compute the albedo. What is the difference in albedo for the two cases, and what does this difference suggest about the potential role of aerosol pollution in the global energy budget?

13.5 General Case

We previously considered the limiting cases of (i) a semi-infinite cloud ($\tau^* = \infty$) with arbitrary $\tilde{\omega}$, and (ii) a nonabsorbing cloud ($\tilde{\omega} = 1$) with arbitrary optical thickness τ^*. Last but not least, we may look at the more general case of (iii) arbitrary τ^* in combination with arbitrary $\tilde{\omega} < 1$.

13.5.1   Albedo, Transmittance, and Absorptance

Starting from our two-stream solutions (13.39) and (13.40), we find that the general expression for the albedo for the case that $\tilde{\omega} < 1$ is

$$r = \frac{r_\infty \left[e^{\Gamma \tau^*} - e^{-\Gamma \tau^*} \right]}{e^{\Gamma \tau^*} - r_\infty^2 e^{-\Gamma \tau^*}}, \qquad \tilde{\omega} < 1, \qquad (13.65)$$

and the total transmittance is

$$t = \frac{1 - r_\infty^2}{e^{\Gamma \tau^*} - r_\infty^2 e^{-\Gamma \tau^*}}, \qquad \tilde{\omega} < 1. \qquad (13.66)$$

Problem 13.6:   Show how (13.65) and (13.66) were obtained.

The dependence of t and r on τ^* is depicted in in Figs. 13.5 and 13.6 for selected values of $\tilde{\omega}$, assuming a fairly typical value of g for cloud droplets in the shortwave part of the spectrum. The cloud absorptance $a = 1 - r - t$ is plotted in Fig. 13.7 .

These figures speak for themselves. For any given value of τ^*, even slight decreases in $\tilde{\omega}$ can potentially lead to pronounced decreases in both t and r and thus an increase in a. We see also that each of these variables tends to have an asymptotic limit with increasing τ^*. The asymptotic limit for r is of course r_∞. Decreasing $\tilde{\omega}$ causes the limit to be reached at smaller optical depth.

Problem 13.7:   At a wavelength of $0.7\mu m$, cloud droplets of 10 μm radius have a single scatter albedo $\tilde{\omega} \approx 0.9997$, a scattering asymmetry $g \approx 0.85$, and an extinction efficiency $Q_e \approx 2$. For a stratiform cloud layer consisting of such droplets and having a vertically integrated liquid water path of 0.01 kg m^{-2}, compute the albedo and absorptance. Repeat for a liquid water path of 0.1 kg m^{-2}.

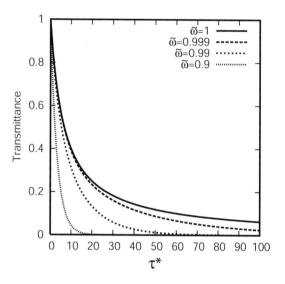

Fig. 13.5: Cloud transmittance t as a function of cloud optical thickness τ^* for $g = 0.85$ and varying values of the single scatter albedo $\tilde{\omega}$.

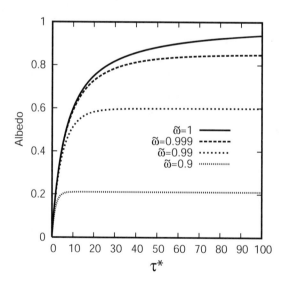

Fig. 13.6: Same as Fig. 13.5, but the plotted quantity is the cloud albedo r.

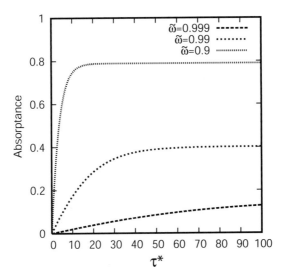

Fig. 13.7: Same as Fig. 13.5, but the plotted quantity is the cloud absorptance $a = 1 - r - t$.

13.5.2   Direct and Diffuse Transmittance

Recall from Section 7.4.4 that the total transmittance t through a cloud layer is actually the sum of two components: the direct transmittance t_{dir} and the diffuse transmittance t_{diff}:

$$t = t_{\text{diff}} + t_{\text{dir}} . \tag{13.67}$$

In particular, t_{dir} describes the fraction of radiation incident on the top of the cloud that passes through to the bottom without either being scattered or absorbed, while t_{diff} describes the fraction that was scattered at least once before emerging from the cloud base. The version of the two-stream equations we derived does not explicitly distinguish between the two types of transmission. Nevertheless, the information is there, for those who know how to get at it.

   We start by considering the special case that the layer is nonscattering, in which case $\tilde{\omega} = 0$, $r_\infty = 0$, and $\Gamma = 2$. Equation (13.66) then reduces to

$$t = t_{\text{dir}} = e^{-\tau^*/\bar{\mu}} , \tag{13.68}$$

where once again $\bar{\mu} = 0.5$. As already mentioned earlier, we're basically saying that the total (flux) transmission in this case behaves as if we were illuminating our nonscattering layer with a single direct beam from an effective zenith angle of 60°. Note also that we are claiming that t in the above equation is the same as the direct transmittance t_{dir}. This is because in the absence of scattering, t_{diff} is by definition zero.

   But wait: if (13.68) gives t_{dir} for nonscattering layer of optical thickness τ^*, then it does so as well for a scattering layer! This is because t_{dir}, by definition, depends only on τ^* and not on $\tilde{\omega}$ or g. So we can subtract t_{dir} from t to get the following expressions for the diffuse component of the transmittance:

$$t_{\text{diff}} = \begin{cases} 0 & \tilde{\omega} = 0 , \\[2mm] \dfrac{1 - r_\infty^2}{e^{\Gamma\tau^*} - r_\infty^2 e^{-\Gamma\tau^*}} - e^{-\tau^*/\bar{\mu}} & 0 < \tilde{\omega} < 1 , \\[3mm] \dfrac{1}{1 + (1-g)\tau^*} - e^{-\tau^*/\bar{\mu}} & \tilde{\omega} = 1 . \end{cases} \tag{13.69}$$

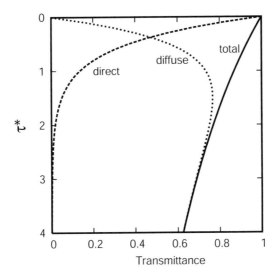

Fig. 13.8: Diffuse, direct, and total transmittance as a function of τ^* in a nonabsorbing cloud with $g = 0.85$.

where we have used (13.64) and (13.66) for the total transmittance in the conservative and nonconservative cases, respectively.

Figure 13.8 shows how the total transmission is partitioned between t_{dir} and t_{diff} as functions of τ^* for a cloud with $\tilde{\omega} = 1$ (conservative scattering). Note that when a cloud is optically thin ($\tau^* \ll 1$), most transmission is direct, and the diffuse component is small. As the layer becomes optically thicker, t_{diff} first rapidly increases, becoming the major contributor to the total transmittance, and then it trails off slowly, long after t_{dir} has gone to zero.

A good real-world example of this behavior can be observed in the thickening layer of clouds that often precedes a warm front. In its early stages, the layer consists of an optically thin veil of cirrostratus that does not significantly block the direct rays of the sun ($t_{\text{dir}} \approx 1$) and also does not scatter enough sunlight to make itself clearly visible against the blue sky ($t_{\text{diff}} \approx 0$). In fact, you may have trouble telling it's even there at all, unless it reveals its presence with a telltale halo.[5] As the cirrostratus layer thickens, it makes the sky

---

[5]The halo around the sun often seen in the presence of cirrostratus is due to a local maximum, near $\Theta = 22°$, in the scattering phase function $p(\Theta)$ for randomly oriented hexagonal ice crystals — see Section 4.3.1.

whiter (t_{diff} initially increases) while the sun's disk rapidly dims (t_{dir} decreases). Eventually, as the layer changes from cirrostratus to altostratus and finally nimbostratus, the sun's disk becomes invisible ($t_{\text{dir}} \approx 0$) and the sky becomes an ever-darker shade of gray ($t \approx t_{\text{diff}} \to 0$).

13.5.3   Semi-Infinite Cloud as Approximation

Our first application of the two-stream solution was to find the albedo of a semi-infinite cloud. It turned out that that albedo is given by r_∞, which is a function of $\tilde{\omega}$ and g. Our more general solution (13.65) reveals that as you increase τ^*, the albedo first increases rapidly and then more slowly. It eventually "saturates" at a value approaching r_∞ and does not increase significantly with further increases in τ^*.

Although a real cloud is never truly semi-infinite, it is reasonable to ask for what value of τ^* a cloud might viewed as *effectively* semi-infinite, in the sense that further increases in τ^* don't significantly change the cloud's overall radiative properties. Another way of posing the same question is to ask how thick a cloud must be, in order that the underlying atmosphere and/or surface has no significant influence on the cloud-top albedo, as seen for example by a satellite imager. If a cloud layer is effectively semi-infinite at a particular wavelength, then the cloud-top radiance at that wavelength can be predicted from the cloud properties alone.

There is more than one way to measure the degree to which a cloud's radiative properties have approached the semi-infinite limit. However, the most straightfoward is the cloud's total transmittance: if $t \approx 0$, then we can be certain that almost none of the photons emerging from cloud-top will have ever "seen" the lower boundary and therefore can't have been influenced by the details of where, exactly, that boundary is found (i.e., what the precise value of τ^* is) or its reflective properties.

Of course, t is *never* exactly zero for finite τ^*, so we have to phrase the question as follows: For what minimum value of τ^* is $t < f$, where we let f be largest value of the transmittance that we still consider to be "negligible?" For example, if we set $f = 0.01$, then we are saying that up to 1% transmittance will be tolerated

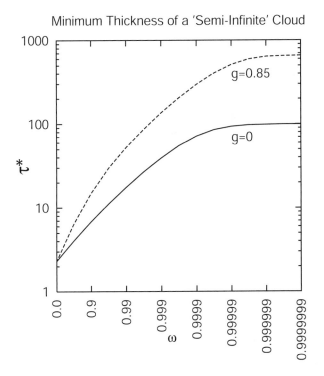

Fig. 13.9: The minimum cloud optical thickness τ^* that qualifies as approximately "semi-infinite", based on the (arbitrary) requirement that the total transmittance be less than 1%.

without invalidating the description "effectively semi-infinite."

Setting $t = f = 0.01$ in (13.66) and solving for τ^* allows us to express the minimum optical thickness as a function of $\tilde{\omega}$ and g. Representative results are plotted in Fig. 13.9. What we see is that a strongly absorbing cloud may be effectively semi-infinite for rather small τ^*, while a strongly scattering cloud layer continues to transmit at least 1% of the radiation incident on the opposite side until τ^* reaches a value of several hundred.

One conclusion we can draw from this result is that even relatively thin water clouds may be treated as opaque at thermal infrared wavelengths for which $\tilde{\omega} \ll 1$, while the same clouds may be far from opaque at visible wavelengths, despite having roughly the same total optical thickness τ^* in both the bands.

Problem 13.8:   A certain cloud consists of drops of radius 10 μm. The total column liquid water path L is 0.05 kg m^{-2}. Assume an extinction efficiency $Q_e \approx 2$ for all wavelengths of interest, and $g \approx$ 0.85.

    (a) Compute the optical thickness τ^* [see (7.74)].

    (b) Determine the range of $\tilde{\omega}$ for which the cloud may be treated as effectively 'semi-infinite', based on the information in Fig. 13.9.

    (c) Examine Fig. 12.10 and determine the approximate range of wavelength over which the cloud *cannot* be considered 'semi-infinite.' Identify the associated spectral band(s).

13.6   Similarity Transformations[†]

In the expressions (13.65) and (13.66) that we derived for albedo and transmittance in the general case, there is an implicit dependence on *three* radiative quantities: the optical depth τ, the single scatter albedo $\tilde{\omega}$, and the scattering asymmetry parameter g. Yet all of this dependence is embodied in only *two* free variables: r_∞ and the product of Γ with τ^*. It follows that any two cloud layers having the same values of both r_∞ and $\Gamma\tau^*$ are *radiatively equivalent* to at least the accuracy of the two-stream approximation.

Because r_∞ itself is a function of both $\tilde{\omega}$ and g, *there is an infinity of combinations of these parameters that map to the same value of r_∞.* So if you were to measure the albedo at the top of a semi-infinite cloud and find, for example, that $r_\infty = 0.80$, you'd have no way of knowing whether you were dealing with $g = 0$ and $\tilde{\omega} = 0.988$, or with $g = 0.8$ and $\tilde{\omega} = 0.998$, or with any other combination that produces the same albedo. What you *can* uniquely determine, however, is the *similarity-transformed (or adjusted) single scatter albedo*, which is defined as

$$\tilde{\omega}' \equiv \frac{1-g}{1-g\tilde{\omega}}\tilde{\omega}\,. \qquad (13.70)$$

It tells you what single scatter albedo *in combination with isotropic scattering ($g = 0$)* would give you the same r_∞ as your actual g and

$\tilde{\omega}$. Note the effect of $g > 0$ (the usual case) is to make $\tilde{\omega}' < \tilde{\omega}$, except of course when $\tilde{\omega} = \tilde{\omega}' = 1$.

Similarly, the *similarity-transformed (or adjusted) optical depth* is defined as

$$\tau' \equiv (1 - g\tilde{\omega})\tau \,. \tag{13.71}$$

It tells you what optical depth *in combination with isotropic scattering* ($g = 0$) *and adjusted single scatter albedo* $\tilde{\omega}'$ will give you the same value of $\Gamma\tau$ as would the "real" τ in combination with your cloud's actual $\tilde{\omega}$ and g. For $g > 0$ and $\tilde{\omega} > 0$, we find that $\tau' < \tau$.

> **Problem 13.9:** Verify the above interpretations of (13.70) and (13.71) by showing that $r_\infty(\tilde{\omega}', 0) = r_\infty(\tilde{\omega}, g)$ and that $\Gamma(\tilde{\omega}', 0)\tau' = \Gamma(\tilde{\omega}, g)\tau$.

The physical interpretation of (13.71) is straightforward. If g is close to unity, then scattered radiation will tend to continue more or less in the original direction of travel, almost as if it hadn't been scattered at all. Therefore, radiation will be able to traverse a greater optical depth without being absorbed than would be the case if g were smaller. The definition of τ' gives an "effective" optical depth that takes into account this phenomenon.

The interpretation of (13.70) is only slightly more subtle. The idea here is that if $g > 0$, then photons incident at cloud top will have a harder time "turning around" from their original downward path than would be the case for $g = 0$. On average, a greater number of scattering events will have to occur in order for a photon to have a good chance of re-emerging from the cloud top and contributing to the albedo. Of course, the greater the number of scatterings, the greater the fraction of photons that will be absorbed first, if $\tilde{\omega} < 1$. The definition of $\tilde{\omega}'$ takes into account the role of g in the overall absorptive properties of the cloud.

> **Problem 13.10:** Given $\tilde{\omega} = 0.99$ and $g = 0.85$, compute $\tilde{\omega}'$ and r_∞.

13.7   Clouds Over Non-Black Surfaces

In order to obtain our solutions (13.39) and (13.40) to the two-stream equations, we had to supply two boundary conditions. We chose to take $I^\downarrow(0) = I_0$ and $I^\uparrow(\tau^*) = 0$. The latter condition states that the lower boundary is perfectly black; i.e., there is no radiation incident on the cloud base from below.

If the lower boundary were in fact non-black, then radiation transmitted by the cloud would reach the surface, partially reflect upward and impinge on the cloud base from below. Some of that radiation would be transmitted back through the cloud. Some of the remainder would be reflect back downward, increasing the illumination of the surface, and so on, *ad infinitum*. The net result would be (a) an increase in the total downward flux incident on the surface and (b) an increase in the albedo at cloud top.

In principle, we could re-solve the two stream equations with a new lower boundary condition to account for a non-black surface. The new boundary condition would be $I^\uparrow(\tau^*) = r_{sfc}I^\downarrow(\tau^*)$, where r_{sfc} is albedo of the surface. But there is a simpler way, at least if we are content with finding the modified fluxes at the upper and lower boundaries.

Imagine that we have already used (13.65) and (13.66) to find the reflectivity r and total transmittance t of a cloud layer with specified τ^*, $\tilde{\omega}$, and g. The reflectivity and transmittance are intrinsic to the cloud itself, because there is no contribution from the lower boundary. The upward flux of radiation from cloud top is

$$F^\uparrow(0) = F_0 r , \qquad (13.72)$$

where F_0 is the incident solar flux. The downward flux below cloud base is

$$F^\downarrow(\tau^*) = F_0 t . \qquad (13.73)$$

Now let's place the same cloud layer over a surface with albedo r_{sfc}. Of the downward flux given by (13.73), a fraction r_{sfc} is reflected back toward the cloud. A fraction t of *that* is transmitted *through* the cloud, adding to the original $F^\uparrow(0)$ given by (13.72). An additional fraction r is reflected back downward toward the surface. A fraction r_{sfc} of *that* is reflected back upward, where it again contributes to an

a) Combining cloud layer with reflecting surface

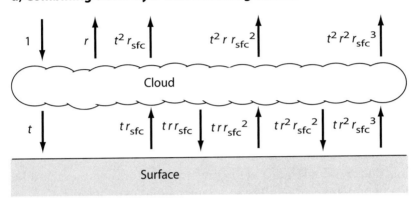

b) Combining two cloud layers

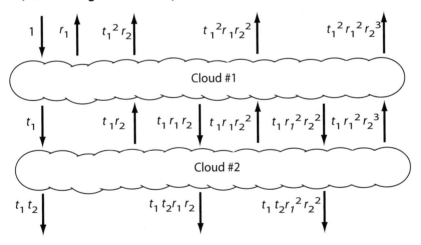

Fig. 13.10: Depiction of the first few transmittance and reflectance contributions when multiple reflections occur between (a) a cloud layer and a non-black surface, and (b) two cloud layers.

increase in $F^\uparrow(0)$ as well to the flux reflected back downward from cloud base.

Figure 13.10a depicts the first few terms in the infinite series of reflections between a cloud layer and the surface. The total upward flux at cloud top is now the sum of the cloud-reflected component and each of the transmitted contributions due to successive reflections from the surface:

$$F^\uparrow(0) = F_0(r + r_{sfc}t^2 + r_{sfc}^2 rt^2 + r_{sfc}^3 r^2 t^2 + r_{sfc}^4 r^3 t^2 + \dots) \quad . \quad (13.74)$$

We can rewrite the above equation as

$$\tilde{r} \equiv \frac{F^\uparrow(0)}{F_0} = r + r_{sfc}t^2[1 + r_{sfc}r + (r_{sfc}r)^2 + (r_{sfc}r)^3 + \dots] \quad . \quad (13.75)$$

This does not look like a very convenient solution, unless you happen to remember the following power series expansion:

$$\frac{1}{1-x} = 1 + x + x^2 + x^3 + \dots \quad , \quad (13.76)$$

in which case you'll recognize that an equivalent closed-form expression for $\tilde{r}$ is

$$\boxed{\tilde{r} = r + \frac{r_{sfc}t^2}{1 - r_{sfc}r}} \quad . \quad (13.77)$$

Using similar reasoning, we get

$$\boxed{\tilde{t} = \frac{t}{1 - r_{sfc}r}} \quad , \quad (13.78)$$

where

$$\tilde{t} \equiv \frac{F^\downarrow(\tau^*)}{F_0} \quad . \quad (13.79)$$

Problem 13.11:   Derive (13.78).

Let's consider first the modified cloud-top albedo $\tilde{r}$ given by (13.77). We note that if either the cloud transmittance t or the surface reflectivity r_{sfc} are equal to zero, then the second term on the right vanishes and we're back to the original reflectivity r computed for a black lower boundary. The second thing we notice is that if both t and r_{sfc} are *not* zero, then the second term on the right is greater than zero, implying an enhancement of the albedo relative to the original r. The third thing we notice is that if $t = 1$, then r must be zero (because $r + t + a = 1$); therefore $\tilde{r} = r_{sfc}$. The last case is of course equivalent to having no cloud at all. All of these inferrences make physical sense.

Recall that $\tilde{t}$ is the ratio of the flux incident on the surface below the cloud to the original flux F_0 incident at cloud top. If $t = 0$, then $\tilde{t}$ is also zero. If either r_{sfc} or r is zero, then $\tilde{t} = t$. Again, these results make sense.

But now consider the case that $r_{sfc} > 0$ and the cloud absorptance $a = 0$ so that $r = 1 - t$. We then get

$$\tilde{t} = \frac{1 - r}{1 - r_{sfc}r} \quad > \quad t = 1 - r. \tag{13.80}$$

Multiple reflections between the ground and the cloud thus enhance the downward flux at ground level, relative to what the flux would have been with a black surface. In other words, making the ground more reflective below you makes the sky brighter above you! If you live in a part of the country that gets snowfall, you will undoubtedly have noticed that an overcast sky is substantially brightened by the presence of snow on the ground.

More surprising, perhaps, is that if $r_{sfc} = 1$ and $a = 0$, then $\tilde{t} = 1$, implying that *the downward flux below cloud base is then exactly as large as it is above cloud top*, even when a large fraction of the incident radiation is reflected back to space before even passing through the cloud! In other words, in the absence of absorption, the presence of the cloud makes no difference whatsoever to the downward flux measured by an observer at the surface!

Although the above conclusion might seem counterintuitive, there is a simple physical explanation based on energy conservation: if there is no loss of radiative energy due to absorption in or below the cloud layer, then the upward flux of radiation below cloud base must increase through multiple reflection until just as much energy is lost by transmission upward through the cloud as is gained by downward transmission of the incident flux above the cloud. Since the transmittance of the cloud is the same in both directions, steady state is achieved when the two fluxes are equal. And since the upward flux below cloud equals the downward flux when the surface is perfectly reflective, the downward flux below cloud equals the downward flux above cloud.

Problem 13.12: The above argument can be equally well applied to the downward and upward flux (and thus intensity in the two-stream approximation) of radiation at an arbitrary level τ within a semi-infinite, nonabsorbing cloud. Specifically, we expect $I^{\downarrow}(\tau) = I^{\uparrow}(\tau) = I_0$.

(a) Outline the physical argument, drawing an analogy to the case of a finite cloud layer overlying a perfectly reflecting surface.

(b) Demonstrate the stated relationship, using the equations given earlier for the intensity in a semi-infinite layer.

(c) Demonstrate the stated relationship, using the equations given for the intensity in a nonabsorbing layer.

Problem 13.13: Assume that the incident flux of visible radiation on the top of a stratiform cloud layer is $F_0 = 400$ W m^{-2}. The cloud itself has a transmittance $t = 0.2$ and does not absorb. The surface albedo is initially $r_{\text{sfc}} = 0.05$, but the cloud produces snowfall which blankets the surface, eventually raising r_{sfc} to 0.95.

(a) Create a table with two rows and six columns. The rows correspond to "before snowfall" and "after snowfall". The first three columns will contain, respectively, the downward flux, upward flux, and net flux at the surface. The last three columns will contain the same quantities, but at cloud top.

(b) By what percentage did the *downward* flux at ground level increase after the snowfall?

(c) For either case, compare the net flux at ground level with that at cloud top. Is one greater than the other? Why or why not?

13.8 Multiple Cloud Layers

We previously considered what happens when a cloud layer that partially reflects and partially transmits radiation is combined with a non-black (i.e., partially or totally reflective) surface. We can undertake a similar analysis to find the combined radiative properties of two cloud layers, the first with reflectivity r_1 and transmittance t_1; the second with r_2 and t_2. Figure 13.10b depicts the first few terms in the infinite series of reflections between the cloud layers. It can be shown that the total reflectance of the two-layer combination is given by

$$\tilde{r} = r_1 + \frac{t_1^2 r_2}{1 - r_1 r_2} \,, \qquad (13.81)$$

and the total transmittance is

$$\tilde{t} = \frac{t_1 t_2}{1 - r_1 r_2} \,. \qquad (13.82)$$

Problem 13.14: Write out the derivation for the above two equations.

Equations (13.81) and (13.82) apply to a combination of just two layers, but they can be used to compute the combined reflectance and transmittance of any number of layers. First, find the reflectance and transmittance of one adjacent pair of layers. Then treat this pair as a single layer to be combined with a third layer, and so on, *ad infinitum*.

Problem 13.15: Three nonabsorbing layers have transmittances $t_1 = 0.2$, $t_2 = 0.3$, and $t_3 = 0.4$.
  (a) Compute their combined reflectivity and transmittance.
  (b) Compare the computed transmittance with that predicted by Beer's Law for combinations of nonscattering layers, and explain the difference.

(c) Under what condition(s) is (13.82) consistent with Beer's Law, and why?

Although we implicitly assumed we were dealing with two distinct cloud layers separated by clear space, the space between the layers plays no role (as long as it is nonscattering and nonabsorbing, of course). Therefore, we can apply (13.81) and (13.82) equally well to two contiguous layers of the same cloud, as illustrated by the following problem:

Problem 13.16:   A certain cloud layer has total optical thickness $\tau^* = 12$, single scattering albedo $\tilde{\omega} = 0.99$, and asymmetry parameter $g = 0.85$.

(a) Use (13.66) and (13.65) to compute the total reflectivity and transmittance of the cloud layer.

(b) For the same values of $\tilde{\omega}$ and g, compute the reflectivities and transmittances of layers having $\tau^* = 3$ and $\tau^* = 9$, respectively.

(c) Use (13.81) and (13.82) to combine your results from (b) in order to find the total reflectivity and transmittance of the layer with $\tau^* = 12$. Do your results agree with your answers to (a)?

13.9   Accurate solution methods[†]

The two-stream method and its close relatives (e.g., the so-called *Eddington approximation*) are often adequate for computing shortwave fluxes, including albedo and total transmittance, in plane-parallel clouds, given τ^*, $\tilde{\omega}$, and g. However, you should not forget that it is an approximate solution based on several fairly drastic assumptions, such as uniform intensity ($I(\mu, \phi) = $ constant) in each hemisphere. Ninety-nine percent of the time when you're outside during the daytime, your own eyes tell you that shortwave radiant intensity $I^\downarrow$ is a strong function of direction.[6]

You should therefore should not rely on the two-stream method in either of the following cases:

---

[6]The other one percent of the time, your eyes are probably closed.

- You require the ability to compute fluxes with high accuracy, taking into account the details of the scattering phase function $p(\Theta)$ and the surface bidirectional reflectance function $\rho(\theta_i, \phi_i; \theta_r, \phi_r)$; or

- You require the ability to calculate radiant *intensities* in one or more specific directions, such as those viewed by a remote sensing instrument in space or on the ground.

For such applications, you need a suitable numerical method for solving the full radiative transfer equation (11.13) for a plane-parallel atmosphere. In addition, there are times when you can't safely ignore three-dimensional structure, in which case even the plane-parallel assumption goes out the window and you have to fall back on (11.8) as your starting point.

Fortunately, there are quite a few off-the-shelf radiative transfer codes available that can be adapted to almost any problem that you're likely to encounter. It is therefore not usually necessary even for radiation or remote sensing specialists to derive and program their own radiative transfer codes, unless they have very special needs. And most nonspecialists (i.e., the presumed majority of readers of this book) will not have to deal with these codes at all, let alone know much about what goes on "under the hood."

One of the most popular and flexible plane parallel radiative transfer codes in use today, called *DISORT*, is based on the *discrete ordinates* method. The discrete ordinates method can be thought of as a generalization of the two-stream method to an arbitrarily large number of discrete "streams" of radiation in each hemisphere, each one representing a different direction.

Other common radiative transfer methods suitable for multiple scattering problems include the *adding-doubling* method, *successive orders of scattering*, and the *Monte Carlo* method. The last of these was briefly outlined in section 13.1.

The adding-doubling method may be thought of as a generalization of equations (13.77), (13.78), (13.81), and (13.82). In this method, the scalar reflectance r and transmittance t for each layer are replaced with $N \times N$ matrices $\mathbf{R}$ and $\mathbf{T}$, which represent the coupling of intensities between each of N discrete directions for the incident radiation into each of the corresponding outgoing directions for reflected and transmitted radiation, respectively. Division in the above equations is replaced with the matrix inverse operator. If you then start with a layer which is very thin, then the single scattering approximation applies, allowing **R** and **T** to be computed from the scattering phase function alone. Thereafter, it is only necessary to combine layers successively until you achieve the desired total optical thickness τ^*.

The method of successive orders of scattering is most suitable when dealing with a cloud layer that is either not too thick or else is moderately absorbing. In this method, you first determine the radiation field that results from single scattering of the incident radiation. This field is then used to determine the contribution from radiation that is scattered a second time, and so on. Summing the contributions from all orders of scattering gives the complete field of multiply scattered radiation. Of course, the sum converges after a reasonable number of iterations only if a significant fraction of the radiation is lost from the cloud layer with each successive scattering, either due to absorption or because the radiation escapes from the upper or lower boundary of the cloud.

All of the above numerical methods are covered in far greater depth by L02 (Ch. 6), TS02 (Ch. 8), and GY95 (Ch. 8).

APPENDIX A

Representing the Phase Function

A.1 Legendre Polynomial Expansion

Except in the Rayleigh limit, real particles always have phase functions that can't be expressed exactly using a closed-form mathematical expression (see Chapter 12). Therefore you will *almost always* have to employ some kind of approximate representation. Your approximate representation must allow the shape of $p(\cos\Theta)$ to be encoded to whatever level of accuracy is required for your application. Often, this means expressing $p(\cos\Theta)$ as an infinite series of suitable orthogonal basis functions — in this case, the Legendre polynomials $P_l(\cos\Theta)$:

$$p(\cos\Theta) = \sum_{l=0}^{\infty} \beta_l P_l(\cos\Theta) . \tag{A.1}$$

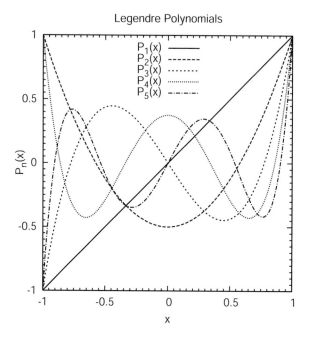

Fig. A.1: Examples of Legendre polynomials.

The first few Legendre polynomials are given by

$$P_0(x) = 1 \tag{A.2a}$$

$$P_1(x) = x \tag{A.2b}$$

$$P_2(x) = \frac{1}{2}(3x^2 - 1) \tag{A.2c}$$

$$P_3(x) = \frac{1}{2}(5x^3 - 3x) \tag{A.2d}$$

$$P_4(x) = \frac{1}{8}(35x^4 - 30x^2 + 3) \tag{A.2e}$$

$$P_5(x) = \frac{1}{8}(63x^5 - 70x^3 + 15x) \tag{A.2f}$$

and they satisfy the orthogonality condition

$$\int_{-1}^{1} P_n(x)P_m(x)\, dx = \begin{cases} 0, & n \neq m \\ \dfrac{2}{2n+1}, & n = m \end{cases} \tag{A.3}$$

Taking advantage of the above property, we can determine the lth coefficient of the expansion as follows:

$$\beta_l = \frac{2l+1}{2} \int_{-1}^{1} P_l(\cos\Theta) p(\cos\Theta) \, d\cos\Theta . \tag{A.4}$$

In practice, only the coefficients of the first N terms are actually utilized, with N being chosen based both on the accuracy and angular detail required for I and on the smoothness of the true phase function $p(\cos\Theta)$:

$$p(\cos\Theta) \approx \sum_{l=0}^{N-1} \beta_l P_l(\cos\Theta) . \tag{A.5}$$

As a general rule, the larger the size parameter x of the atmospheric particles, the more complex the phase function and the larger N must be in order to capture details like the forward diffraction peak, rainbows, glories, etc.

The first coefficient β_0 in a Legendre polynomial expansion of the phase function is always one, because of the normalization condition (11.17). The asymmetry parameter g turns out to be equal to one-third of the second coefficient β_1. Therefore, any radiative transfer solution that uses only g to describe the phase function (such as our two-stream solution) is effectively employing a two-term representation of the phase function and discarding all higher order terms in the expansion. Assuming isotropic scattering is equivalent to neglecting all coefficients except $\beta_0 = 1$.

Problem A.1:   Prove the three assertions made in the previous paragraph, as follows: (a) Show that $\beta_0 = 1$ for *any* phase function $p(\cos\Theta)$. (b) Show that β_0 is the *only* non-zero coefficient in the case of isotropic scattering. (c) Show that $g = \beta_1/3$, based on the definition of g given by (11.20).

Problem A.2:   Find all non-zero coefficients β_l for the Rayleigh phase function (12.10).

Convenient one- or two-parameter models such as the Henyey-Greenstein phase function (see section 11.3.3) are at best crude approximations of real phase functions, and are only useful when you don't care about high accuracy in your calculation of $I(\mu, \phi)$, or when you're interested in testing the general performance of a radiative transfer code using an idealized phase function. But even if you do adopt the Henyey-Greenstein phase function model, with its simple one-parameter mathematical form (11.23), you might still have to re-express p_{HG} as a truncated Legendre polynomial series in order to perform actual radiative transfer calculations, depending on the particular method used.

A.2 δ-Scaling of the Phase Function

As mentioned above, the number of terms in a Legendre polynomial expansion required to adequately represent a given phase function depends on how smooth the phase function is — the larger the angular variations, the larger the number of terms N must be. This in turn generally increases the overall computational effort required to solve the RTE to a desired level of accuracy, as well as increasing the risk of machine precision problems and/or numerical instabilities.

In this regard, one of the most problematic features in typical phase functions for particles with large size parameter x is the forward diffraction peak (see Figs. 12.7 and 12.9), which can be both very narrow and very intense. This peak cannot be accurately reproduced via a sum over just the low-order terms in the expansion, because the polynomials P_l are very smooth for low values of l. You cannot take the sum of a few very smoothly varying functions and expect to be able to reproduce a very non-smooth, spike-like feature.

Not only is the strong forward scattering peak problematic from a computational point of view, but its influence on both the total extinction cross-section σ_e and the scattering asymmetry parameter g of a particle can be deceptive.

Take for example the scattering of visible light by a black bowling ball. Its size parameter x is on the order of 10^6, putting it very firmly in the realm of geometric optics (see Chapter 12). Common sense tells us that it will extinguish only the radiation that is physically incident on it; i.e., its extinction cross-section is equal to the size of its shadow which is in turn equal to its physical cross-section, and its extinction efficiency Q_e is therefore equal to one. Since the bowling ball is black, we can further assume that its single scatter albedo is within a percent or two of zero. Finally, since it is opaque, much of the radiation that *is* reflected from its surface will be directed more or less backwards, so we can anticipate an asymmetry parameter $g \ll 1$.[1]

The same bowling ball examined from the point of view of the exact Mie theory (remember that geometric optics is an approximation!) looks quite different. In the limit of large x, we know that Mie theory predicts $Q_e = 2$. In other words, the bowling ball apparently extinguishes *twice* as much radiation as might be inferred from the size of its shadow alone! Earlier, we referred to this apparent discrepancy as the *extinction paradox*. Also, the Mie theory-derived single scatter albedo will be at least one-half, and the asymmetry parameter will be close to one! These values are all greatly at odds with our intuition, yet they are correct according to the exact theory.

"Common sense"	Exact Theory
$Q_e \approx 1$	$Q_e \approx 2$
$\tilde{\omega} \approx 0.01$	$\tilde{\omega} \approx 0.5$
$g \approx 0$	$g \approx 1$

This admittedly extreme example is one in which the intuitive (approximate) properties are actually more germaine than the exact ones. Why? Because in the exact results for the bowling ball, fully half of the total radiation extinguished is extinguished *only in a very narrow, literal sense of the word*. That half consists of radiation passing *near* the bowling ball that is deflected by an almost infinitesimal amount from its original direction. Technically speaking, it *is* scattered. And of course that infinitesimally deflected radiation factors into the computed values of $\tilde{\omega}$ and g. But for *any practical computational purpose*, it is a red herring, and we'd be better off using the much different, and less "correct," geometric optics results for our bowling ball.

---

[1]For a perfectly reflecting smooth sphere, a geometric optics calculation yields an asymmetry parameter of exactly zero. For an absorbing sphere with specular reflecting surface obeying the Fresnel relations, forward scattering will be slightly favored owing to the higher reflectivity for glancing rays.

   To summarize: Capturing the precise shape and intensity of the forward diffraction peak for a bowling ball would require the inclusion of extremely large number of terms in the Legendre polynomial expansion of the phase function. The forward diffraction peak is not nearly as narrow for cloud droplets as it is for bowling balls, but the same basic problem (in milder form) exists for solar radiative transfer in clouds. The computational effort needed to account for the forward peak in the phase function is not only unwelcome, it is also utterly pointless unless for some reason we really *have* to compute $I(\mu, \phi)$ with extremely high angular resolution.

   The way to deal with this problem is to split the mathematical representation of the phase function into two pieces, one that accounts for the forward diffraction peak and another that captures the rest of the phase function. Specifically, we pretend that the diffraction peak can be adequately represented by a Dirac δ-function:

$$p(\cos \Theta) \approx A p'(\cos \Theta) + 4B\delta(\cos \Theta - 1) , \qquad (A.6)$$

where $p'(\cos \Theta)$ is the *δ-scaled phase function*, and the coefficients A and B determine how the total phase function is partitioned between the two pieces. If we require $p'(\cos \Theta)$ to be properly normalized in its own right, then we can eliminate A as follows:

$$\frac{1}{2} \int_{-1}^{1} \left[A p'(\cos \Theta) + 4B\delta(\cos \Theta - 1) \right] d \cos \Theta = 1 , \qquad (A.7)$$

$$A + 2B \int_{-1}^{1} \delta(\cos \Theta - 1) d \cos \Theta = 1 , \qquad (A.8)$$

$$A + B = 1 \quad \rightarrow \quad A = 1 - B , \qquad (A.9)$$

so that

$$p(\cos \Theta) \approx (1 - B) \, p'(\cos \Theta) + 4B\delta(\cos \Theta - 1) . \qquad (A.10)$$

The asymmetry parameter g' of the scaled phase function $p'(\cos \Theta)$ should be chosen so as to be consistent with the asymmetry g of the original phase function:

$$
\begin{aligned}
g &\equiv \frac{1}{2} \int_{-1}^{1} x p(x)\, dx \\
&= \frac{1}{2} \int_{-1}^{1} x \left[(1-B)\, p'(x) + 4B\delta(x-1) \right]\, dx \\
&= (1-B) \frac{1}{2} \int_{-1}^{1} x p'(x)\, dx + 2B \int_{-1}^{1} x\delta(x-1)\, dx \\
&= (1-B)\, g' + B ,
\end{aligned}
\tag{A.11}
$$

so that the *scaled asymmetry parameter* is

$$
g' = \frac{\beta_1'}{3} = \frac{g - B}{1 - B} .
\tag{A.12}
$$

Note that by finding g', we automatically determine the second coefficient in the Legendre polynomial expansion of $p'(\cos\Theta)$. A similar matching procedure can be used to find subsequent coefficients β_l', given our choice of B and the expansion coefficients β_l for the original phase function.

Although the optimal choice of B is a bit ill-defined, the goal is to put as much of the diffraction peak as possible into the δ-term in (A.6) without doing violence to the rest of the phase function. Specifically, you want to be able to accurately represent the scaled phase function $p'(\cos\Theta)$ with significantly fewer terms in a Legendre polynomial expansion than would have been required for the original phase function $p(\cos\Theta)$.

Recall that the most general form of the radiative transfer equation was given by (11.9). If we neglect thermal emission, it becomes

$$
\frac{dI(\hat{\Omega})}{d\tau} = -I(\hat{\Omega}) + \frac{\tilde{\omega}}{4\pi} \int_{4\pi} p(\hat{\Omega}', \hat{\Omega}) I(\hat{\Omega}')\, d\omega' .
\tag{A.13}
$$

If we substitute (A.10) into the above, we have

$$
\begin{aligned}
\frac{dI(\hat{\Omega})}{d\tau} = &-I(\hat{\Omega}) \\
&+ \frac{\tilde{\omega}}{4\pi} \int_{4\pi} \left[(1-B)\, p'(\hat{\Omega}', \hat{\Omega}) + 4B\delta(\hat{\Omega}' \cdot \hat{\Omega} - 1) \right] I(\hat{\Omega}')\, d\omega' ,
\end{aligned}
\tag{A.14}
$$

which simplifies to

$$\frac{dI(\hat{\Omega})}{d\tau} = -(1 - B\tilde{\omega})\, I(\hat{\Omega})$$
$$+ (1 - B)\frac{\tilde{\omega}}{4\pi}\int_{4\pi} p'(\hat{\Omega}', \hat{\Omega}) I(\hat{\Omega}')\, d\omega'\,. \qquad (A.15)$$

Let's now define the *scaled optical depth* as

$$\boxed{\tau' = (1 - B\tilde{\omega})\,\tau\,,} \qquad (A.16)$$

and the *scaled single scatter albedo* as

$$\boxed{\tilde{\omega}' = \left(\frac{1 - B}{1 - B\tilde{\omega}}\right)\tilde{\omega}\,.} \qquad (A.17)$$

With these definitions, we can rewrite (A.15) as

$$\frac{dI(\hat{\Omega})}{d\tau'} = -I(\hat{\Omega}) + \frac{\tilde{\omega}'}{4\pi}\int_{4\pi} p'(\hat{\Omega}', \hat{\Omega}) I(\hat{\Omega}')\, d\omega'\,. \qquad (A.18)$$

This has exactly the same form as (A.13), except with τ', $\tilde{\omega}'$, and $p'(\hat{\Omega}', \hat{\Omega})$ replacing τ, $\tilde{\omega}$, and $p(\hat{\Omega}', \hat{\Omega})$.

By representing part of the phase function with a δ-function, we are in effect treating that part of the scattered radiation as if it had never been extinguished at all, which is why our scaled optical path τ' is less than the actual optical path τ (as long as $\tilde{\omega} > 0$). Moreover, since the total *absorption* along the path is not supposed to be affected by the scaling of the optical depth, the single scatter albedo must be scaled downward by an appropriate amount; thus $\tilde{\omega}' < \tilde{\omega}$ except in the case of conservative scattering.

If you read section 13.6 concerning similarity transformations, then (A.16) and (A.17) may seem somewhat familiar. In fact, they are identical to (13.71) and (13.70) for the special case that $B = g$. Recall that the similarity-transformed optical depth and single-scatter albedo were derived from the two-stream method by defining a *radiatively equivalent* cloud for which $g = 0$. In fact, if we set $B = g$ and substitute into (A.12), we get $g' = 0$! In short, we have arrived at the same pair of scaling relationships by two completely different paths.

This does not mean, however, that setting $B = g$ is necessarily a good choice when our goal is to approximate $p'(\cos\Theta)$ with the smallest possible set of expansion coefficients β'_l. On the contrary, even with the forward diffraction peak "chopped off" and represented by a δ-function, the residual scattering phase function for cloud droplets in the shortwave band still exhibits marked positive asymmetry. Therefore, the best choice for B will usually give $g' > 0$.

Problem A.3: As discussed above, the extinction efficiency Q_e computed using exact Mie theory has a limiting value of 2 for large spheres. This is exactly twice what you would expect from geometric considerations alone (hence, the so-called extinction paradox). It is due to the very slight deflection, via diffraction, of a large amount of radiation passing *near* the sphere. In the limit of large x, it makes more sense to treat the diffracted component as if it had never been scattered at all and let geometric optics dictate the remainder of the phase function. With this in mind,

(a) write down the desired ratio of τ' to τ,

(b) determine the value of B that achieves the desired scaling for a given value of $\tilde{\omega}$, and

(c) find expressions for the scaled single scatter albedo $\tilde{\omega}'$ and asymmetry parameter g', given $\tilde{\omega}$ and g.

(d) Assume that a pure geometric optics (ray tracing) calculation is applied to a nearly black bowling ball and yields a single scatter albedo of 0.01 and a scattering asymmetry parameter of 0.2. If exact Mie theory were used instead, so that the computed scattering properties included the effects of the forward diffraction peak, what would be the new values of $\tilde{\omega}$ and g?

Problem A.4: For a water sphere with $x = 1000$ and $m = 1.33 + 10^{-3}i$, Mie theory gives $Q_e = 2.02$, $\tilde{\omega} = 0.549$, and $g = 0.968$. Assuming that the excess of 1.02 in Q_e (relative to geometric optics) is due to the forward diffraction peak in the phase function, find the δ-scaled values $\tilde{\omega}'$ and g' that exclude this contribution.

To summarize the key points of this section:

- Regardless of the numerical method employed, it is common to represent the scattering phase function $p(\cos \Theta)$ via a truncated infinite series of Legendre polynomials.

- The number of terms N retained in the above representation depends both on the complexity of the phase function and the desired angular resolution of the computed intensity field.

- When the size parameter x of the scattering particles is large, it is usually advantageous to use δ-scaled versions of the phase function, single scattering albedo, and optical depth. The scaling helps reduce the numerical complications associated with the forward diffraction peak in the phase function. Among other things, it enables the use of smaller N. It also helps resolve the large inconsistency between scattering properties derived using the geometric optics (ray tracing) approximation and those obtained from the exact Mie theory.

APPENDIX B

Symbols Used

Symbol	Meaning [example units, if applicable]
a	absorptivity
a	radius (e.g., of a rain drop) [m]
a	acceleration [m s^{-2}]
a_n, b_n	Mie scattering coefficients
a_{lw}, a_{sw}	longwave, shortwave absorptivity
$\bar{a}$	graybody absorptivity
a_λ	monochromatic (spectral) absorptivity
A	albedo
A	area [m^2]
$\mathcal{A}$	band-averaged absorption (equals $1 - \mathcal{T}$)
b	backscatter fraction (as used in two-stream solution)
B	occasionally, shorthand for B_λ
B	rotational constant (in quantum rotational transitions) [Hz]
$\bar{B}$	average of Planck function over a spectral interval
B_λ, B_ν	Planck function, expressed as function of wavelength [W m^{-2}sr$^{-1}\mu$m^{-1}] or frequency [W m^{-2}sr^{-1}Hz^{-1}]
$\vec{B}$	magnetic induction [T]
c	speed of light in a vacuum; see Appendix D
c'	speed of light in a medium [m s^{-1}]
c_p	specific heat capacity of air at constant pressure; see Appendix D
C	heat capacity [J K^{-1}]

438

dBZ	radar reflectivity factor Z expressed in decibels relative to one standard unit
D	distance [m]
D	drop diameter [m]
D	penetration depth [m]
D_m	distance between the earth and moon; see Appendix D
D_s	distance between the earth and sun; see Appendix D
$\vec{D}$	electric displacement [C m^2]
E	energy (e.g., of a photon) [J]
E	scalar amplitude of electric field
E_{bond}	chemical binding energy [J]
E_{kr}	rotational kinetic energy [J]
E_{kt}	translational kinetic energy [J]
$\vec{E}, \vec{E}_c$	electric field; complex electric field [V m^{-1}]
$\vec{E}_0$	electric field associated with the incident wave
$\vec{E}_{scat}$	electric field associated with a scattered wave
$f(\nu - \nu_0)$	line shape function for a line centered on frequency ν_0 [Hz^{-1}]
$f_D(\nu - \nu_0)$	Doppler line shape [Hz^{-1}]
F	force [N]
F	flux density (a.k.a. flux, irradiance, exitance) [W m^{-2}]
F_0	incident flux (e.g., at the top of the atmosphere) [W m^{-2}]
F_i, F_r	incident, reflected flux [W m^{-2}]
F_λ	spectral (monochromatic) flux [W m$^{-2}\mu$m^{-1}]
F_{BB}	flux emitted by a perfect blackbody, equal to σT^4 [W m^{-2}]
F^{net}	net flux (broadband), defined as $F^\uparrow - F^\downarrow$ [W m^{-2}]
$F^\uparrow, F^\downarrow$	upward-, downward-directed flux (broadband) through a horizontal plane [W m^{-2}]
$F_\lambda^\uparrow, F_\lambda^\downarrow$	monochromatic counterparts to $F^\uparrow, F^\downarrow$ [W m$^{-2}\mu$m^{-1}]
g	acceleration due to gravity; see Appendix D
g	the scattering asymmetry parameter
$g(k)$	cumulative distribution function of k (as used in k-distribution method)
h	Planck's constant; see Appendix D
H	depth or altitude [m]
H	scale height [m]
$\vec{H}, \vec{H}_c$	magnetic field; complex magnetic field [A m^{-1}]
$\mathcal{H}$	local heating rate [K s^{-1}]
I	moment of inertia [kg m^2]
I	radiant intensity (or radiance) [W m^{-2}sr^{-1}]
$I^\uparrow, I^\downarrow$	intensity associated with radiation having an upward, downward component

$\mathbf{I}$	Stoke's vector
I_1, I_2, I_3	principle moments of inertia [kg m^2]
I_λ	spectral (monochromatic) intensity [W m^{-2}sr$^{-1}\mu$m^{-1}]
I_s	average intensity of the sun's disk [W m^{-2}sr$^{-1}\mu$m^{-1}]
$\Im(x)$	imaginary part of x
J	rotational quantum number
$J(\hat{\Omega})$	source function for radiation traveling in direction $\hat{\Omega}$
$\vec{J}$	electric current vector [A m^{-2}]
k	absorption coefficient (as used in k-distribution method)
k_s, k_a, k_e	mass scattering, absorption, extinction coefficients [m^{2}kg^{-1}]
$k(g)$	inverse of $g(k)$
k_B	Boltzmann's constant; see Appendix D
k_W	Wien's constant; see Appendix D
$\vec{k}$	wave propagation vector [m^{-1}]
$\vec{k}'$	real part of $\vec{k}$
$\vec{k}''$	imaginary part of $\vec{k}$
L	angular momentum [J s]
L	cloud liquid water path (vertically integrated cloud water density) [kg m^{-2}]
L	latent heat of vaporization of water ; see Appendix D
L_f	latent heat of fusion/melting/freezing (of water); see Appendix D
m	relative index of refraction (complex)
m	mass [kg]
m'	reduced mass (in the calculation of a moment of inertia) [kg]
$n(r)$	drop size distribution [m^{-3} μm^{-1}]
n_r, n_i	real, imaginary parts of N
$\hat{n}$	unit normal vector
N	concentration of particles [m^{-3}]
N	index of refraction (complex)
N_0	intercept parameter of an exponential size distribution [m^{-3} μm^{-1}]
N_A	Avogadro's number; see Appendix D
$\mathcal{N}$	rate of incident photons [m^{-2} s^{-1}]
p	air pressure [Pa]
p	momentum [kg m s^{-1}]
$\bar{p}$	effective pressure (in a band transmittance model applied to an inhomogeneous path) [Pa]
$\vec{p}$	electric dipole moment [C m]
$p(\Theta)$	scattering phase function (unpolarized) as function of scattering angle Θ only

$p(S)$	distribution of line strengths
$p(\hat{\Omega}', \hat{\Omega})$	scattering phase function (unpolarized) for arbitrary combinations of incoming and scattered directions
p_0	standard sea level pressure; see Appendix D
$p_{HG}(\Theta)$	the Henyey-Greenstein phase function model
P	power [W]
$\mathbf{P}(\hat{\Omega}', \hat{\Omega})$	scattering phase matrix for fully polarized scattering calculations
Q	second element of Stoke's vector
Q_b	backscatter efficiency
Q_s, Q_a, Q_e	scattering, absorption, extinction efficiencies
r	reflectivity
r_{eff}	effective cloud drop radius [m]
r_λ	monochromatic (spectral) reflectivity
$\bar{r}$	graybody reflectivity
r_∞	parameter in two-stream solution
R	rainfall rate; typically [mm/hr]
R, r	radius (e.g., of a sphere, disk, droplet, etc.) [m]
R_E	mean radius of the earth; see Appendix D
R_d	gas constant for dry air; see Appendix D
R_m	radius of the moon; see Appendix D
R_p, R_s	Fresnel reflectivity for radiation polarized parallel, perpendicular to plane of reflection
R_s	radius of the sun; see Appendix D
R_v, R_h	Fresnel reflectivity for vertically, horizontally polarized radiation (for reflection from a horizontal surface, $R_v = R_p, R_h = R_s$)
R_{normal}	Fresnel reflectivity at normal incidence
$\Re(x)$	real part of x
s	geometric distance along an optical path [m]
S	actual solar flux at TOA (depends on solar output and orbital distance) [W m^{-2}]
S	line strength; units depend on context
$\bar{S}$	mean line strength
$\vec{\mathbf{S}}$	Poynting vector [W m^{-2}]
S_0	solar "constant"; i.e., the long-term average solar flux (normal to the beam) at TOA; see Appendix D
S_λ	solar intensity (spectral) [W m^{-2} μm^{-1}]
T	temperature (absolute, except where noted) [K]
T	torque [N m]
T_a	air temperature (e.g., in an isothermal atmosphere) [K]
T_B	brightness temperature [K]
T_E	radiative equilibrium temperature [K]

T_s	surface temperature [K]
TOA	top of the atmosphere
t	time [s]
t	transmittance
t_{diff}	diffuse transmittance
t_{dir}	direct transmittance
$t_F(z_1, z_2)$	flux transmittance (monochromatic) between levels z_1, z_2.
t^*	total atmospheric transmittance
$\mathcal{T}$	band transmittance in a spectral band of finite width
U	wind speed [m s^{-1}]
U	third element of Stoke's vector
$\mathbf{U}$	the four-element vector $(1, 0, 0, 0)$
u	mass path (integrated density) between two points [kg m^{-2}]
$\bar{u}$	effective mass path, as used in a band transmittance model applied to an inhomogeneous path [kg m^{-2}]
$\tilde{u}$	non-dimensional mass path
u_{tot}	total mass path, usually measured vertically through the atmosphere [kg m^{-2}]
V	fourth element of Stoke's vector
V	water vapor path (vertically integrated water vapor density) [kg m^{-2}]
v	speed [m s^{-1}]
v	vibrational quantum number
w	constituent mixing ratio
W	equivalent width of one or more absorption lines in a spectral interval (units depend on context)
W	total insolation at a location over a 24-hour period [J m^{-2}]
$W(z)$	emission/absorption weighting function [m^{-1}]
$W^\uparrow(z)$, $W^\downarrow(z)$	Emission/absorption weighting functions with respect to upward intensities seen from TOA, downward intensities seen from the bottom of the atmosphere [m^{-1}]
$W_F^\uparrow(z)$, $W_F^\downarrow(z)$	Same as $W^\uparrow(z)$, $W^\downarrow(z)$, but for fluxes instead of intensities [m^{-1}]
x	general position coordinate [m]
x	normalized position relative to center of a sphere
x	size parameter of a spherical particle, defined as $2\pi r/\lambda$
x	wavenumber parameter (in a band transmittance model)
$\vec{x}$	position vector [m]
y	"grayness" parameter (in a band transmittance model)
z	height or altitude [m]
Z	radar reflectivity factor, typically [mm^6 m^{-3}]
Z_e	effective (apparent) radar reflectivity factor [mm^6 m^{-3}]

α	electric polarizability (complex) of a particle [C m^2 V^{-1}]
α_0	Lorentz linewidth parameter at standard temperature and pressure [Hz]
α_D	Doppler linewidth parameter [Hz]
α_L	Lorentz linewidth parameter [Hz]
$\alpha_{1/2}$	half-width at half-maximum (for an absorption line) [Hz]
$\beta_s, \beta_a, \beta_e$	volume scattering, absorption, extinction coefficients [m^{-1}]
Γ	atmospheric temperature lapse rate [K m^{-1}]
Γ	parameter in two-stream solution
γ	angle between $\vec{E}_0$ and the scattered direction $\hat{\Omega}'$
ΔT	change of temperature [K]
$\delta(x)$	Dirac δ-function
ε	emissivity
ε_λ	monochromatic (spectral) emissivity
$\varepsilon_v, \varepsilon_h$	emissivity for vertically, horizontally polarized radiation
ϵ_{av}	effectivity dielectric "constant" of a heterogeneous mixture
ϵ	dielectric "constant" (complex; equal to N^2)
ϵ', ϵ''	real, imaginary parts of ϵ
ε	electric permittivity [F m^{-1}]
ε_0	electric permittivity of free space [F m^{-1}]
η	backscatter cross-section per unit volume of air [m^{-1}]
Θ	scattering angle (angle between incident and scattered ray)
Θ	angle of scattered radiation relative to incident direction
Θ_0	critical angle (e.g., for total internal reflection); rainbow angle
Θ_B	Brewster angle
$\Theta_i, \Theta_r, \Theta_t$	angle of incident, reflected, transmitted rays, relative to local normal
θ	zenith angle
θ_s	solar zenith angle
Λ	slope parameter of an exponential size distribution [m^{-1}]
λ	wavelength [m]
λ_{max}	wavelength of maximum emission [m]
μ	magnetic permeability [H m^{-1}]
μ	$\cos(\theta)$ or $|\cos(\theta)|$
μ_0	magnetic permeability of free space [H m^{-1}]
$\overline{\mu}$	effective μ value for which beam transmittance equals flux transmittance
ν	frequency [Hz]
$\tilde{\nu}$	wavenumber [m^{-1}]

ρ	density [kg m^{-3}]
ρ	electric charge density [C m^{-3}]
$\rho(\theta_i, \phi_i; \theta_r, \phi_r)$	bidirectional reflectance function (BDRF)
ρ_a	density of air [kg m^{-3}]
ρ_l	density of pure water [kg m^{-3}]
ρ_w	cloud water density [kg m^{-3}]
σ	Stefan-Boltzmann constant; see Appendix D
σ	electric conductivity [S m^{-1}]
σ_b	backscatter cross-section [m^{-2}]
$\sigma_s, \sigma_a, \sigma_e$	scattering, absorption, extinction cross-sections [m^{-2}]
τ	optical thickness, optical depth, or optical path
τ'	similarity-transformed (scaled) optical depth
τ^*	total atmospheric (or cloud) optical depth
$\tau^{*'}$	similarity-transformed (scaled) total optical depth
Φ	azimuthal scattering angle (angle between scattering plane and an arbitrary reference plan that includes the incident ray)
ϕ	azimuthal angle
χ	electric susceptibility
$\hat{\Omega}$	unit vector indicating direction of propagation
$\hat{\Omega}_i, \hat{\Omega}_r$	unit vectors describing directions of incident, reflected rays
ω	angular frequency [s^{-1}]
$\tilde{\omega}$	single scatter albedo (defined as β_s / β_e)
$\tilde{\omega}'$	similarity-transformed (scaled) single scatter albedo

APPENDIX C

Further Reading

Some of the following textbooks offer more detailed treatments of many of the topics introduced here, as well as providing comprehensive bibliographies. Others give the broader meteorological or climatological context for studies of atmospheric radiation. The keys appearing at the beginning of each entry below are used to cite these works throughout this book.

BH83 Bohren, C.F., and D.R. Huffman, 1983: *Absorption and Scattering of Light by Small Particles* (paperback). Wiley-Interscience, New York, 536 pp. (ISBN 0-47-129340-7)

FB80 Fleagle, R.G., and J.A. Businger, 1980: *An Introduction to Atmospheric Physics.* Academic Press, San Diego, 432 pp. (ISBN 0-12-260355-9)

GY95 Goody, R.M. and Y.L. Yung, 1995: *Atmospheric Radiation: Theoretical Basis* (2nd ed., paperback). Oxford University Press, New York, 544 pp. (ISBN 0-19-510291-6)

H94 Hartmann, D.L., 1994: *Global Physical Climatology.* Academic Press, San Diego, 411 pp. (ISBN 0-12-328530-5)

L02 Liou, K.-N., 2002: *Introduction to Atmospheric Radiation* (2nd Ed.). Academic Press, San Diego, 583 pp. (ISBN 0-12-451451-0)

S94 Stephens, G.L., 1994: *Remote Sensing of the Lower Atmosphere: An Introduction.* Oxford University Press, New York, 523 pp. (ISBN 0-19-508188-9)

TS02 Thomas, G. and K. Stamnes, 2002: *Radiative Transfer in the Atmosphere and Ocean.* (paperback) Cambridge University Press, Cambridge, UK, 517 pp. (ISBN 0-52-189061-6)

WH77 Wallace, J.M., and P.V. Hobbs, 1977: *Atmospheric Science: An Introductory Survey.* Academic Press, San Diego, 467 pp. (ISBN 0-12-732950-1)

Useful Physical and Astronomical Constants

Universal constants

Avogadro's number (N_A)	6.022×10^{23} mole^{-1}
Boltzmann's constant (k_B)	1.381×10^{-23} J K^{-1}molecule^{-1}
Magnetic permeability of free space (μ_0)	1.257×10^{-6} N A^{-2}
Permittivity of free space (ε_0)	8.854×10^{-12} F m^{-1}
Planck's constant (h)	6.626×10^{-34} J s
Speed of light (c)	2.998×10^8 m s^{-1}
Stefan-Boltzmann constant (σ)	5.670×10^{-8} W m^{-2} K^{-4}
Wien's constant (k_W)	2897 μm K

Astronomical constants

Mean distance, sun to earth (D_s)	1.496×10^8 km
Mean distance, earth to moon (D_m)	3.84×10^5 km
Mean radius of the earth (R_E)	6373 km
Mean radius of the moon (R_m)	1740 km
Mean radius of the sun's photosphere (R_s)	6.96×10^5 km
Mean solar flux at TOA (S_0)	1370 W m^{-2}
Gravitational acceleration (g)	9.81 m s^{-2}

Air and water

Average sea level pressure (p_0)	1.013×10^5 Pa
Dry air gas constant (R_d)	287 J kg^{-1} K^{-1}
Specific heat capacity, dry air (c_p)	1004 J kg^{-1} K^{-1}
Latent heat of fusion, ice (L_f)	3.34×10^5 J kg^{-1}
Latent heat of vaporization, water (L)	2.50×10^6 J kg^{-1}

Index

Absorptance, *see also* Absorptivity
  in cloud, 195
  optical path, 163
Absorption
  band-averaged, 288, 289
  exponential atmosphere, 190–193
  weighting function, 190–193
Absorption coefficient, 76, 155
  homogeneous medium, 30
  mass, 167–169
    small particle, 356–358
  volume, 167–169
    mixtures, 168–169
Absorption cross-section, 167–169
Absorption efficiency, 167–169
  small particle, 354–355
  spheres, 363–364
Absorption index, 76
Absorptivity, 98–99
Adding-doubling method, 425–426
Advanced Microwave Sounding Unit (AMSU), 231
Aerosols
  extinction efficiency, 362
  indirect cooling by, 199–200
  properties, abundance, 184, 199, 344
Albedo, 101, *see also* Reflectivity, Reflectance
  clouds, *see* Clouds, radiative properties
  natural surfaces, 102

  planetary, 137, 142
  shortwave, 132
Atmosphere
  composition, 176
  emission spectra, 219–228
  emissivity of, 211–212
  transmission spectrum, 174–185
    microwave, 181
Atmospheric heating/cooling
  cooling-to-space approximation, 312
  equations, 306–312
  examples
    longwave, 316–319
    shortwave, 314–316
Azimuthal angle, 36

Band transmission
  isolated line, 288–293
    equivalent width, 288–292
    Lorentz line, 290–292
    square line, 289–290
    strong line limit, 291–292
    weak line limit, 289
  models, 284–299
    comparison, 298
    defining, 293–294
    Elsasser, 294–297
    HCG approximation, 298–299
    random/Malkmus, 297–298
Bands, spectral, 57–67
  and diabatic heating, 60
  and photochemistry, 60

and remote sensing, 60
gamma rays and X-rays, 61
infrared, 64–66
microwave, 66–67
radio, 66–67
ultraviolet, 61–63
visible, 63–64
BDRF, *see* Bidirectional reflection function
Beer's law, 78, 161, 286
    as limiting case, 296, 298
Beer-Bouguer-Lambert law, 78, *see* Beer's law
Bidirectional reflection function (BDRF), 105–107, 111, 112
    and remote sensing, 110–111
    sun glint, 111
Blackbody, 115–117
Blackbody emission, 115–123
    broadband flux, 122
Blueing, 361
Boltzmann's constant, 118
Boundary layer
    daytime heating of, 23
    marine, 148
BRDF, *see* Bidirectional reflection function
Brewster angle, 89, 90
Brightness temperature, 127–130, 383
    in IR images, 148–150
    in satellite images
        diurnal variation, 150
    microwave, 128
    ocean, 152–153
Broadband radiation
    definition, 19
Bruggeman dielectric mixing formula, 81

Carbon dioxide
    15 μm band, 180, 221, 224, 274–277, 311
    4.3 μm band, 180, 275
    absorption in near IR, 180
    as greenhouse gas, 65, 142
    atmospheric abundance, 176, 177
    dipole moment, 251

in Martian atmosphere, 70
    IR absorption spectrum, 272–277
    molecular structure, 247
Carbon monoxide
    atmospheric abundance, 176
    IR absorption spectrum, 272
    molecular structure, 247
CCN, *see* Cloud condensation nuclei
CFCs, *see* Chlorofluorocarbons
Chapman layer, 192
Chlorofluorocarbons (CFCs)
    and ozone depletion, 73
    as greenhouse gas, 65
    atmospheric abundance, 176
    molecular structure, 247
Cloud
    extinction coefficient, 197
Cloud condensation nuclei (CCN), 199
Cloud droplets
    asymmetry parameter, 374
    effective radius, 202–203
    extinction efficiency, 363
    monodisperse vs. polydisperse, 196
    number concentration, 344
    single scatter albedo, 374–376
    size distribution, 200–203, 372
    typical sizes, 194
Cloud water
    microwave extinction coefficient, 382
    microwave remote sensing, 153, 358, 382–386
Clouds
    as contaminant in satellite measurements, 150
    effective radius
        remote sensing, 376
    in IR images, 149
    radiative properties, 373–376
        albedo, 195, 401–403, 407, 409
        dependence on drop size, 375
        dependence on phase, 375
        diffuse transmittance, 412–414
        direct transmittance, 194–200
        flux and heating profiles, 404–405

general case, 408–414
multiple layers, 423–424
non-absorbing, 406–408
optical thickness, 194–203
over non-black surfaces, 418–422
semi-infinite, 400–405
transmittance, 407–409, 412–416
Collision broadening, see Pressure broadening
Color and wavelength, 63
Color temperature, 121
Conductivity, electric, 25
Continuum absorption, 267–270, 282
water vapor, 269–270, 316, 318
microwave, 182
Cooling to space, 311
as approximation, 312
Corona, 370–371
Cosmic rays, 61
Crepuscular rays, 370
Cross-section
absorption, 167–169
extinction, 166–169
scattering, 167–169

Dew formation, 144–146
Diamond, refraction and reflection by, 89
Dielectric constant, 79–82
effective, 81–82
of heterogeneous mixtures, 80–82
relationship to index of refraction, 79–80
Dipole radiation, 347–351
Discrete ordinates method, 425
Doppler broadening, 261–263
compared with pressure broadening, 266–267
Doppler effect, 17–18, 262
Doppler wind profilers, 67

Eddington approximation, 424
Effective emitting temperature
Sun, 122
top of atmosphere, 137
El Niño, 150
Electric charge density, 24, 25

Electric conductivity, 25
Electric current vector, 24
Electric displacement, 24
Electric field, 24
Electromagnetic radiation
absorption of, 29–30
coherent and incoherent, 19–21
electric, magnetic fields, 11–12
energy, 22–23
frequency, 16–18, 56–57
mathematical description, 24–30
Maxwell's equations, 24–26
monochromatic and broadband, 19
phase speed
and reflection, refraction, 75
in a medium, 76
polarization, 20–22
circular, 20
degree of, 22
elliptical, 21
linear, 20
neglect of, 22
properties, 11–36
quantum properties, 31–33
quasi-monochromatic, 19
wavelength, 16–18, 56–57
wavenumber, 57
waves, 13–30
homogeneous, 26, 28
phase speed, 27–28
plane, 26–28
time-harmonic solution, 25–26
Emission, 113–115
infrared spectra of earth, atmosphere, 129
weighting function, 207–210
when it matters, 130–132
Emissivity, 123–125
graybody, 124–125
in IR images, 148
longwave, 132
microwave, 128
land and ocean, 151–153
polarization dependence, 152
wind speed dependence, 152–153

monochromatic, 124
Equilibrium temperature
    Earth's surface, 142
    moon's surface, 133, 134
    of sphere, 134–136
Equinox, 51
Error function, 296
Exitance, radiant, 23, *see also* Flux
Extinction
    absorption vs. scattering, 157
    by aerosols and clouds, 184–185
    classroom demonstration, 156–158
    extended path, 161–163
    infinitesimal path, 160–161
Extinction coefficient, 156, 158
    in cloud, 197
    mass, 163–165, 167–169
    scattering plus absorption, 159
    volume, 164, 167–169
        mixtures, 168–169
        size distributions, 201, 372
Extinction cross-section, 165–169
Extinction efficiency, 166–169
    absorbing sphere, 363–365
    nonabsorbing sphere, 359–363
        limiting value, 359
    small particle, 354–355
Extinction law, 78, *see* Beer's law
Extinction paradox, 166–167, 370, 430–431, 435

Far infrared, *see also* Infrared radiation
    absorption by water vapor, 180
Flux, 23, 33–35
    absorbed, 99
    and photons, 31
    broadband, 34
    monochromatic, 34, 212–215
        transmittance, 213, 283
        typical units, 34
        weighting function, 213
    net
        and heating profile, 284, 306–308
        definition, 47
    reflected, 99
    relationship to intensity, 36, 46–48
        for isotropic intensity, 47
        general, 47
        spectral, 34
Flux density, 23, 29, 33, *see also* Flux
Fogbow, 372
Forward diffraction peak, 365, 368, 370, 429, 430
    truncation of, 431–433
Fourier decomposition, 18
Frequency, 16–18, 56–57, 69
    decomposition, 18–19
Fresnel relations, 86, 92, 96, 152
Frost formation, 114, 144–146

GCM, *see* General circulation models
General circulation models (GCMs), 143, 284
Geometric optics, 430
    and extinction paradox, *see* Extinction paradox
    and rainbow, halo, 90
    as alternative to Mie theory, 359
Gigahertz (GHz), definition, 66
Global energy budget, 6–7
Global heat engine, 4–6
Global warming, 142
    countered by aerosols, 200
Glory, 368, 371
Graybody approximation, 100–101, 132
Grayness parameter, 295
Greenhouse effect, 142
Greenhouse gases, 65, 142

Halo, 94
HITRAN spectroscopic data base, 280
Hydroxyl radical (OH), 72–73

Ice
    index of refraction, 76, 77
    microwave emissivity, 128
Ice crystals, 95
Ideal gas law, 169
Index of refraction, 28
    and phase speed, 28
    complex, 28, 75
    imaginary part, 76–78
        relationship to absorption coefficient, 30

Kramer-Kronig relations, 75
  of air, 76
  of ice, 76, 77
  of water, 76, 77
  real part, 76
  relative, 87, 346
Infrared
  spectral window, 148, 180
Infrared (IR) radiation, 64–66
  and greenhouse gases, 65
  atmospheric absorbers, 270–279
  atmospheric absorption, 180
  atmospheric transmission spectrum, 179
  far IR band, 66
  near IR band, 65–66
  significance for energy exchange, 64, 65
  thermal IR band, 66
Infrared radiation
  thermal
    significance of, 3, 68
Insolation
  daily average, 52
  global, 49–50
  regional and seasonal, 50–52
Intensity, 33, 35–48
  and polarization, 43–45
  as Stokes vector, 44
  conservation of, 42–43
  formal definition, 41–42
  relationship to flux, 36, 46–48
    for isotropic intensity, 47
    general, 47
  scalar, 43
IR radiation, see Infrared radiation
Irradiance, 23, see also Flux

k-distribution method, 284–286, 299–305
  correlated-k, 303–305
Kirchhoff's law, 115, 125–127, 132

Lambertian reflection, 103–106
  in radiative transfer equation, 216–217
Latent heat flux, 108
Legendre polynomials, 427–429

expansion of phase function, 427–430
Lightning detection systems, 67
Line strength, 261
Line strength distribution models, 294
Line-by-line (LBL) calculations, 281–284
Local thermodynamic equilibrium (LTE), 126–127, 238–239
Longwave radiation, 113, see also Infrared (IR) radiation
  separation from shortwave, 131
Lorentz line shape, 263–265
LTE, see Local thermodynamic equilibrium

Magnetic field, 24
Magnetic induction, 24
Magnetic permeability, 24
  of free space, 28
Marine haze
  scattering phase function, 332
Mass absorption coefficient, see Absorption coefficient, mass
Mass extinction coefficient, see Extinction coefficient, mass
Mass path, 189, 288
  nondimensional, 290
Mass scattering coefficient, see Scattering coefficient, mass
Maxwell Garnett dielectric mixing formula, 81
Maxwell's equations, 24–26
Methane
  absorption in near IR, 180
  as greenhouse gas, 65
  atmospheric abundance, 176
  IR absorption spectrum, 278–279
  molecular structure, 247
Microwave imaging
  transparency of clouds, 382
Microwave radiation, 66–67
  atmospheric transmission, 180–182, 384
  brightness temperature, 128
Microwave radiometers, 382–383
Microwave remote sensing, 67, 128, 151–154, see also Remote sens-

ing, microwave
resolution, 153
transparency of clouds, 151
Mie theory, 358–372
    absorption efficiency, 363–364
    asymmetry parameter, 364–365
    extinction efficiency, 358–365
    forward diffraction peak, 365, 368,
       370
    phase function, 365–372
    scattering coefficients, 358
    scattering efficiency, 358
    series truncation, 359
    single scatter albedo, 363–364
Model atmospheres, 312–314
Molecular absorption and emission
    combined transitions, 258
    continuum, 267–270
    electronic transitions, 256–258
    line positions, 240–242
    line shape, 258–267
        Doppler broadened, 261–263
        pressure broadened, 263–266
        van Vleck-Weisskopf, 265
        Voigt, 267
    physical basis, 238–239
    rotation spectra, 249–250
    rotational transitions, 243–251
    transition types, 242
    vibration modes, 254–256
    vibration/rotation spectra, 253–
       254
    vibrational transitions, 251–256
Molecular scattering
    polarization, 353
    transmission spectrum, 183–184
Molecules
    dipole moment, 250–251
    moments of inertia, 243–247
    quantized angular momentum, 247–
       248
Monochromatic radiation, 19
Monte Carlo model, 392, 425
μ, definition, 171, 325
Mueller matrix, 45

Net flux

and atmospheric heating, 306–308
    definition, 47
Nitrogen
    atmospheric abundance, 176
    lack of dipole moment, 251
    molecular structure, 247
Nitrogen oxides, 71
Nitrous oxide
    absorption in near IR, 180
    atmospheric abundance, 176
    IR absorption spectrum, 279
    molecular structure, 247
Number density (of particles), 166

OLR, see Outgoing longwave radiation
Optical depth, 161, see Optical thickness
    δ-scaled, 434
    as vertical coordinate, 173–174
    exponential atmosphere, 189
    similarity transformed, 417
Optical path, 161
    additive property, 162
    constant extinction coefficient, 162
Optical thickness, 172, see also Optical
      depth
    clouds, 194–203
Outgoing longwave radiation (OLR),
     136, 137
    zonally averaged, 4
Oxygen
    118 GHz band, 181, 384
    60 GHz band, 181, 231, 384
    atmospheric abundance, 176
    binding energy of, 32
    dipole moment, 251
    molecular structure, 247
    photodissociation of, 32, 69
Ozone
    9.6 μm band, 180, 222, 278
    as pollutant, 71–72
    atmospheric abundance, 176
    formation of, 69
    importance for heating profiles,
      314–318
    IR absorption spectrum, 277–278
    molecular structure, 247
Ozone layer, 60, 62, 69–70

and atmospheric temperature structure, 70
depletion of, 70

P-, Q-, R-branches, 254
Parhelia, 94
Particles
atmospheric, 344–345
nonspherical, 347
physical properties, 345–347
size distributions, 372–373
size parameter, 345
Penetration depth, 78
water, ice, 78
Permittivity
in a medium, 26
of free space, 24, 28
relative, 79
Peroxyacetyl nitrate (PAN), 71
Phase function, 323, 326–332
δ-scaling, 430–436
compared with similarity trans-
formation, 434
asymmetry parameter, 329–332
Henyey-Greenstein, 330–332
double, 332
isotropic, 327–329
Legendre polynomial expansion,
427–430
marine haze, 332
normalization, 323, 327
Rayleigh, 330
relation to phase matrix, 359
size distributions, 373
spheres, 365–372
Photochemistry, 60
and air pollution, 60, 70–72
Photodissociation, 32, 268–269
of oxygen, 32, 69
Photoelectric effect, 31
Photoionization, 268
Photon, 31
energy, 31–32
Planck's constant, 31, 118
Planck's function, 114, 117–120, 127, 131
as function of frequency, 119
physical dimensions, 118

Plane parallel approximation, 169–174
and Earth's curvature, 170
validity for atmosphere, 169
validity for clouds, 170
Planetary albedo, 137, 142
Polarization, 16, 20–22, see also Electromagnetic radiation, polariza-
tion
and microwave emissivity, 152
and Rayleigh scattering, 351–354
and reflectivity, 87–90
in radiative transfer equation, 324
Stokes representation, 43–45
vertical and horizontal, 88
Polarized sunglasses, 22, 89, 353
Poynting vector, 28–29
Precipitable water, 151
Pressure broadening, 263–266
compared with Doppler broadening, 266–267

Quantum number
rotational, 248–250
vibrational, 252, 254–256

Radar, 17, 21, 67, 151, 358, 376–382
backscatter cross-section, 376
backscatter efficiency, 377
dependence on phase, 378
hailstones, 378
raindrops, 378
Rayleigh, 378
equivalent reflectivity factor, 380
operation, 376
reflectivity factor, 379
Radiance, 33, see Intensity
Radiant intensity, 33, see Intensity
Radiation budget, 132–148
Radiation, ionizing, 61
Radiative cooling
atmosphere, see Atmospheric heat-
ing/cooling
cloud top, 146–148
surface, 144–146
Radiative equilibrium, 132
in vacuum, 133–136
of Earth, 136–138
of sphere, 134–136

on moon, 133–134
two-layer system, 139–144
Radiative transfer
    as diabatic process, 1–2
    relevance for climate and weather,
        1–7
    relevance for remote sensing, 7–10
Radiative transfer equation
    azimuthally averaged, 392–393
    Lambertian lower boundary, 216–
        217
    polarized, 324
    simplified for microwave radiome-
        ter, 384
    single scattering, 333–336
    specular lower boundary, 215–216
    with absorption and emission, 206
        plane parallel, 210–211
    with absorption and scattering,
        388
    with extinction only, 161
    with scattering, 322–326
        plane parallel, 324–326
    with source function, 323
Radio band, 66–67
    and remote sensing, 67
Rain rate
    Marshall-Palmer size distribution,
        381
    microwave remote sensing, 153
    radar estimation, 376–382
    Z–R relationship, 381
Rainbow, 55, 75, 91–94
    from Mie theory, 368, 372
    primary, 92
    secondary, 94
Ray tracing, 90, see also Geometric optics
Rayleigh-Jeans approximation, 123, 128,
        152, 382
Reddening, 361–363
Reflectance, 195, see also Albedo, Reflec-
        tivity
Reflection, 75
    angle, 82–84
    critical angle, 85
    homogeneous medium, 82–90
    Lambertian, 103–106

specular, 83, 102, 105
    total, 85
    water surfaces, 103
Reflectivity, 98–99, see also Albedo, Re-
        flectance
    directional dependence, 102–107
    homogeneous medium, 86–90
    natural surfaces, 99–100
    normal incidence, 88
    of water, 88–89
    polarization dependence, 87–90
Refraction, 75
    angle (Snell's law), 84–85
    homogeneous medium, 82–90
Remote sensing, 7–10, 60, see also Satel-
        lite
    active and passive, 151
    humidity profiles, 235
    infrared, 128
    microwave, 22, 67, 88, 128, 151–154
        cloud water, 153, 358, 382–386
        rain rate, 153
        snow, 153
        water vapor, 153, 384–386
    ocean wind speed, 152–153
    radio band, 67
    satellite, 8–10
    sea surface temperature, 150–153
    split window method, 151
    sung lint, 132
    temperature profiles, 130, 228–233
    water vapor, 151
Retroreflective beads, 371

Satellite, see also Remote sensing
    images, 8–10
        clouds, 149, 150
        infrared, 8–10, 111–112, 148–151
        microwave, 151–154
        visible, 8, 64, 109–112
        water vapor, 9–10, 233–235
    infrared spectra, 129
    surface classification, 112
Scattering, 156
    as source, 320–321
    by aerosols, 184–185, 337–338
    by clouds, 184–185

clear air, 183–184
   multiple, 387–392
      visualizing, 389–392
   Rayleigh, 347–358
      frequency dependence, 351, 356
      phase function, 351–353
      polarization, 353–354
      single and multiple, 332–333
Scattering coefficient
   mass, 167–169
   volume, 167–169
      mixtures, 168–169
      size distributions, 373
Scattering cross-section, 167–169
   small particle, 355–357
Scattering efficiency, 167–169
   small particle, 354–355
Scattering phase matrix, 324, 359
Scattering, isotropic, 327–329
Schwarzschild's equation, 205–206
Sea surface temperature
   from IR images, 150–151
Semi-infinite cloud
   as approximation, 414–416
   flux and heating profiles, 404–405
   radiative properties of, 400–405
Sensible heat flux, 108
Shortwave radiation, *see also* Solar radiation
   ation
   separation from longwave, 131
Similarity transformations, 416–417
   compared with δ-scaling, 434
Single scatter albedo, 159, 167
   δ-scaled, 434
   clouds, 375–376
      dependence on drop size, 375
      dependence on phase, 375
   mixtures, 169
   similarity transformed, 416
   size distributions, 373
   small particle, 355–356
   spheres, 363–364
Single scattering co-albedo, 375
Size parameter, 345
Skylight
   blue sky, 337, 358

from single-scatter approximation, 336–338
Slab geometry, *see* Plane parallel approximation
Smog, photochemical, 70–72
Snell's law, 84–85, 91, 96
Solar constant, 134
Solar heating
   atmosphere, 311
   surface, 107–108
Solar radiation
   absorbed, 49
      by snow, 108
      globally averaged, 136
      zonally averaged, 4
   at top of atmosphere, 49
      indirect measurement, 185–187
   atmospheric heating, 311
   in clouds, 387–389
   infrared, 2, 65–66
   non-overlap with terrestrial radiation, 68
   significance of, 2–3, 68
   spectrum of, 64
   ultraviolet, 3, 61–63
   visible, 63–64
   wavelength range of, 68
Solid angle, 37–41
Solstice, 51
Source function, 323
Spectral window, 148, 182
   "dirty", 183, 221
Spectrometer, 219
Specular reflection, 83, 102, 105
   in radiative transfer equation, 215–216
Speed of light, 28, 76
   in nonvacuum, 28
   in vacuum, 28
Spherical polar coordinates, 36–37
Split window method, 151
Stefan-Boltzmann law, 115, 122, 125
Steradian, 37–41
Stokes parameters, 44, 324
Stratocumulus, 146–148
   albedo, 408

microwave brightness temperature, 386
Successive orders of scattering, 425–426
Sun
    color temperature, 121
    effective emitting temperature, 122
Sun glint, 111, 132
Sundogs, 94, see Parhelia
Susceptibility, 24

Terrestrial radiation, 68, see also Infrared (IR) radiation
    non-overlap with solar radiation, 68
Thermal emission, see Emission
Thermal infrared radiation, see Infrared radiation, Longwave radiation
Transmissivity, see Transmittance
Transmittance, 78, 161–163
    band-averaged, 286
    diffuse, 195, 392, 412
    direct, 194, 412
    exponential atmosphere, 187–194
    monochromatic flux, 213
    multiplicative property, 78, 162
    plane parallel, 172, 174
    small optical path, 162
Two-stream method, 388, 392–400
    backscatter fraction, 396–397
    boundary conditions, 400
    solution, 398–400
    two-stream approximation, 393–394
    two-stream equations, 395–396

Ultraviolet (UV) radiation, 61–63
    absorption by oxygen and ozone, 69, 178
    as ozone source, 69–70
    biological hazards of, 62, 70
    significance of, 62–63
    UV-A, 62, 70
        and tropospheric chemistry, 71
    UV-B, 62, 69–70
    UV-C, 62, 69–70

van Vleck-Weisskopf line shape, 265

Visibility, 338–342
Visible radiation, 63–64
    contribution to solar output, 63
    reflectivity of clouds for, 63
    transmission spectrum, 179, 183
    transparency of atmosphere to, 63
Voigt line shape, 267
Volatile organic compounds (VOC), 71
Volume absorption coefficient, see Absorption coefficient
Volume extinction coefficient, see Extinction coefficient
Volume scattering coefficient, see Scattering coefficient

Water
    index of refraction, 76, 77
    microwave emissivity, 128
Water vapor
    183.3 GHz band, 181
    22 GHz line, 181, 386
    6.3 μm band, 180, 221, 233
    6.7 μm imagery, 233–235
    absorption in near IR, 180
    as contaminant in satellite measurements, 150
    as greenhouse gas, 65
    atmospheric abundance, 176
    continuum absorption, 269–270, 316, 318
        microwave, 182
    dimers and trimers, 269
    far IR absorption, 180
    importance for heating profiles, 314–318
    IR absorption spectrum, 273–274
    microwave remote sensing, 153
    molecular structure, 247
    profile retrievals, 235
Wavelength, 16–18, 56–57, 69
    and color, 63
    units of, 57
Wavenumber, 57, 69
    units of, 57
Weighting function
    absorption, 190–193
    band-integrated flux, 308

emission, 207–210
in profile retrievals, 229–232
monochromatic flux, 213
Wien's Displacement Law, 114, 118,
    120–121

Zenith angle, 36

Ordering Information

Although this textbook may be ordered through bookstores in the usual way, the recommended method is to purchase directly from the Sundog Publishing. Here's why:

Wholesale price - By ordering directly from this publisher, you avoid the bookstore retail markup of 20%–25% or more.

Free domestic shipping - The discounted direct order price includes free shipping to addresses in the United States.

Detailed ordering information is provided on the following page. To allow for the slight possibility of back orders, please submit orders *at least six weeks* in advance of the start date of the course.

Have you found this textbook useful? If so, please consider letting your instructor, fellow students, and/or colleagues know about it!

A free examination copy may be requested by instructors of qualifying courses.

A First Course in Atmospheric Radiation by G.W. Petty

Orders may be submitted via the following methods
(1) Online at www.sundogpublishing.com/AtmosRad.htm (credit card),
(2) Regular mail or FAX using this form (check or credit card).
(3) E-mail (bookstore orders and requests for examination copies).

Mail or FAX orders to: Sundog Publishing, PMB 111, 1360 Regent Street, Madison, Wisconsin, 53715. Fax No.: (206) 600-6406 E-mail: sales@sundogpublishing.com

Direct-Order Price: $36.00 per copy (includes Media Mail shipping to U.S. addresses). This is a 25% discount off the list price of $48.00.

For non-U.S. orders or for upgraded shipping, include the shipping cost as calculated on the ordering web page (see URL above), or send e-mail to sales@sundogpublishing.com to request pricing.

Wisconsin residents please add 5.5% sales tax to total.

Copies ordered:_____ **Payment: US$:** _____

Method of payment:

Check ☐   Credit Card ☐

Billing address (please print clearly):

Name_____

Address_____

Address_____

City/State/Zip_____

Credit Card No. _____Exp. mo/yr _____

Shipping address (please print clearly):

Name_____

Organization_____

Address_____

Address_____

City/State/Zip_____

E-mail address (for order follow-up):_____